LAST SURVIVORS

CREATED AND PRODUCED
BY
EDITA LAUSANNE

Noel Simon   ·   Paul Géroudet

LAST SURVIVORS

The Natural History of Animals in Danger of Extinction

Illustrations by Helmut Diller and Paul Barruel

Preface by H. R. H. The Prince of the Netherlands

President of the World Wildlife Fund

PSL

PATRICK STEPHENS

LONDON

ISBN 0 85059 059 0

CONTENTS

PREFACE

Threatened animals ... endangered species.... These warnings are not new but we have long ignored them. Today, we are alarmed because we know that the destruction of nature directly menaces our common heritage. Once an animal species disappears, it can never be revived, a fact which must be stressed again and again. This is why I am particularly happy to welcome this book by Noel Simon and Paul Géroudet. Their collaboration, one working on mammals and the other on birds, in association with the well-known animal artists Helmut Diller and Paul Barruel, has given us an authoritative work on the present status of 36 mammals and 12 birds which are threatened with extinction. Each of the chapters is a true story, based on a profound knowledge of nature. The reader experiences a feeling of sadness, even indignation, at the actions of his fellow-men.

The authors are not describing the sorry end of the many species that have already disappeared. Rather, they introduce us to species still living, whose existence hangs on a slender thread which we can strengthen or break. Even in apparently hopeless cases, determined men can sustain life.

The battle has begun. The World Wildlife Fund and the International Union for Conservation of Nature and Natural Resources, working in collaboration, have already many successes to their credit. There could be many more if the Fund had greater financial resources.

If we look at the economic expansion attained in this century—often at the detriment of nature— the costly voyages into space, the ruinous wars, is it too optimistic to ask for a few tens of millions for conserving nature? There is still a chance of saving these vanishing species, but it should be seized at once, since any delay will lengthen the list of those already extinct. We and the coming generations must decide. Let us make up our minds and act now.

H.R.H. The Prince of the Netherlands
President of the World Wildlife Fund

Authors' Note

This book introduces thirty-six wild mammal and twelve bird species, selected from among the large number whose future is, in varying degrees, endangered. The choice of species is necessarily arbitrary, but has been guided by several considerations: we have tried to make the selection as representative as possible of the main continental regions and of the zoological orders.

Our choice has also been influenced by the need to give examples of some of the principal problems, political as well as ecological, which impede the protection of many endangered animals; and to indicate some of the efforts currently being made to resolve them. A further aim is to show some of the positive achievements in the field of fauna conservation which have been accomplished or assisted by the International Union for Conservation of Nature and Natural Resources (I.U.C.N.), the World Wildlife Fund (W.W.F.), and other organizations.

INTRODUCTION

The history of conservation is dominated by man's confrontation with nature. The causes and results of this situation require to be better understood, if only to provide practical examples of the prodigal attitude of our own species towards the world's living natural resources.

The majority of species extinctions during the last three centuries are attributable to man, either directly through deliberate slaughter or indirectly through the inability of many wild animals and plants to adapt themselves to fundamantal changes in their living conditions resulting from man's degradation of the environment. Included among the better-known names are such recently extinct animals as the aurochs, the quagga, Steller's sea-cow, the dodo, and the passenger pigeon. A few drawings, museum specimens, and eye-witness accounts are all that remain to remind us of their appearance and former existence.

The list of extinctions lengthens in pace with increasing human exploitation of the world's natural resources. Today, almost 600 forms of mammals and birds—to say nothing of other fauna and flora—are moving towards extinction. Their ultimate fate depends on a single species; our own. Although human rapaciousness, ignorance, apathy, and negligence have led to the annihilation of entire species, it is equally true that man has it within his power to conserve those that remain, if he is so minded.

Much has been said about the inevitability of species extinction as a normal, natural phenomenon, indeed as an integral part of evolution. It is certainly correct that innumerable prehistoric forms, of which only relatively few are known to us from their fossil remains, disappeared from the face of the earth long before man became the preponderant animal. But let it not be forgotten that the whole essence of evolution is its creativeness: inadequate animals or plants may be ruthlessly discarded along the way, but they are replaced by more successful life forms. Such a process of natural selection, spread over long periods of geologic time, is essentially positive in terms of the replenishment and enrichment of life. Species extinction by man, on the other hand, is the very antithesis of the evolutionary progress, as it is characterized by biological impoverishment.

Although a number of animal species are known to have disappeared within historical times, it was not until the development of a comprehensive system of zoological classification in the seventeenth century that reliable records could be kept. It has been estimated that approximately 120 forms of mammals and 150 of birds have ceased to exist since 1600. Referring to the birds, Dorst states that about 10 species and subspecies died out before 1700; about 20 in the eighteenth century; a further 20 from 1800 to 1850; about 50 from 1851 to 1900; and a similar number since 1901. The quickening momentum of this process is undeniable: over the last century an average of one form has disappeared each year; and this relates to birds alone.

Deliberate slaughter by man is one of the principal causes of extinction; either by excessive (often commercialized) exploitation or by the eradication of species regarded as "vermin". In some instances extinction has been brought about either by thoughtlessness or, worse still, by the sheer pleasure of destruction for its own sake.

But the most significant single reason is the destruction or degradation of natural habitats. Deforestation, agricultural and pastoral expansion, and spreading urbanization are some of the factors which have contributed to this situation. Environmental change, often in combination with intentional eradication of the native fauna, has been particularly rapid and extensive—and the more devastating for that—in newly independent countries.

Introductions of exotic animals and plants have also had calamitous consequences through the disruption of long-established, and sometimes delicately held, natural checks and balances. Insular species, which have evolved in isolation, offer many examples of plants and animals which are incapable of withstanding competition or predation from more aggressive, or more readily adaptable, alien forms, or of resisting the diseases which sometimes accompany them.

Sufficient evidence is presented in this book to show that human expansion, both demographic and technological, is the underlying cause of faunal decline. There are, however, other subsidiary factors.

The ability of animals to adapt themselves to changing environmental conditions varies from one species (and even from one race) to another according to the particular biological and ecological circumstances. A basic consideration is the balance between mortality and reproduction. Some of the endangered forms are handicapped by having a naturally low reproductive rate. Under optimum conditions this may be no great disadvantage, but it can

have serious repercussions if normal reproduction is thwarted by undue disturbance or by such factors as the weakening of a species' vitality through fragmentation of the population.

At what point should an animal species be considered in danger of extinction? It is impossible to give a generalized reply to this question, as the answer will vary widely according to the species and to the prevailing conditions. Theoretically, a species can be regarded as endangered when losses (from whatever cause) so exceed recruitment that the total population begins to approach the minimum number necessary to sustain a viable population. This so-called "threshold number" varies greatly from one type of animal to another; it will naturally be higher for a gregarious species than for a non-gregarious species. In practice, however, so little is known about this aspect of the subject that any strictly numerical criterion is bound to be highly speculative. Assessment of a species' status must therefore be based on such diverse factors as the relative numerical rate of decline; the size and condition of the habitat; the availability of food, water and cover; the incidence of disease; the effects of human and animal predation; the nature and degree of exploitation (either of the animal or of its habitat); and the effectiveness of protective measures.

Information under these headings is not always adequate for firm conclusions to be drawn. Natural impediments to research are sometimes imposed by the habits of the animals themselves, or by the environmental and climatic conditions under which they live; to say nothing of political circumstances. Furthermore, even under optimum conditions certain species are naturally low in numbers either because of their restricted distribution or of their specialized ecological requirements: a species can thus be rare without necessarily being endangered. A number of forms in this category inhabit islands. So long as the ecological equilibrium remains unimpaired they are capable of maintaining themselves satisfactorily, but the balance may be so finely adjusted that only a slight push is required to set them on the path to extinction. The

Galapagos penguin and the long-tailed roller of Madagascar are two examples of this situation.

Should the work on rare and endangered fauna be conducted at the level of the species or of the subspecies? Despite the inevitable uncertainties and occasional inconsistencies inseparable from working at the subspecific level, there are both technical and practical advantages in doing so: most races are sufficiently well characterized to warrant admission as distinctive taxonomic entities, and many are represented by several separate populations isolated from one another in either geographical or in political terms, each of which merits careful watching. The imperial eagle, for example, is not endangered as a species; but its western race unquestionably is. Unless due recognition is given to its status as a separate and taxonomically valid entity, the discrete population isolated in south-western Europe will inevitably be neglected.

A global evaluation of the status of a widely distributed mammal such as the tiger would be masked if done at the species level; the true situation is not fully revealed until each race is examined separately. Moreover, although the taxonomic status of some animals is open to criticism and subject to wide divergence of specialist opinion, such controversies are not confined to the subspecific level. To give two examples from among the mammals mentioned in this book, it would have been perfectly justifiable to have accorded the rank of full species to the Spanish lynx *(Felis lynx pardina)*, and to have regarded the walia ibex *(Capra walie)* as only a subspecies. But such taxonomic conundrums lie outside the scope of this work; whichever solution is adopted does not in any event affect the situations mentioned here.

The number of endangered animals continues to increase. The *Red Data Book* catalogues 275 species and races of mammals, of which 67 are considered to be gravely endangered; and more than 300 birds, 60 of them giving rise to extreme anxiety. It is perhaps remarkable that so few European animals should be listed in the *Red Data Book*. This is explained by the fact that eligibility for the international list of rare and endangered species is based on an assessment of status over an animal's entire geographical range. Many Palearctic species are unquestionably rare in individual European countries, but are nevertheless relatively abundant farther east: they cannot therefore be considered rare in the international context, despite being in need of stringent protection at the national level.

The present book is concerned with fewer than ten per cent of the rare and endangered mammals and birds on the world list. Reading these accounts it is at once apparent that the principal causes of decline and extinction, enumerated earlier in this Introduction, have lost none of their force. In particular it is necessary to stress the effects on wildlife and the natural scene arising either directly or incidentally from the impact of modern technology, which, in addition to stimulating the exploitation of areas which had hitherto been protected by their remoteness or inaccessibility, has already exacted an appalling toll in terms of environmental destruction and pollution.

The unbridled exploitation of the world's living natural resources touches all continents, and extends even to the depths of the oceans. Pressure on wildlife and the pristine increases at the same rate as the constantly expanding human population. The need merely to feed, clothe and house this growing human multitude is in itself a potent factor in the decline of wildlife and wilderness.

What constructive action can be taken to redress the situations mentioned in this book, some of which seem almost beyond hope of solution? It is essential to appreciate that ultimate responsibility for the conservation of wildlife and other living natural resources rests squarely with the governments concerned. International and other organizations can assist in a variety of ways as, for instance, by drawing a government's attention to a particular situation; advising on suitable measures to meet it; suggesting ways of introducing or strengthening protective legislation; arranging for qualified personnel to undertake field studies; drawing up comprehensive management plans; and financing approved conservation programmes.

But effective action can be taken only with the support and collaboration of the government or responsible local authority. Not all governments are receptive to such advice. One of the biggest problems facing both national and international conservation organizations lies in convincing governments that action is really necessary. It is seldom easy to convince those in political control of the need to look to the long-term advantages inherent in the conservation of wildlife and natural resources instead of being guided by short-term expediency. Political considerations assume an importance which should not be underrated. It is in this direction that public opinion—providing it is well informed—can exert such a beneficial and even decisive influence. Even when that difficulty has been surmounted, there remains the need for vigorous implementation and subsequent follow-up action, without which even the best conceived programme becomes almost valueless.

The basic requirement for the perpetuation of a rare or endangered species normally involves setting aside and protecting at least one undisturbed part of its natural habitat adequate in extent to ensure the continuance of a viable population. Given such conditions, most species of wild animals can be relied upon to look after themselves.

This is why national parks and other sanctuaries are of such importance. As the world's wild lands contract, the future of rare species, and of wildlife in general, is becoming increasingly dependent on the creation and efficient maintenance of sanctuaries in which the interests of wildlife take precedence over all other considerations. But the real value of any national park or equivalent reserve depends in large measure on the degree of competence with which it is administered. This requires not only a devoted staff; it also calls for a well-founded management plan, with clearly defined objectives, as the essential framework on which the administration of the area can be based.

Such an ideal solution is not always attainable; indeed most of the world's species are not represented in any national park. For this reason the paramount conservation requirement lies in the creation of further well-administered national parks and sanctuaries in suitable areas before they are taken over for other purposes, and the opportunity thus lost for ever.

In considering means of safeguarding rare and endangered species, priority must invariably be given to retaining them within their natural habitats. Circumstances sometimes arise, however, when this aim proves impossible; there is then usually no alternative other than to establish stocks in semi-captivity or confinement. There are many animals, however, which appear unable to adapt themselves to living and breeding under unnatural conditions. Several of the leading zoological gardens have taken up this challenge, and are making a valuable contribution to wildlife conservation by working to resolve some of the complex problems relating to the propagation of certain rare species in captivity. Some notable successes have already been achieved.

It is important that the breeding of rare and endangered animals in captivity should be regarded not as an end in itself but as an interim measure aimed at keeping a species in being until such time as conditions improve sufficiently for it to be reinstated in the wild.

A further constructive measure involves capturing wild animals in the regions where their continued survival is no longer guaranteed and transferring them to a reserve or other suitable area. The recent development of immobilizing techniques based on the use of tranquillizing drugs fired from syringe guns has made possible the re-introduction of several species of wild mammals—few bird species are amenable to such treatment—into areas from which they had disappeared. There is always the danger that a rare species confined to a single locality could be wiped out. The risk of such losses can be reduced by establishing viable populations in several localities.

It is self-evident that the work of conservation cannot succeed without a solid scientific base. Information on the habits, biology, and ecology of many rare animals is insufficiently precise to enable sound conservation programmes to be drawn up. Investigation and research are therefore essential preliminaries.

The International Union for Conservation of Nature and Natural Resources (I.U.C.N.), through its Survival Service Commission, is responsible, among other things, for compiling and maintaining the official international list of rare and endangered species, and for recommending appropriate ways of ensuring their protection. The organization of the Survival Service Commission is based on a series of "specialist groups", supported by a world-wide network of correspondents, which feed in the information on which the status of species can be assessed and conservation programmes drawn up. The Survival Service Commission works in close conjunction with the International Council for Bird Preservation (I.C.B.P.), which has special responsibility for rare and endangered birds.

These two organizations collaborate in compiling and publishing the *Red Data Book*, a series of volumes designed to provide concise reports on each of the world's rare and endangered species. These volumes are arranged in a way that allows the data sheets to be revised and brought up to date whenever necessary. The Mammalia and Aves volumes of the *Red Data Book* are the framework around which this present work is constructed. Further volumes in the *Red Data Book* series are in course of preparation; these will be devoted to Amphibia and Reptilia; Pisces; and Angiospermae. Others will follow.

Since its creation at the end of 1961, the World Wildlife Fund (W.W.F.) has worked side by side with I.U.C.N., with the specific task of fund-raising, thus providing the indispensable means of giving practical effect to approved conservation programmes and projects. Through the activities of its various National Appeals, which have already been established in fifteen countries, and the generosity of numerous donors and benefactors, the W.W.F. has from 1962 to 1969 dispensed more than 20 million Swiss francs in support of 296 approved conservation projects, many of them concerned with the conservation of rare and endangered flora and fauna. Without the timely financial support provided by the W.W.F. it is possible that neither the Javan rhinoceros nor the aye-aye of Madagascar would still be living; other rare and endangered species also have received practical assistance at the hands of W.W.F.

These three international organizations—all of which are non-governmental and therefore politically independent—work in close collaboration with U.N.E.S.C.O. and F.A.O. and with many national and regional organizations.

The materialist may dispute the purpose of attempting to safeguard endangered flora and fauna. What possible advantage can be gained from supporting a cause that must surely be destined to ultimate failure? The acceptance of such an abject philosophy would condemn man himself to a barren future. Most people, to be sure, do not in the least care about the survival of the blue whale, the mountain gorilla, the kakapo, and many other creatures which live in such remote or little known regions that they lie beyond the realm of normal experience.

But much more is at stake than the preservation of an exotic animal or an area of wilderness. Man's attitude towards the world of nature is a barometer which can be used to gauge his capacity for dealing with fundamental issues affecting his own well-being and survival. The diverse but mutually inter-related living components of the biosphere—which include not only fauna and flora but soil, water, and air—are indispensable to human existence; and they are far from inexhaustible. Man's future will unquestionably be influenced by the measures he takes, or fails to take, to conserve them. The need is for ecology to become not so much an abstract scientific discipline as the touchstone of human purpose.

Man alone of all Creation has the power of rational thought; he has consistently used this power to advance his own immediate short-term interests. The crucial test is whether he has the wisdom to take the longer view and to appreciate that ecological anarchy is likely to be as disastrous to the human race as to other forms of life.

17

AMERICA

1, Haitian solenodon — 2, Volcano rabbit — 3, Red wolf — 4, Northern swift fox — 5, Mexican grizzly bear — 6, Giant otter — 7, Mountain tapir — 8, Vicuna — 9, Galapagos penguin — 10, Californian condor — 11, Whooping crane — 12, Attwater's prairie chicken — 13, Kirtland's warbler

HAITIAN SOLENODON

Solenodon paradoxus

The family Solenodontidae is represented by two living species: *Atopogale cubana*, the Cuban solenodon; and *Solenodon paradoxus*, the Haitian (or Hispaniolan) solenodon. The family was once more widely distributed, but there is no evidence that the Haitian species has ever existed anywhere except on the island of Hispaniola.

Solenodons are the largest living insectivores to be found in the New World. They are the only surviving representatives in the New World of a group of insectivores whose nearest living relatives are the otter shrews of the genera *Potamogale* and *Micropotamogale* from western and central Africa, and the tenrecs, which are found only in Madagascar.

The relationship of the solenodons and the tenrecs is a question that has been frequently debated. Allen conjectures that "the presence of long coarse hairs in the pelage in addition to the finer ones in *S. paradoxus* may indicate a step toward the spiny condition of certain other insectivora".

Very little is known about the solenodon's reproductive biology, but the little information that exists seems to bear out the belief that the rate of reproduction is slow. Individual animals have lived longer than six years in captivity, but there are no records of the species ever having bred in captivity. Females which were pregnant at the time of capture have, however, given birth. According to Allen, the females bear from one to three (usually two) young at a birth; and may breed twice a year. Paul Thumb, who in the mid-1930s used specially-trained dogs to collect about twenty living solenodons, states that dens are usually in holes among broken rocks, but that solenodons sometimes occupy hollow logs. It seems more probable, however, that they enter hollow logs only in search of food.

The Haitian species is rat-sized. Its body is about a foot long, and its naked tail almost as long again. It is a nocturnal animal, with very small eyes, large ears, and unusual dentition. Its snout is remarkably long, and its sense of smell highly developed. There is considerable individual colour variation, ranging from a mixture of black and buff-yellow to deep reddish-brown. Its feet and the lower extremities of its limbs are almost hairless. Each foot is equipped with claws, those on the fore feet being particularly large.

Allen describes the Haitian solenodon as "a rather slow-moving creature, constantly on the move with a shuffling gait, sniffing everywhere with its long nose, and scraping and scratching here and there with its long claws, exploring for food. It is capable of delivering a sharp bite if too much disturbed, however." It is believed that the solenodon—like some of the shrews—has poisonous saliva, but this has not been definitely established.

The Haitian solenodon was first described in 1833, but very few further specimens were obtained. It was not until 1907—by which time the animal was thought to be extinct—that A. Hyatt Verrill found it still living in the interior of the Dominican Republic. He obtained three specimens for the American Museum of Natural History: several others were collected three years later.

The most recent information from the field was obtained by Murray L. Johnson in 1967. He states that the species still exists in a number of different localities in the Dominican Republic. Most recent records are from forested or bushy areas which have not yet been greatly disturbed by man. Unfortunately, however, undisturbed areas are becoming scarce. The rising human population and increasing cultivation of the land have resulted in the destruction of much indigenous forest.

The cause of the solenodon's decline has often been attributed to predation by exotic animals. Allen postulates that the extinct Antillean insectivores of the genus *Nesophontes*, which are known only from cave deposits, "may have become extinct only since white occupation. . . . Anthony adduces some evidence that the *Nesophontes* were abundantly represented in the deposits prior to the deposition of rat bones, so that the introduction of the rat may have been the decisive factor in extermination of the insectivores."

The theory that the introduced mongoose is responsible for the decline of the Haitian solenodon is refuted by Johnson. He points out that the mongoose has been present on the island for almost a century, and is now well established and widely distributed. It seems unlikely, therefore, that the solenodon is as vulnerable to mongoose predation as has sometimes been claimed. The principal cause of decline is unquestionably the destruction or modification of the natural habitat, caused by the spread of human settlement into previously unoccupied parts of the country.

Luis S. Varona's studies of the Cuban species have brought him independently to the same conclusion. He points out that the mongoose is rare in Cuba's Oriente Province, and it does not in any event frequent the dense forests. Furthermore, the solenodon is not hunted by the local people, few of whom would recognize one if they saw it. Varona states unequivocally that the decline of the Cuban solenodon is entirely attributable to deforestation.

A subsidiary factor has been the recent demand from zoos. Since 1966, more than 40 solenodons have been captured in the Domini-can Republic for sale to zoos, principally in Europe. As solenodons are difficult animals to keep alive under artificial conditions the mortality rate is heavy. The high market value of the animal is an irresistible incentive for local collectors; this could lead to the extinction of local populations.

The Haitian solenodon has been legally protected since March 1967, but the most practical method of enforcing the law lies in stringently controlling the export of living animals. It seems important, moreover, that they should go only to reputable scientific organizations for breeding purposes.

Both the living species of solenodon are rare and are therefore listed in the *Red Data Book*. The Cuban species, *Atopagale cubana*, which is believed to be even rarer than the Haitian, is now found only in the mountainous region of Sagua-Baracoa in the north-eastern part of Oriente Province, and in the Sierra Maestra. The most recent record is of a pair collected in 1956 in the Sierra Maestra, to the west of Santiago de Cuba.

The Cuban Academy of Sciences has recently established the Jaguani Reserve in the montane forests near Baracoa, to protect both the Cuban solenodon and the equally rare ivory-billed woodpecker, *Campephilus principalis bairdi*.

VOLCANO RABBIT

Romerolagus diazi

The volcano rabbit, or *teporingo* to use one of several colloquial names, has a very restricted range on the upper-middle slopes of Popocaté-petl, Ixtacihuatl and the peak of Ajusco, on the south side of the Valley of Mexico. A narrow strip running along the edge of this one valley, about 20 miles long and 10 miles wide, is the only place in the world where the species occurs. This small area lies at an altitude of between 9,000 and 12,000 feet, and is thus at the upper limit of the pine tree. The volcano rabbit's habitat consists of open pine forest with a dense undergrowth of coarse *zacaton* grasses.

It is interesting to note that another member of the same subfamily, the Ryukyu rabbit *(Pentalagus furnessi)*, has a similarly restricted range, being confined to the two small Japanese islands of Amami Oshima and Toko-no-Shima, south of Kyûshû. This form also is listed in the *Red Data Book*.

The general appearance of the volcano rabbit is very distinctive, though Leopold draws attention to its striking resemblance to the northern pika, or cony, of the genus *Ochotona*. Both are tailless and short-eared, and both possess high-pitched penetrating voices which

SOLÉNODON DE HAÏTI   *Solenodon paradoxus*   HAITIAN SOLENODON

they use frequently. They are the only vocal members of a normally silent family.

Durrell describes two distinct cries, one "a squeaking noise like somebody rubbing a wet thumb over a balloon and [the other] a short, high-pitched bark, rather similar to that of a chinchilla, but not repeated. They utter this noise when handled. They will also thump the hind legs on the ground in a manner similar to the European wild rabbit."

The fur of the *teporingo* is a uniform dark brown colour on the back and dark brownish-grey beneath. The overall length is about 12 inches, the legs and feet are short, the ears small and rounded, and the tail so rudimentary that it is invisible.

The animals live in burrows either beneath the ground or under rock piles. Durrell notes "that their burrows were generally dug on gently sloping ground facing south" and that they appear to live in small colonies, each containing perhaps 150 to 200 individual animals. They move through the tall coarse vegetation by a network of well-maintained tunnel-like paths running beneath the overhanging *zacaton* grass.

This grass grows in large tussocks which attain a height of up to three feet, but require soft, deep volcanic soil. The areas occupied by the plant are separated by what Nelson describes as "hot slopes on which it cannot maintain itself. These breaks are not wide and can be readily crossed by small mammals."

Burrows are dug in the soft soil on which the *zacaton* grows. Underground the burrow is very complex, and normally contains a number of different openings to facilitate escape. Durrell writes that "on two occasions we found down short side burrows small circular chambers which contained a small quantity of dried leaves, grass and on one occasion a small quantity of rabbit fur, which we took to be preliminary nest making, as it was the beginning of the breeding season".

Breeding takes place during the spring and early summer, from March to the beginning of July. Litters vary from one to four young, but three is said to be the usual number. Two different females collected by Durrell for the Jersey Zoo each bore twin young. He also succeeded in establishing the gestation period at 38 to 40 days.

The animal appears to be equally active by day and by night. Leopold notes that "in good weather the volcano rabbit spends much time above ground, playing, fighting, foraging or sleeping among the clumps of bunchgrass. It is especially active in the evening and early morning, usually resting quietly in the middle of the day. When surprised it utters its sharp call and scuttles away along a runway to one of its burrows."

Little detailed information is available on the animal's diet. Durrell observed that it feeds on *zacaton*, generally "sitting on top of a tussock . . . and apparently feeding on both the old and the new grass, as a number of tussocks we discovered had been chewed flat as a mown lawn on top, only leaving a rim of overhanging grass around the edge". It is also reputed to consume the aromatic mint *Cunila tritifolium* which

grows in the region. Villa speaks of the volcano rabbit being attracted to this plant and sometimes smelling strongly of it. Despite a deliberate search, however, Durrell "could find no aromatic mint in the area in which we caught *Romerolagus*, neither did the captured specimens smell of this or, indeed, of anything else".

In 1893, when the animal was first described, the range did not differ greatly from today. In recent years, however, agricultural development has gradually advanced higher up the mountain. Each year the slopes are burned to increase the acreage under cultivation, and fire is progressively reducing the pine-*zacaton* zone.

The species is nominally protected, but the law is difficult to enforce. Not only do the local people regard the *teporingo* as vermin, but the area in which it lives is becoming increasingly popular with the inhabitants of Mexico City who go there for recreational purposes and, in the course of hunting quail and other game birds, find the *teporingo* useful for target practice. Many are destroyed in this way. The animal is not regarded as suitable for human consumption, possibly because the strong mint flavour makes the meat unpleasant to the palate, but it is sometimes used for dog food.

In 1968, Gerald Durrell led an expedition to Mexico with the purpose of acquiring a breeding nucleus. Several specimens were collected and are now installed in the Jersey Zoo where it is hoped to establish the first captive colony. Attempts to keep wild rabbits in captivity have hitherto seldom been successful largely because of their susceptibility to parasitism, particularly coccidiosis, but Durrell is confident that these problems can be overcome.

At the same time there is a self-evident need for the Mexican authorities to prevent further encroachment of the remaining pine-*zacaton* formation, which alone can ensure the continued survival of a species unique to that country.

RED WOLF   *Canis rufus*

Although closely resembling the coyote (*Canis latrans*) in general appearance, the red wolf is a significantly larger animal, and its fur is usually a little coarser. It occurs in three distinct colour phases—grey, black and red. Its normal coloration is grey or tawny and closely resembles that of the coyote; the black and red phases are much less common.

Three races are recognized: the Texas red wolf, *C. r. rufus*, the smallest of the three forms, which once inhabited eastern Oklahoma, central Texas, and extended into Mexico; the Mississippi red wolf, *C. r. gregoryi*, characterized by Goldman as "decidedly larger and grayer, less tawny" than the nominate race, found mainly on the western bank of the Mississippi River in Louisiana, eastern Texas, Mississippi, Arkansas, south-eastern Oklahoma, southern Missouri, southern Illinois, south-western Tennessee, and south-western Kentucky; and the Florida red wolf, *C. r. floridanus*, which differs from *gregoryi* by its skull and dentition, and which ranged eastwards into southern Alabama, Georgia, and Florida.

These three races form a cline. The eastern race is the largest of the three, some specimens being almost as big as the timber wolf (*Canis lupus*). Towards the west, red wolves become progressively smaller, and less distinguishable from the coyote.

This gradual merging of the red wolf with the coyote has resulted in the occurrence of animals intermediate in size between the two species, thus making positive identification difficult. Coyotes have frequently been mistaken for red wolves, and this mis-identification has led to the publication of inflated accounts of their numbers and status. As Pimlott and Joslin have pointed out, this difficulty is further increased by the fact that the colour of the coyote's fur during the grey or reddish phases is indistinguishable from either the grey wolf or the red wolf. "Characteristics, such as tawny coloration, smaller size, more slender build, smaller rhinarium and foot pads . . . are very subjective and do not permit separation of the species either in the field or in museums."

These same authors point out that the black phase was long regarded as a distinctive feature of the red wolf, the occurrence of black-phase animals being generally accepted as conclusive proof that the animals concerned were red wolves. Indeed, the scientific name originally assigned by Bartram to the species in 1791 was *Lupus niger*—black wolf. This belief was widely held until Pimlott and Joslin made a special

LAPIN DES VOLCANS   *Romerolagus diazi*   VOLCANO RABBIT

collection of skulls from black-phase animals in Arkansas; all were shown to be from medium-sized coyotes. The coyotes examined by McCarley in eastern Texas and eastern Oklahoma also showed a high degree of melanism.

Widely contrasting opinions have been expressed on the classification of the red wolf. One body of opinion questions whether it is justifiable to regard the animal as a distinct taxonomic entity. Some biologists consider the red wolf to be a race of the coyote. This opinion is supported by Goldman's belief that it is impossible to distinguish between small red wolves and large coyotes; and by Paradiso's study of skulls collected in eastern Texas after 1960, which caused him to suggest that the red wolf and the coyote had probably interbred, which, if correct, would mean that the two animals were only subspecifically distinct.

Lawrence and Bossert, on the other hand, argue convincingly that the red wolf is a race of the timber wolf; they agree with McCarley's contention that the red wolf has probably undergone hybridization with other species of the genus *Canis*.

An interesting aspect of this issue has been the use by Pimlott and Joslin of their "wolf-howling method"—the playing of tape-recorded wolf howls, to which the wolves respond—which enabled red wolves and coyotes to be distinguished in the field "on the basis of differences in vocal characteristics. The coyote has a peculiarly sharp rise in pitch to its call which the wolf call lacks. Moreover, its call is generally higher in pitch, and each call is usually of shorter duration. The howling of dogs, though in many ways more similar to that of wolves, can almost always be differentiated by the inclusion of barking. Wolves almost never bark, except in extreme threat situations."

Lack of knowledge about the status of the species led the World Wildlife Fund to finance a field survey which was undertaken by Pimlott and Joslin during 1964 and 1965. This study revealed that contrary to some earlier reports which suggested that red wolves were still common, the species had disappeared from the greater part of its range. "Our studies showed that red wolves still existed in at least two areas along the flood plain of the Mississippi River, in one area of north-central Louisiana, and in south-eastern Texas. . . . In Texas, the red wolf appears to be restricted to three south-eastern counties. . . . In Arkansas the existence of a pure strain of red wolves appears very unlikely."

Subsequent investigations have shown that the Florida race, *C. r. floridanus*, has been extinct since the early 1940s: the Mississippi race, *C. r. gregoryi*, is close to extinction but may still exist in a few remote parts of north-eastern and south-western Louisiana, the adjoining part of Texas, and possibly a few parts of Arkansas: the Texas race, *C. r. rufus*, is known in its pure form only from the coastal prairie marshes of the Gulf coast of Texas.

The decline of the red wolf is primarily attributable to environmental changes which have favoured the coyote, a more aggressive animal with which the red wolf is unable to compete. The coyote has therefore gradually extended its ranges at the expense of the red wolf.

Nowak draws the conclusion that environmental change "certainly played a role in the coyote invasion of Louisiana, but it might be mentioned that the full-scale coyote movement into the state did not come until after the period of intensive clearing had passed and reafforestation begun. The heavy coyote migration through Louisiana did correspond exactly, however, to the period immediately following the hard-hitting control programs directed against the wolf. Therefore it seems logical to suppose that the two events were related. Indeed, one could easily believe that the coyote, formerly kept out by the presence of the natural wolf population, was now moving in to fill a predatory vacuum left when the wolf was killed off. If this premise is correct, then the intensive war waged against the wolf in Louisiana not only failed to achieve the desired result, but actually greatly increased the problems of those persons who dislike predators, for the coyote is now present in far larger numbers and is allegedly doing much more damage than the wolf ever was . . . the true wolf was never particularly harmful and would usually try to stay as far from civilization as possible, but the coyote now

29

prefers to live within agricultural areas and sometimes takes to raiding domestic animals."

Habitat change has been both rapid and extensive in many parts of the animal's range. In the Mississippi Valley, for instance, large areas of typical wolf habitat have recently been developed either for conventional agricultural purposes, for oil production, or flood control schemes. Joslin states that "the activities of the Corp of Engineers to inhibit annual flooding over the bottomlands has opened up many areas to further human development. In such areas where flood control does not yet exist building construction is favoured along the few natural ridges. In many areas such ridges are the only available sites for denning." Pimlott and Joslin comment that the conversion of forest into agricultural land "not only creates unsuitable habitat for red wolves but it also results in the creation of a niche that is suitable to the coyote".

The surviving red wolf population is small and highly vulnerable to hunting. Pimlott and Joslin state that red wolves "are more vulnerable to trapping and hunting than are coyotes, and the evidence suggests that these mortality factors have been important in the final decline of the species. The intensive trapping in central and south-western Louisiana, for example, occurred immediately before the wolf disappeared from these areas."

The difficulty of distinguishing between the coyote and the red wolf, and the tendency for hunters to shoot any predator on sight has moreover resulted in heavy pressure from sportsmen. Most hunters are not aware of the precarious status of the red wolf and, even if they knew, few would have much sympathy for a wolf.

In devising means of safeguarding a wide-ranging species such as the red wolf formidable difficulties have to be overcome. As Pimlott points out, a pack of red wolves probably roams over an area of 50 to 100 square miles: "We have returns on timber wolves taken 80 to 90 miles from where we originally captured them, and I think the red wolf has similar capability of movement." There would thus be a tendency for a pack to wander far beyond the boundaries of any normal-sized santuary that might be established.

The red wolf is a forest and thicket dweller—an ecological characteristic that it shares with the timber wolf—while the coyote is a creature of the open plains, prairies, and deserts. The aim of a programme for the conservation of the red wolf should therefore be to carry out a series of field surveys to determine where pure populations still exist, and to set aside suitable areas of red wolf habitat to be added to existing refuges such as Anahuac and Brazoria National Wildlife Refuges. The prairie marshes of the Gulf Coast of Texas are of particular importance for this purpose as they contain the only known pure population of the Texas race. It is therefore vital for the survival of the species that means should be found to preserve these marshes intact.

The establishment of sanctuaries should be carried out in conjunction with a programme for the destruction of any coyotes found in the vicinity of the refuges; with a scheme for compensating ranchers for any livestock losses they may incur from wolf predation; and with an educational campaign designed to obtain the collaboration of hunters. Unless these measures are taken, there is little prospect that the red wolf will survive.

The Fish and Wildlife Service has already assigned field staff to investigate the status and distribution of the species. These studies have done much to clarify the taxonomic status of the animal, and to show that under certain conditions hybridization with the coyote will occur; they have also been instrumental in discovering at least one pure population of red wolves in the coastal marshes of Brazoria County, Texas.

As an interim measure it would seem advisable to establish captive breeding stocks for introduction into suitable areas if the need should arise in the future. This proposal has been put in hand by the Wild Animal Propagation Trust (W.A.P.T.), with the development of a captive breeding programme. For reasons which have already been discussed, the taxonomic separation of the red wolf from the timber wolf, coyote, and their hybrids rests on skull measurements. The committee appointed to co-

30

LOUP ROUGE   *Canis rufus*   RED WOLF

ordinate the programme has the difficult preliminary task of establishing criteria for the positive identification of red wolves.

Five zoological gardens are at present co-operating with the W.A.P.T. Red Wolf Committee in establishing captive breeding groups: Chicago Brookfield, Illinois; Dallas; Oklahoma; San Antonio; and St. Louis. Philip W. Ogilvie, chairman of this committee, explains that "all participating zoos have agreed to co-operate with the Committee on the placement of progeny in other zoos and also to co-operate in any testing programme deemed advisable by the Committee to further establish the identity of these animals. The Committee has given first consideration for the placement of these animals to zoos located within the former range of the red wolf but as more animals become available, consideration will be given to zoos located in other parts of the United States and abroad."

NORTHERN KIT FOX   *Vulpes velox hebes*

This diminutive fox is only about two-thirds the size of the red fox *Vulpes vulpes*, or a little bigger than a well-built cat. A full-grown adult stands no more than about 12 inches at the shoulder, seldom exceeds 3 feet in overall length, and weighs from 4 to 5 pounds. It has a prominent bushy brush tipped with black, and large, erect, pointed ears. The general colour is yellowish-brown speckled with silvery, black-tipped guard hairs.

The diet consists mainly of small rodents, such as field mice and prairie gophers, as well as rabbits, birds, lizards, large insects and the like, which means that the kit fox performs valuable service in controlling certain pests, even if occasionally it imposes a modest fee of a chicken in return. Although seldom indulged, this practice does not endear it to the ranchers: in their eyes the animal is a nuisance, chewing at saddlery or anything else encountered during the course of its nocturnal wanderings.

The kit fox is impressively graceful in its movements and so remarkably swift and agile over short distances that in some parts it is known as the swift fox. When chased it dashes at high speed across the plain, brush fully extended, jinking violently or turning suddenly in its own length to throw off pursuit. Its intelligence and agility are well shown by Dr. Thomas Childs, a Canadian federal government veterinarian, who writes of a sport that was very popular in the southern parts of Alberta half a century ago: the hunting of coyotes by horsemen with dogs of the stag-hound, wolfhound, or greyhound type which, being crossbreds, combined speed and stamina with exemplary fighting qualities.

"During such hunts it was quite common to rouse a Kit Fox and of course the dogs would take off after the fox. Dogs which could, without too much difficulty, overhaul and destroy a coyote, could outrun the Kit Fox. However, catching the little rascal was definitely not an easy matter. When the fox realized the dogs were overhauling him, he would reduce speed just enough to encourage the dogs to even greater efforts; then when it appeared he would surely be picked up, the fox would swing his tail assembly (brush) hard aport or starboard, leap sideways as lightly as a puff of thistledown, reverse his course and float away at top speed. The dogs—strong, weighty animals, travelling at top speed—would invariably overrun the point at which the fox reversed course, and after braking to a stop, and reversing course to renew the chase, would find the fox had opened a very substantial lead. That sort of performance usually continued until either the dogs were exhausted and gave up the chase, or the fox had managed to disappear from view.

"If there was a barbed wire fence in the vicinity—such fences usually consisted of three strands of barbed wire strung on posts, with the lower strand of wire 16 or 18 inches from the ground—little vulpes astuta would invariable lead the pursuing dogs directly to the fence, and pass under the lower strand of wire at top speed; the pursuing dogs, having their eyes on the fox and nothing else, would usually strike the lower wire at top speed—frequently with disastrous results to the dogs, and terminating the chase very abruptly. The writer has seen this form of vulpine strategy in operation on more than one occasion.''

It is surprising that so little has been recorded about the life history of an animal that once was so common. Indeed, it was not until 1902 that the distinctive northern race was scientifically described, by which time it had already become scarce.

Much of what we know about the animal comes from the writings of Ernest Thompson Seton. The cubs, normally four or five to a litter, are born in the spring, and by May or thereabouts are to be seen frolicking around the entrance to the den, in which the adult male spends much of his time until the cubs are old enough to fend for themselves. Being largely nocturnal creatures, they do not normally go far from the burrow during the hours of daylight: their day begins at dusk when they become very active. Seton excavated one grass-lined den which was situated five feet beneath the surface at the end of a nine-foot long entrance tunnel. Greater lengths have been recorded. Each burrow is normally equipped with several alternative exits for emergency use.

The adult pair remains together throughout the year, and may mate for life. This is in character with the kit fox's disposition which, in marked contrast to the legendary wiliness of the red fox, is gentle and trusting and wholly without guile. Unfortunately for the kit fox this failure to develop any fear of man was one of the factors leading ultimately to its extinction.

The artless, unsuspicious nature of the kit fox resembles that of the Falklands Island fox *Dusicyon australis*, from the opposite end of the continent, which was exterminated in 1876. It, too, was entirely without fear of man. Allen (1942) records that the animal was so absurdly tame that "the Gauchos would capture them by holding out a bit of meat to a fox in one hand

and stab the animal with a knife held in the other, when the fox came within reach''.

Various predators—coyotes, wolves, and eagles, among others—took their toll of the kit fox, but its reproductive rate was sufficiently high to sustain such natural losses. But the coming of the white man and the impact of advancing civilization soon altered all that.

The kit fox remained abundant until about the middle of the last century. It ranged throughout the higher and drier southerly parts of the prairie provinces of Canada, extending south across the international border into North and South Dakota and Wyoming. According to Bailey (1926) it "at one time covered the whole of the prairies of North Dakota", but the encroachment of settlement exerted increasing pressures on the little kit fox which it was powerless to resist. Much of its natural cover was either destroyed or altered by agricultural activities, and untold numbers were trapped and snared. Soper records one shepherd who even as recently as the turn of the century succeeded in trapping 60 in a season: many others were poisoned by consuming baits laid for coyotes and wolves. Destruction was on such a scale that within a few decades the kit fox had slipped quietly towards oblivion. The final stages of its demise were perhaps accelerated by the more adaptable and agressive red fox taking over and dominating at least some parts of its habitat.

By the turn of the century the kit fox had everywhere become scarce and had vanished completely from large sectors of its former range; so scarce, in fact, that Fowler, writing in 1937 of the High River district, stated that "only those people who were here before 1900 can recall having seen a Kit-fox. My father states that the last bunch of Kit-foxes he saw was in the summer of 1897".

A few managed to cling to existence in some of the wilder and more inaccessible parts of the country, but by the 1920s most of these scattered remnants had gone. The last specimens in Saskatchewan were taken in 1927 and 1928 at Ravenscrag and Govenlock respectively, though a handful of pairs or solitary outliers probably persisted for another ten years or so. This was

RENARD VÉLOCE D'ALBERTA   *Vulpes velox hebes*   NORTHERN KIT FOX

the pattern on both sides of the international border; and by the late 1930s the animal had probably gone forever.

Careful inquiries made in 1969, and involving an extensive correspondence with specialists in every state and province in which the animal formerly occurred showed conclusively that the graceful little northern kit fox no longer exists, except possibly in the Cypress Hills of south-western Saskatchewan where there is a slight chance that it might, almost miraculously, still cling to existence.

As a child, Mr. J. David Chandler, an active Saskatchewan naturalist, became familiar with the animal's distinctive call, which he describes as "soft and plaintive, somewhat suggestive of the mourning dove", and which was heard only during the still of spring evenings.

On a number of occasions in the mid-1950s Mr. Chandler was surprised to hear this unmis-takable call coming from a location where the kit fox was once known to exist. On the evening of May 20th, 1964 he heard it again, from the direction of some abandoned coal mines. Since then it has not been repeated. The silence of the ensuing years tells its own story.

The southern race of the kit fox, *Vulpes velox velox*, has been subjected to similar pressures but, oddly enough, has fared much better than the northern. Within the last few years it has even staged a come-back. Increasing numbers of sightings in Kansas have led to speculation that the species is gradually spreading north-wards from the Oklahoma Panhandle, New Mexico and Texas, This is credited to the intro-duction of more specific methods of coyote control, which thus avoids destroying the smaller predators. But this sophisticated devel-opment has come too late to help the little kit fox of the northern prairies.

MEXICAN GRIZZLY BEAR   *Ursus horribilis nelsoni*

Although this southernmost race of the grizzly bear is a little smaller than the northern forms it is none the less a huge animal, often attaining a length of six feet or more and weighing up to 660 pounds. A mature grizzly has a massive head, with a wide forehead, small ears, a very prominent shoulder hump, which distinguishes it from the black bear, *Ursus americanus*, and claws which are only slightly curved, as distinct from those of the black bear which are designed for climbing trees. The general coloration is of varying shades of brown.

The Mexican race was not described until 1914, from the type specimen collected in Chihuahua fifteen years previously by Dr. E. W. Nelson. Its existence had been known for many years, but it had not previously been recognized as a distinct type.

The original range was extensive, including northern Baja California as well as parts of New Mexico and Arizona. The date of its disappear-ance from Baja California is not known, but none has been recorded there for many years. In 1855, at the time the International Survey was delin-eating the boundary between the United States and Mexico, the animal was said to be abundant in the northern Sierra Madra, especially in the San Luis Mountains and at Los Nogales.

Grizzlies were in fact still plentiful in the San Luis Mountains, along the Chihuahua/New Mexico border, until as recently as 1892 when the second International Boundary Survey was in progress. Dr. E. A. Mearns, who participated in the survey, was of the opinion that the pre-sence of Billy the Kid's gang of desperados and the grizzly bear, were sufficient reasons why law-abiding folk should give this region a wide berth.

By the end of the last century the grizzly had already become scarce along the Arizona/Sonora border, and in 1937, when Starker Leopold visited the Chihuahua/Sonora boundary to the west of Pacheco, he found that the last grizzlies in this region had been killed several years previously. He wrote: "Thus in a period of less than half a century the grizzly bear was reduced from abundance to extinction along the United States border and in the northern Sierra Madre."

This exemplified the situation throughout the animal's range. By the end of the Second World War the Mexican grizzly bear had been exterminated throughout its range except for a small region about 50 miles north of the city of Chihuahua, in the Cerro Campana and adjoining Santa Clara and Nido ranges.

Koford defines this area as "about 15 miles in diameter centering in the upper Arroyo del Mesteño and ranging southeast into the drainage of Cañon del Alamo and northward into Arroyo del Alamo, Cañon de la Madera, and upper branches of Cañon del Nido". This ultimate retreat comprises a plateau about 4500 feet above sea level from which the mountains ascend abruptly to about 9,000 feet. The vegetation varies from the semi-desert of the plateau to open grassland, oak woodland and pine forest at the higher elevations, although most of the timber has been cut out.

The entire region has been taken up for cattle ranching, but the mountainous parts are not used because they lack permanent water and, in Leopold's words, are "too rough for the cowboys to muster cattle on horseback. A Mexican cowpuncher, who despises walking from the corral to the ranch house, is not likely to be found chasing cows around a mountain afoot. It has been the custom therefore, on ranches situated around these highlands, to maintain drift fences that preclude the ascent of range stock into the cumbres and breaks. There is very little timber in these highlands, nor have any important mineral discoveries been made. Mexican ranch folk do not idly go into rough mountains unless there is a financial motive. Lacking one, the little Sierra del Nido is rarely visited and the big bears have escaped attention. There they have persisted long after the more spacious but rolling timberlands to the west were overrun with loggers, miners, and grazing operations, and pretty well stripped of wildlife."

Leopold also points out that the grizzly favours the brush-covered foothills because,

although omnivorous, its main diet consists of acorns, nuts, roots, berries and fruits of various kinds which do not occur in heavy coniferous forest. For this reason it was originally less likely to be found at the higher elevations than the black bear. This ecological factor militated against the grizzly and was unquestionably one of the underlying causes of its decline, for the reason that the lower country was most suited to pastoralism, and thus the grizzly came at once into conflict with human interests.

The number of grizzlies steadily diminished, and by the 1950s there were about 20 to 30 animals. These were hunted incessantly by ranchers and visiting sportsmen.

Little is known of the breeding biology of the Mexican grizzly, but it is thought that breeding age is not reached until the fourth or fifth year and that the animal is not fully grown until the age of eight or ten. Litters seldom exceed two cubs, and in normal circumstances females do not reproduce more frequently than every second or third year. The cubs develop even more slowly than black bears and remain under maternal care and control for two full seasons before being capable of leading an independent existence. This low reproductive rate is one of the factors which helps to explain the species' vulnerability to excessive exploitation.

In 1961, possibly as the result of prolonged drought that caused both food and water to become scarce, one grizzly turned stock killer and destroyed sixteen cattle. The rancher concerned retaliated by adopting a policy of deliberate extermination of all bears by shooting, trapping and poisoning. Commencing in the winter of 1961-62, and for the two ensuing winters, a poisoning campaign was mounted, using 1080-treated meat baits obtained from the Oficina Sanitaria Panamericana. The numbers killed are not known, but it is evident that the campaign resulted in a drastic decrease in the grizzly population. This happened despite the grizzly having been since 1959 on the official list of protected Mexican mammals, a measure which was endorsed by a more formal proclamation issued by the President in July 1960.

Among the recommendations made by Starker Leopold in 1959 was a proposal for a field

Ursus nelsoni

OURS GRIZZLY DU MEXIQUE

MEXICAN GRIZZLY BEAR

survey to ascertain how many Mexican grizzlies were left, and the measures required to protect them. This recommendation was strongly supported by Dr. Rodolfo Hernandez Corzo, Director General of Wildlife for Mexico, and resulted in the Government prohibiting the hunting of bears. Plans were also prepared for the establishment of a preserve, but progress was frustrated by shortage of field staff without which law enforcement was impossible, as well as being hampered by lack of money with which to purchase the 50,000 acres of private grazing land necessary for the establishment of a reserve.

Funds for the proposed field study did not become available until 1967. In that year the Conservation Foundation and the World Wildlife Fund jointly financed a survey by Dr. Carl B. Koford. His study extended over a period of

three months, and included reconnaissance flights over the area by helicopter as well as extensive foot treks throughout the country known to have been inhabited by the grizzly. He also interviewed ranch owners, *vaqueros* and others with an intimate knowledge of the range, in an attempt to acquire evidence.

"The vaqueros knew of no recent bear carcasses, bones, or other remains and I discovered none. In addition, I found no areas of ground torn up as by large-clawed bears seeking rodents or roots, nor any broken up manzanita bushes or madrone trees. These features had been observed by Leopold and others in 1959 after three years of drought; their lack in 1968 may have been due to the comparative abundance of manzanita berries, acorns, and other bear foods. On some ranches steel traps are set for wolves: I recovered the skull of a wolf recently trapped on Rancho El Mesteño and saw trap holes and discarded trap pads on Rancho Compana. Because bears are generally more easily trapped, failure to take them in recent years is another indication of their scarcity."

In this type of country it is difficult to differentiate with certainty between grizzly and black bear sign. The droppings are almost indistinguishable and although grizzly tracks are heavy and include marks made by the fore-claw, so much of the Sierra is rocky that tracks are visible in only a few places, such as stream beds and sandy stretches.

After a careful appraisal of all the evidence, Koford tentatively concluded that grizzlies were present in the area until 1960 but by 1962 they had gone. He stresses, however, that his study was not exhaustive and that despite the lack of firm evidence, it is possible that a few grizzlies may still survive in some remote canyon seldom visited by man.

The story of the grizzly is best told by Leopold himself: "Of all the mammals native to Mexico there is not one to take the measure of the grizzly bear. In size, in power, and in self-reliant independence the grizzly has no match. He fears no beast. Mountain lions, wolves, and black bears withdraw discreetly, even from their own kills, when the grizzly comes to feed. The strongest range bull cannot match his strength. Yet for all his majesty, the grizzly has been virtually exterminated by man and his dogs, traps, poisons, and 30-30 rifles. That so noble a species, the very symbol of wildness and rugged freedom, should be trampled to extinction under the heel of progress is a sad commentary on our civilization."

GIANT OTTER   *Pteronura brasiliensis*

Pteronura is the largest of the world's otters, averaging between 5 and 6 feet from nose to tip of tail, though larger specimens have been recorded. It bears a superficial resemblance to a bigger version of the common otter *(Lutra)*, except that it has an extensive area of coalescing cream-coloured blotches on the chest, throat, and underside of the head and chin.

The fur on its back is a rich chocolate colour, fading to a lighter tone on the under-surface. Its head is flat, wide and seal-like, and its neck so thick that in old animals it is sometimes broader than the head. Its jaws are extremely powerful. Its nose is tipped with a narrow strip of very short fur dividing the nostrils. Its small rounded ears are placed far back. Its tail—which accounts for almost a third of its total length—is more beaver-like than that of any other otter: it is a flattened paddle-shaped appendage, broader in the centre than at the root. Its feet are well webbed to the ends of the toes, and set on short, stout legs, which are used with great effect in the water. It is sometimes said that the limbs are almost useless on land, but this suggestion is refuted by Douglass Branch, who has successfully reared a cub from the age of one week. Branch states that the animal can trot perfectly well, with the gait—but not the speed—of a weasel, and is capable of galloping fast enough to catch a man running slowly.

Under water, *Pteronura* uses its hind feet, tail, and body for propulsion, while its fore feet are kept close to its sides. In this way it is not only a fast swimmer but capable of rapid manœuvring. On the surface, however, it usually prefers to swim on its back, partly because in this position its field of vision is improved.

The *perro de agua*, or *lobo de rio*, to use two of its vernacular names, inhabits river courses in the northern part of South America. Two races are recognized: *P. b. brasiliensis*, which lives in suitable parts of the Amazon river system in north-eastern Brazil, the Guayanas, southern Venezuela (the Orinoco River marking the northern extremity of the range), eastern Colombia, and north-eastern Peru; and *P. b. paranensis*, of southern Brazil, north-eastern Argentine, Paraguay, and Uruguay.

With such a wide distribution, covering the greater part of South America, it might be expected that the animal was fairly well known; but very little has been recorded of it. Insufficient observations have been made on the species in the wild state to allow firm conclusions to be drawn about its ecological requirements, behaviour or status. One of the few recent accounts to throw much-needed light on this subject is Grimwood's report on the wildlife of Peru. He observes that the species "is confined to the low selva zone of the Amazon region, within which it is principally found in the 'black water' regions of clear but peat-stained lakes, lagoons, and interconnecting water-ways of the lower basins of the main Amazon tributaries. . . . At times of low water they are found principally in the rivers themselves, but during the flood season they follow the spawning fish into even the smallest creeks and drains and are, or were, found in great numbers in the *cochas*, or oxbows, left where a river has changed its course. They are apparently never encountered in the clear, fast-flowing upper reaches of the rivers (i.e. the 'white water'), which are the preserve of *Lutra incarum*." This no longer applies to Venezuelan Guayana where, as Glass points out, persecution has driven *Pteronura* from the lower stretches of rivers into the upper reaches.

The giant otter is monogamous, and is believed to pair for life. The holt is normally a tunnel in a river bank with an entrance above water level; but hardly anything is known of the animal's breeding habits, except that litter size varies from one to four cubs, though two is the usual number, and the cubs are blind for the first month of their lives. There are widely differing opinions on the length of the gestation period. Some state that it is three months; others that it may be as much as six to nine months or more.

If the longer period is correct, it could be attributable to delayed implantation. The

LOUTRE GÉANTE   *Pteronura brasiliensis*   GIANT OTTER

North American otter, *Lutra canadensis*, is known to exhibit this phenomenon; but until further evidence is forthcoming it is impossible to do more than conjecture whether it also occurs with the giant otter. Studies on captive specimens should help to answer this question. Crandall, writing in 1964, mentions no captive breeding records. More recently, however, successful breeding has occurred on several occasions at the Parque del Este, in Caracas; but, with one exception, the male has invariably killed the young.

Pteronura can be very courageous in defence of its young. Its boldness is noted by Branch, who cites the example of a large male chasing, and indignantly hissing at, a *curiara* (dug-out canoe) which came too close to a family of giant otters. In Branch's experience, it is an intelligent and affectionate animal, much addicted to basking in the sun on rocks and boulders in the rivers.

The giant otter appears to be more gregarious than other otter species. Grimwood tells of it being commonly seen in bands of up to twelve or fifteen animals. Its main food is fish, which it usually eats on land. Molluscs and crustaceans are also eaten; as well as birds, eggs, and small mammals on occasion. Its favourite meal is undoubtedly the paca *(Cuniculus paca)*, the large spotted rodent whose flesh is greatly relished not only by Indians but by every carnivore in Latin America.

The extent of natural predation on the giant otter is not known. It seems likely that losses are caused by various carnivores, such as the jaguar, cougar, and ocelot. Harris quotes a report of a giant otter being found in the stomach of a large water snake. But such losses are insignificant compared with those caused by man.

In the Guayanese outback, for example, the giant otter is killed at sight, as the fishermen accuse it of robbing the fish traps. No doubt this allegation is correct but, as Branch points out, the loss of some fish seems a modest price to pay for the service the giant otter renders in preying on the deadly *piranha*.

In some parts of its range, on the other hand, the giant otter is venerated by the local people.

Branch states that the Sanema group of the Yanoama (Guaica) Indians, living in the Pacaraima Mountains on the Venezuela/Brazil frontier, regard the animal as sacred, and look upon all giant otters (of both sexes) as female relatives of the tribe.

The Makiritare are another tribe of Indians who do not kill *Pteronura*, "unless their love of gain is played on by hide-hunters".

The status of the giant otter is hard to determine, owing to the lack of sufficiently precise information. In some of the more remote and inaccessible parts of its range it is probably still relatively abundant; but such localities are few, and in the greater part of its range—particularly along the more accessible rivers—the species is believed to be scarce and progressively declining. In Peru, for example, Grimwood states that it has "disappeared from nearly all its former haunts, and probably only small and isolated relict populations now exist . . ." Indeed, the only place in Peru where the species remains well represented is in the recently created Manu

National Park. The credit for this unusually favourable situation is chiefly due to the effective guardianship of the Amawaka Indians, whose warlike activities have thus far deterred the professional hide-hunters.

Hide-hunters—who frequently employ native Indians to hunt for them—are responsible for the decline of the giant otter. Grimwood remarks on the relative ease with which the animal can be hunted. He attributed this to "their diurnal habits, intense curiosity, lack of timidity, and because their grunts and cries draw attention to their presence in any swamp or cover in which they may be hidden". He adds that because their carcasses sink when they are killed "it is probable that two or three are killed for every skin that reaches the market".

The giant otter's pelt is an extremely valuable commodity, comparable in price to that of the jaguar. Grimwood states that in 1966 dealers in Iquitos, Peru, were paying 1,700 sols (£23) for a single skin. He also provides statistics showing the yearly export of giant otter pelts from Peru, which "reflect the dwindling numbers of this species and show how its skins have nearly disappeared from the market despite the incentive of soaring prices and an ever-increasing number of hunters in the field":

1946	2,107	1953	918	1960	1,002
1947	1,248	1954	1,213	1961	293
1948	751	1955	2,169	1962	850
1949	1,403	1956	1,766	1963	435
1950	1,437	1957	1,066	1964	672
1951	1,635	1958	1,278	1965	223
1952	854	1959	1,114	1966	210

Pelts originating in Venezuela are usually marketed in Colombia where they fetch a higher price. Furthermore, by a curious anomaly, *Pteronura* pelts entering the United States under the vernacular name are not considered otters, and are not therefore eligible for the import duty levied on other otter skins.

There is self-evident need to afford the species more effective protection in its natural environment; but this hope is unlikely to be realized owing to the greater part of the animal's range lying far beyond reach of the law. The main hope for its survival lies in action by the governments of the principal importing countries agreeing to introduce stringent controls over the trade in otter pelts; but this could only be effective if all of them co-operated.

MOUNTAIN TAPIR   *Tapirus pinchaque*

Three of the four living species of tapirs inhabit the New World: the fourth, *Tapirus indicus*, lives in South East Asia (in Burma, Malaya, Thailand, and Sumatra). Although separated by several thousand miles, the Malayan tapir is closely related to the American forms, and similar in general appearance, except for colour and marking.

The tapirs are the only living representatives in the New World of the order Perissodactyla (odd-toed ungulates), the order of mammals which also includes the horses, asses, zebras, and rhinoceroses. The five or six living genera of perissodactyls are merely a remnant of a once much bigger group. Extinction has been more extensive in this order of mammals than in any other—more than 150 extinct genera are known from fossil remains. It is also the most endangered of all the mammalian orders: of the 16 living species, 11 are under threat of extinction and are thus included in the *Red Data Book*.

The appearance of the tapirs has altered little since their forbears inhabited the earth during the Pleistocene. Their most distinctive feature is the long flexible snout which, like the elephant's trunk, is invaluable for food-gathering. Tapirs are the only living perissodactyls with four toes on each front foot; the hind feet have only three.

The existence of a tapir in the higher parts of the northern Andes was known since the early years of the Spanish occupation, but was assumed to be the same animal as the lowland form. It was not until 1829, when Roulin described a specimen obtained while he was resident in Bogotá, Colombia, that it was recognized as a distinct species. He called it *pinchaque*, which is said to be a derivative of the native Indian name for a mythical monster.

The mountain tapir—also called the woolly, hairy, Andean, or Roulin's tapir—is the smallest of the four tapir species. Its general colour is black or dark brown, its head down to the neck being paler. Its lips are usually rimmed with white; and there is a ring of bare white skin above its toes. On either side of its rump is a bare or thinly-haired patch. Its body is covered in thick curly hair about an inch long. Unlike the Central American form *(Tapirus bairdi)*, *Tapirus pinchaque* has no mane and no crest between the ears.

Very little is known about the breeding biology of the mountain tapir. The gestation period is uncertain, but is assumed to be of similar length to the other species of tapir—about 13 months. Mature females are believed to reproduce every two years, a single young being the normal rule: there appears to be no particular breeding season. The juvenile coat is distinguished by conspicuously patterned horizontal stripes and spots.

The greater part of the mountain tapir's range is in Colombia and Ecuador; with minor extensions southward into Peru, and northward into the Sierra de Mérida in Venezuela.

The Colombian sector of the range is mainly restricted to the central and eastern cordilleras, to the south of Mount Tolima. The species has never been recorded from the western cordillera, and has disappeared from several areas where it was known twenty years ago. The animal is still believed to exist, however, in the northern part of Colombia's eastern cordillera, close to the Venezuelan frontier and isolated from the main distributional zone.

The principal population inhabits Ecuador where the species lives in a few restricted and isolated parts of the eastern cordillera: there are no records from the western cordillera, despite the existence of suitable habitat.

The range crosses the southern frontier of Ecuador into a small part of northern Peru where the animal lives in the departments of Piura and Cajamarca, in the high country south to about 6°S. Grimwood states: "The mountain tapir is locally reported to be common in the mountains between the towns of Ayabaca and Huancabamba and to the east of the latter town, where it inhabits thick, bushy country in the zone of wind-dwarfed *Polylepis* trees and *Hypericum*. It is probably also to be found along the mountainous ridges running south from Huancabamba, for several small groups are known to exist where those ridges

are cut by the Olmos-Jaen road some 60 kms. to the south, including one party of 5 to 7 animals living at only 2,000 m., 35 kms. east of Olmos. The species is also known from several localities near Tabaconas and Chontali in the Jaen Province."

The species was once more widely distributed. Hershkovitz conjectures that it "inhabits an area representing part of the original Colombian Central Land Mass, the South American side of the intercontinental land bridge where Tertiary mammals entering from North America established a foothold". The mountain tapir arrived at a time of temperate climatic conditions at sea level in equatorial regions. As the climate at sea level became warmer, and the Andes rose higher, the mountain tapir did not lose its preference for cool climatic conditions. "Newly established tropical zone habitats at the base of the Andes were invaded subsequently by other kinds of tapirs."

Within its overall range, the species is confined to the upper subtropical and temperate parts of the Andean cordilleras above 8,000 feet. It is not known from lower altitudes, which are inhabited by other tapir species.

Hershkovitz comments: "Within the geographic limits defined, tapirs may occur in practically any wooded or grassy habitat with good surface supplies of water. Forests and thickets are usual daytime retreats, while bordering exposed areas such as grass or scrublands, marshes, lakes and streams with herbaceous banks, and grassy islands are favored nocturnal feeding resorts. Streams, whether narrow, torrential watercourses of mountain gorges or wide, sluggish rivers of the interior and coastal plains are indispensable refuges of all tapirs attacked by enemies, be they of the itch-producing, external parasitic kind, or tigers, jaguars, and man."

Water is an exceptionally important factor in the lives of mountain tapirs: indeed it is essential for their existence. They are completely at home in water, and spend much time wallowing. If pursued, they take refuge in a river, lake, or swamp. They are excellent swimmers, and it is said that they can remain submerged for long periods.

The habitat favoured by the mountain tapir differs greatly from that of other tapirs. It includes two principal zones: the humid mist forest from 8,000 to 12,000 feet; and the *paramo* grasslands from 11,000 to 13,000 feet. Occasionally the tapir goes even higher; its tracks have been seen above the permanent snow line at altitudes of over 15,000 feet.

The mist forest is characterized by stunted tree growth; at the higher elevations this gives way to almost impenetrable bush and scrub much of it criss-crossed by a labyrinth of tunnel-like tapir trails. These paths are usually the only route by which a man can move through the area.

Tapirs are nocturnal animals, spending the day in the depths of the forest, and emerging at night to feed. They are exclusively herbivorous, much of their diet consisting of aquatic vegetation in rivers and swamps. Where settlement has intruded into their range, they frequently enter the cultivated areas at night to feed on the standing crops. This habit sometimes results in considerable damage, and naturally brings the tapirs into conflict with man.

The mountain tapir is particularly shy and retiring, unable either to tolerate disturbance by man and his domestic livestock or to adapt itself to changing environmental conditions. The transformation of the environment, which has been brought about by settlement and various kinds of development, has driven the animal from many parts of its range into the more remote and inaccessible places.

Undisturbed natural forest is essential for the tapir's existence: widespread deforestation in the Colombian and Ecuadorian Andes has been the principal cause of decline. Much of this forest destruction occurred towards the end of the nineteenth century when charcoal burning was practised on a large scale, for both domestic and industrial purposes. Since then, the pace of environmental degradation has quickened; roads are penetrating deeper into the Andes, and fingers of cultivation are constantly reaching higher into the cordilleras. These developments, in combination with the expansion of pastoralism into the open grasslands of the *paramo* above 12,000 feet, have imperilled the mountain tapir. Concern at reports of the species' depletion caused the World Wildlife Fund to organize

and finance a survey to ascertain the animal's current status. This reconnaissance, covering a large part of the Ecuadorian Andes, was undertaken by Schauenberg in July 1968. Although numbers cannot be gauged with certainty, he estimated that the population probably totals no more than a few hundred animals, and cannot number more than 2,000 at the most.

In 1968, a sudden demand from zoological gardens for mountain tapirs stimulated dealers in Ecuador to undertake a series of expeditions to capture living specimens. The method of hunting usually adopted involves employing thirty or forty Indian beaters to encircle the area chosen for the operation; they station themselves on high ground, and move slowly downhill towards the centre. When the tapir is flushed from cover it normally dashes away to plunge into the nearest river. Hounds are used to bay the animal until it can be lassoed. These hunts may last from a few hours to several days. According to Schauenberg, for every tapir captured and exported alive, many others are destroyed by drowning and other causes.

As the situation appeared to be getting out of hand, I.U.C.N. sought the collaboration of I.U.D.Z.G. (International Union of Directors of Zoological Gardens) and A.A.Z.P.A. (American Association of Zoological Parks and Aquariums) in placing an embargo on the purchase by zoos of further specimens of *Tapirus pinchaque* until the precise status of the species was better known. The two organizations agreed to this request and imposed restrictions on the purchase of further specimens by their members.

The Government of Ecuador has shown its concern for the species by introducing in 1969 legislation imposing certain restrictions on the export of fauna from the country. The species is legally protected in Colombia; its name has also been included in the list of animals to be accorded total protection in Peru when control of hunting is introduced.

Responsibility for the ultimate survival of the mountain tapir rests with the governments of Ecuador and Colombia. The inability of the species to adapt itself to changing environmental conditions means that the only hope for its continued existence lies in the introduction and

TAPIR PINCHAQUE   *Tapirus pinchaque*   MOUNTAIN TAPIR

enforcement of stringent protective legislation in every country in which it occurs. This should be done in conjunction with the establishment of well protected national parks or similar sanctuaries in some of the few unspoiled forests that remain, and where the animal is known to exist in greatest numbers. One of the most important zones which should be secured for this purpose is in the eastern cordillera of Ecuador. The World Wildlife Fund is doing everything possible to promote the establishment of a national park in this region.

VICUNA

Vicugna vicugna

The vicuna is a member of the camel family which originated in western North America during the Eocene, and spread into South America and Asia before becoming extinct in its place of origin. There are four contemporary species in Latin America, the llama, guanaco, alpaca and the vicuna, all bearing a superficial resemblance to each other, though differing in size and other characteristics. Of these, the llama and the alpaca have long been domesticated, the llama primarily as a pack animal, and the alpaca, the Andean counterpart of the sheep, as a source of wool and meat. Both were domesticated by the pre-Inca inhabitants of Latin America, and played a significant part in the cultural development of the Andean civilizations.

The vicuna is the smallest of the four species, standing from 28 to 35 inches at the shoulder and weighing only around 100 pounds. Apart from size, the most obvious feature that distinguishes the vicuna from the other species is the prominent tuft of long pure-white hair on the lower part of the throat, which stands out prominently against the fawn brown coat. It has the added distinction of being the only living artiodactyl with continually-growing lower incisors like those of the rodents.

The vicuna has never been domesticated, cannot be used as a beast of burden, and yields less wool than the alpaca; but these disadvantages are more than compensated by the supreme advantage of providing the lightest and finest quality fleece obtainable.

The range extends over 1,300 miles from the south of Ecuador through Peru and Bolivia into extreme northern Chile and north-western Argentina. Knowledge of the animal's distribution in Chile is scant, and the southern limits are not known with certainty. According to Molina (1782), the range at one time included the Chilean provinces of Coquimbo and Copiapo, but there is little likelihood that any now remain in either Chile or Argentina, and the animal has definitely gone from Ecuador.

Within this overall range the vicuna has adapted to the extreme environmental conditions of the *puna* zone, which consists of a series of discontinuous plateaux, separated by high mountains and deep gorges, sandwiched between the higher parts of the main Andean Cordilleras. These high altitude short-grass pastures lie above the limits of tree growth and cultivation (except for occasional small patches of potatoes), and immediately beneath the snow line. This bleak and desolate region, characterized by extreme cold, rarified air, and scarcity of water, is the vicuna's chosen environment.

Vertical distribution is determined by availability of suitable forage. The animal forages from the upper limits of vegetation at 16,000 feet or more, down to the limits of green pasture. The *puna* is moist, with green herbage the year round; whereas below 12,000 feet the vegetation tends to be not only more arid but also coarser and taller, which, in addition to being less succulent, hinders freedom of movement.

Distribution was not greatly affected by man or his domestic livestock until recently, but as human activities, including ever increasing pastoralism and mining, encroached deeper into the Andes, the vicuna was obliged to retreat to the higher and more remote areas.

49

Vicunas occur in small herds, usually of about five to fifteen animals, presided over by an adult male. The immature males are expelled from the herd at about ten months of age, when they congregate in bachelor herds of from twenty to a hundred or more.

A single young is the general rule, and a major limiting factor is the high infant mortality rate. Koford shows that about half the young die during the late foetal or infant stage. No doubt poor range conditions in some seasons affect fertility, and predators, both animal and human, take their toll of the new-born young. Little is known of the reproductive biology of the species, however, or the factors militating against successful breeding.

Vicuna wool is of incomparable quality and the fabric derived from it is by far the most luxuriant and valuable of all wool products. This fact has long been recognized, and during the era of Inca supremacy robes and garments made from vicuna wool were reserved for the exclusive use of the royal family, as well as for the beautification of the temples, and sacrificial offerings to the sun. The spinning and weaving of vicuna wool was the principal privilege and responsibility of the Virgins of the Sun.

Inca culture showed a profound respect for Nature's bounty and an innate comprehension of ecological precepts that was in marked contrast to the methods adopted by their successors. Their system of soil conservation, for example, was marvellously accomplished, and their prescience extended to the conservation of wildlife.

Hunting was the prerogative of the Inca himself, and was conducted on rational game management lines that permitted a "crop" to be harvested without impairing the basic stocks. A royal hunt, or *chaco*, employed between 20 and 30 thousand men who encircled a huge area, perhaps as much as 60 or more miles in circumference, and gradually advanced towards the centre driving the wild animals before them. Large numbers of deer and other animals hemmed in by the phalanx of human beaters were clubbed or speared and the meat distributed to the common folk; but the vicuna were captured alive and, after being shorn, were released. A *chaco* was not held in any district more fre-

quently than every three to five years, thus permitting stocks to recover, as well as giving time for the vicuna fleece to grow.

With the coming of the Spaniards all this changed. The Inca system of carefully regulated conservation gave way to unbridled slaughter; and this has been a constant feature of the wildlife situation in Peru from the overthrow of the Incas down to the present day.

Simon Bolivar, the Liberator of Peru, introduced protective legislation as long ago as 1825. A century later the law was strengthened to prohibit both hunting and the commercialized use of vicuna wool and hides, as well as the export of the living animal without special authorization.

Similar regulations apply in Argentina and Bolivia, but nowhere is enforcement effective. Moreover, Bolivian law expressly authorizes the manufacture and sale of articles made from imported vicuna products, as the result of which a thriving industry has developed around this legal loop-hole. Not only does this encourage the killing of vicuna in Bolivia but quantities of wool and skins are smuggled into the country from Peru, often with the connivance of frontier officials. Vicunita robes, made entirely from infant fleeces, and other vicuna products then acquire an official certificate of Bolivian origin, after which they can be legally exported.

The highland Indians of Peru prefer vicuna meat to any other, and Koford states that they commonly capture new-born vicunas within half an hour of birth, after which the animal is too agile to be easily caught by hand. Grimwood notes that shepherds "can rarely resist picking up newly-born lambs, and kill considerable numbers of adults with their dogs". Generally speaking however, the Indian is a subsistence hunter and Koford considers it "improbable that pastoral Indians greatly reduce the vicuna population by shooting. Because of the expense and legal complications of obtaining guns, few Indians have them. The guns they do have are normally low-powered single shot arms, often muzzle loaders. Further, an Indian usually kills but one animal and this he utilizes fully before he hunts another. Lastly, as Indian hunters are more likely to get within range of an immature

VIGOGNE   *Vicugna vicugna*   VICUNA

male than within range of a female, they kill relatively few females." An incipient threat, however, lies in the Indian practice of maintaining constantly increasing numbers of domestic animals in the *puna*, with consequent degradation of the fragile habitat through over-stocking.

The decline of the vicuna is primarily attributable not to the Indian but to the sophisticated motorized hunters from the towns, miners, road workers, government officials and the like, armed with modern rifles, who deliberately and openly violate the law by shooting vicunas for amusement and profit. The police themselves are often the worst offenders. Because the females invariably stand by the male after he is killed, the hunters first pick off the flock male and then shoot all the females and young at their leisure. Entire herds are wiped out in this manner.

The scale of the slaughter during the last decade can be gauged from comparative population figures. In 1957, Koford estimated the total at approximately 400,000, of which about 250,000 were in Peru. In the fifteen years that have elapsed since his study, numbers in Peru have fallen to about 15,000. Although the Peruvian population is greatly impoverished it is nevertheless by far the largest in existence: the only other country where the species now occurs is Bolivia, where since 1965-66 numbers have dropped to less than a thousand.

This relentless commercialized poaching arises from international demand for vicuna wool and skins, notably from the United States and Great Britain. One British manufacturer has been importing between two and three tons of vicuna wool a year, equivalent to the yield from about 4,000 animals, all of which are of course killed in the process. The resultant high quality cloth is exported, principally to the United States, where a vicuna coat fetches about $800 and is regarded as a symbol of affluence and status.

Various attempts have been made to domesticate the vicuna, but with little success. The rearing of the young presents no great difficulty, provided they are captured at a very early age. Vicunitas make charming pets but with increasing age they become less tractable, and captive animals refuse to mate. The animal appears to be temperamentally allergic to domestication.

The only recent success was achieved by Francisco Paredes, owner of the Hacienda Cala Cala in the Azangaro Province of the Department of Puno, who spent many years attempting to domesticate the vicuna. He started with a nucleus of ten hand-reared animals, accustomed from the earliest age to being handled, which were kept in large enclosures under semi-wild conditions: but eighteen years elapsed before the first breeding success was obtained. Since then the herd has gradually increased to about 500 to 600 animals, all ranch born.

A further difficulty is that in spite of vicuna wool being the most valuable of all natural fibres (the wholesale price of cloth being about

£60 a yard), the annual yield of about a third to half a pound per animal is so low that, paradoxically, domestication is uneconomic.

Attempts have therefore been made to cross the vicuna with the alpaca, and thus produce a hybrid combining the quality of the vicuna fleece with the heavier yield of the alpaca. While some success has been achieved, the resultant progeny are invariably sterile, and it has thus been impossible to establish a new cross-breed.

Peru remains the vicuna's main bastion. Even though the animal has disappeared from many areas where it was formerly common, small scattered herds can still be seen. But the only place in which the species can be regarded as abundant is the Pampas Galeras region of the Lucanas Province in the Department of Ayacucho where, in 1965, 1,200 to 1,300 vicunas were counted in an area of roughly 250 sq. miles. This includes land measuring 19,768 acres and owned by the village of Lucanas. With the support and encouragement of the government, the commune plans to manage the herd in a way that will provide the villagers with a valuable source of meat and wool, as well as an income through the development of tourism.

In 1967, some 17,250 acres of the Pampas Galeras was declared a National Vicuna Reserve, and the government provided funds for its maintenance. The reserve carries between 400 and 600 of the 2600 vicuna now known to exist in the region, and employs about a dozen guards to enforce the prohibition of hunting not only within the reserve but also in the adjacent area belonging to the commune.

The Peruvian Government is now negotiating for the purchase of the 10,000-acre Hacienda Cala Cala, with the purpose of developing part of the ranch as a second reserve for pure-bred vicuna, while using the remainder for experimental work designed to improve the wool of alpaca and llama by crossing with vicuna.

The basic requirements for ensuring the future of the vicuna are the establishment of further firmly administered reserves to ensure the protection of wild stocks; the continuation of experimental breeding work; the implementation of effective legislation, including adequate provision for ensuring that the U.S.A. and Great Britain do not continue to contribute to the destruction of the species by providing an outlet for the purchase of contraband vicuna wool or other products; and the extension by Bolivia of the existing ban on the sale or export of vicuna wool and skins of Bolivian origin to include all vicuna products, irrespective of origin.

The vicuna is a further example of a wild animal occupying a highly specialized ecological niche where it is not in competition with man. It possesses the useful attribute of being capable of thriving on the sparse high altitude vegetation of the *puna* and of converting it into wool and meat of superlative quality. Retention of the vicuna is the wisest as well as the most rewarding form of land-use to which the *puna* zone can be put. It is self-evident that under a properly regulated management system the animal could make a significant contribution to rural economies.

THE GALAPAGOS PENGUIN   *Spheniscus mendiculus*

On the Equator, about 600 miles from the western shores of South America, the Galapagos Islands rise out of the Pacific Ocean. After their discovery in 1535, they were first visited by pirates and whalers and then by settlers, who, with a taste for adventure and solitude, have also defied the arid lava and the scarcity of soft water. Since Charles Darwin's celebrated visit in 1835, the Galapagos have had a special significance for naturalists. Some of the observations and ideas from this voyage helped him to formulate his famous theories on the origin of species and evolution. A remarkable fact about the Galapagos is the wealth of flora and fauna

endemic to this volcanic archipelago. In addition to the giant land tortoises, from which its name is derived, and curious marine iguanas, the birds are of special interest. Out of 89 breeding forms, 50 are peculiar to the Galapagos, 27 endemic species and 23 subspecies. Lack of fear exposes most of them to dangerous contact with man; an unexpected form amongst them is the penguin.

On the Equator, the presence of this representative of a group of birds generally associated with the frozen shores of the Antarctic, seems paradoxal. However, out of 15 species of Spheniscidae, several inhabit the southern coasts of

Australia, South Africa and South America, by reason of colder waters rich in plankton and fish. It is thanks doubtless to the Humboldt Current, a true stream of marine life reaching as far as the Galapagos, that these equatorial islands are privileged to possess *Spheniscus mendiculus*. Its resemblance to the Humboldt penguin, which frequents the coasts of Chili and Peru, shows their ancestral relationship; but differences have developed in isolation, above all a reduction in size.

The Galapagos Penguin is one of the smallest that exist, measuring about 20 inches in total length and weighing five pounds. The plumage is a dark blue-grey on the upper side and white on the under side with white "eye-rings" and a dark pectoral collar. On land, sometimes lying on its belly, sometimes standing on its sturdy feet, it seeks the cool shadows in the clefts of the old lava flows washed by the sea. Like the other species of this very primitive group, it cannot fly, but is an expert diver and swimmer and feeds on fish. A sociable bird, it fishes in pairs or in groups numbering as many as 60 penguins, according to Lévêque (1963). On the other hand, local conditions do not allow it to constitute spectacular breeding colonies.

Brosset stated that this penguin does not lay its eggs in the open, but in secure cavities in the "often complicated labyrinth which extends under the lava crevasses or under piles of broken rocks at the edge of the sea". Lévêque saw six nests at Punta Mangle, on the coast of Fernandina (Narborough), "in cavities situated in a mass of lava between three and seven feet above high-tide". The incubating birds are usually well hidden and sheltered by lava blocks; in one case, they were almost completely in the dark.

At Elisabeth Bay, the nests were built between huge boulders. Two pairs without eggs were found in the same hole and, in another case, two penguins had laid eggs almost "at a beak's distance" one from the other. It is, therefore, the localization of favourable sites that compels these penguins to nest separately. Brosset (1963) even thinks that the number of adequate sites is insufficient and that each nest is occupied by different pairs in turn, which leads him to suppose that the sexual cycles are individual, probably without connection to the cycle of the seasons. According to Lévêque, breeding takes place during the cooler season, from May to August, with maximum activity in June and July. The female lays two eggs, of which the length of incubation is not known. The young are clad in down for a long period, from June to December (Harris, 1969). They are greatly attached to their customary area; a penguin ringed by Lévêque on March 12th, 1960 at Punta Espinosa was found by him in the same place on July 1st, 1961 and again in the middle of December of that same year.

The population of the species is fairly low, but it is difficult to obtain a precise survey of its numbers. Estimates vary between 1,500 birds, according to Lévêque, and Brosset's estimation of 5,000, which may be excessive. An average total of some 2,000 to 2,500 penguins seems reasonable.

Breeding appears to be confined to two islands only. According to Lévêque's observations, the penguins are spread out all around Fernandina Island (Narborough) and on the western coast of Isabela (Albermarle), including Elisabeth Bay where three islets shelter an important colony. Around these two neighbouring islands, the water is very deep, cool with a wealth of fish and the coastlines are favourable for nesting. Until now, reproduction has not been proved on other islands. Although some penguins occur here and there in the archipelago, they are mostly rare and spasmodic, for example on Santa Maria (Charles Island), Santa Cruz (Indefatigable) and James (San Salvador). In 1969, an unusual dispersal was observed, the causes of which are still unknown; on May 14th, J. Black observed a gathering of 500 birds at Pta Tortuga, Isabela; later, in June, penguins were noted at Santiago, Baltra, Rabida, Pinzon, Santa Cruz, Plaza Sur, Española, which considerably enlarges the actual, known area of distribution (according to Perry, 1969).

Is the Galapagos penguin an endangered species? Judging by the figures it does not appear that its population has decreased, nor that it is threatened; it has probably always been limited in number but fairly stable in its own small radius and also restricted by its natural enemies in the sea, such as sharks. However, man is certainly a danger to this trusting bird: "It is often captured by yachtsmen or passing fishermen owing to the fact that it is not at all shy and lets a man approach to within a few yards," stated Lévêque, and this is a risk that could be avoided. Like all the other species peculiar to the Galapagos, the penguin is protected by the Ecuadorian law of 1934, but its application appears to be very difficult and it is almost impossible to discover and punish all the violations committed by too-interested visitors, often for commercial purposes.

Conservation of the natural treasures of this archipelago is certainly not an easy task. Since the seventeenth century, human interference has continually endangered the fauna and flora, either by direct destruction or through the introduction of domestic animals, which, on returning to the wild, have multiplied in liberty to the detriment of the frail balance of nature. For numerous endemic species, this pillage has already caused regrettable damage. In this way, the several insular populations of the famous giant tortoises have died out and their future appears to be uncertain on the few islands where they still exist. Clandestine commercial abuse continues even today. The iguanas, fur seals, several species of birds and even the native rats are threatened in various ways, whereas the vegetation suffers from introduced herbivora.

In 1934, in response to an appeal from scientific organizations and the International Office for the Protection of Nature, the Government of Ecuador promulgated the first protective laws and 14 islands were proclaimed nature reserves. But this legislation is ineffective: during and after World War II, Laruelle observed that there was a boom in the tortoise trade and fishermen massacred seals with impunity. In 1954, when Eibl-Eibesfeldt landed on the Galapagos with the "Xarifa" expedition, he was so deeply struck by the signs of destruction that he described his impressions in a report to the International Union for Conservation of Nature and Natural Resources (I.U.C.N.) upon his return. He concluded that a biological station and a permanent observer would ensure protection in the long run. In 1957, he took part in the combined mission organized by UNESCO and I.U.C.N., at the request and with the collaboration of the Ecuadorian authorities, to examine the situation and choose the site for the future station.

In 1959, the "Charles Darwin Foundation for the Galapagos Islands" was formed in Brussels, under the patronage of UNESCO and I.U.C.N., to direct the study and protection of wildlife in the archipelago. The Charles Darwin Research Station, of which R. Lévêque began the construction on Santa Cruz (Indefatigable) in 1960, was inaugurated in 1964 and since then has been constantly occupied. The financial requirements of the foundation and the station were, to a great extend, covered by generous donations from various American countries and Europe, and by UNESCO; also with the help of the World Wildlife Fund which is concerned with six projects in the Galapagos.

The Republic of Ecuador also gave all possible support to this remarkable effort. Its government established the Galapagos National Park, thus confirming its intention to conserve the natural habitat of the islands under its protection. If the international co-operation outlined above had not intervened, the fauna and flora of the Galapagos would have been rapidly depleted without any valid economic justification whatsoever. No doubt the task of conservation is not ended, but the progress made in a short time gives hope of a calmer future.

CALIFORNIA CONDOR

Gymnogyps californianus

The American continents have the privilege of possessing the largest birds of prey in the world, the condors. The two species existing today are superficially alike, but differ enough for systematists to place them in separate genera. The great condor *(Vultur gryphus)*, occurring in the Andes, is the largest; the slightly smaller California condor is one of the most rare and endangered birds in the world. With a wing spread of almost nine feet (on an average 9 feet, maximum 9.6 feet), weighing 17 to 30 pounds, it is a gigantic raptorial bird, spectacular in flight. Like a great black glider with white underwing coverts, it soars effortlessly over the mountains floating on the currents of air. When circling in wide sweeps, the tips of its remiges spread out like fingers produce an almost musical whistling sound. Man has always been fascinated by the condor's size and this has led to its down-fall.

The California condor is harmless, it is a vulture, a scavenger that has never been known to attack a living creature. With steady, gliding flight it covers vast areas searching incessantly for carrion with its piercing eyesight. In the olden days, when it still patrolled the Pacific Coast, it was able to find the carcasses of seals, sea-lions and whales stranded on the beaches; inland, there were the corpses of deer and antelope. Then came the great herds of domestic livestock, brought west by the settlers, which provided most of its food. First sheep later cattle—especially calves killed by disease or accident—and, finally, horses. Even ground squirrels, victims of systematic poisoning, were part of its diet, perhaps also a reason for its decline. There is no economic justification for this great bird's destruction.

According to McMillan's account, the first written record of the California condor dates from 1602; a Spanish priest, member of an expedition, wrote in his journal that a flock of these vultures were eating the corpse of a whale washed up on the beach in Monterey Bay. In 1769, Spanish explorers assisted at the ritual sacrifice of a condor at an Indian encampment. It is a plausible theory that such ceremonies

were handed down from a distant age; many condor bones, nearly 8,000 years old according to the carbon-14 test, have been found at an archaeological site in Oregon. This human exploitation of the enormous bird, either for ritual sacrifice or for its feathers, is very ancient. It is likely that such exploitation gradually depleted the original population, accentuated its fear of man and encouraged it to nest in the most inaccessible areas possible.

The first specimens were collected in 1792 for a museum in England. Since then, shooting has been a major factor in determining the condor's fate. For more than a century it was quite natural to shoot it, sometimes as a splendid addition to a collection, sometimes for the pleasure of aiming at such a large target. The influx of settlers resulted in its disappearance over large areas of its former territory.

The range of the California condor once extended from the Columbia River in the State of Washington, south to the mountains of Baja California, an elongated territory bounded by the Pacific Ocean to the west and to east by the flanks of the Sierra Nevada, overlooking the Sacramento Valley. However, it is questionable as to whether it ever nested north of San Francisco Bay. Koford believes that condors reported from San Francisco to the Columbia River were juveniles or solitary adults on regular forays in these areas. In any case, all the early nesting sites were in the coast range between San Francisco and San Diego. From the fossil record of prehistoric cave deposits in Nevada, New Mexico and Texas, the species' original distribution would seem to have been much more extensive.

The data accumulated by Koford show a constant shrinkage of the condor's territory since the beginning of the nineteenth century. About 1840, it abandoned the Columbia River basin; in 1860 it disappeared from Sacramento Valley, and, in 1890, from all areas north of San Francisco. The last nesting reported in San Diego County occurred about 1900, south of Monterey in 1920, and the species has not been seen in Baja California since 1932, where it was already rare in 1914. Since the 1930s, the big vulture occupies an area reduced to eight or nine counties in the mountains northeast of Los Angeles. In this last stronghold, it maintained a population of some 60 individuals until 1952 (the year Koford completed his study). Each year, this figure included 10 nesting —or five nests a year—30 non-breeding adults and about 20 juveniles. The latter are easily recognized by the grey head and neck, as distinct from the adult's naked orange-coloured skin, bordered with red at the base of the neck. After a period of relative stability, the population declined for reasons as yet unknown. The 1964 census showed some 40 birds, one-third of which were immatures. In 1967, except for three nests, each with one young bird, a total of 46 individuals was seen. This is the latest information on the total world population of the California condor.

All the available evidence indicates that the species is gravely endangered. However, its imminent extinction was already predicted in 1890, and, since then, several experts have been pessimistic about its future and have considered its final disappearance inevitable. Its continued survival seems to discredit the concept of a species "at the end of its tether", an anachronism, essentially doomed. The reasons for its survival, no doubt due to the measures taken on its behalf, will be dealt with after the reasons for its decline have been examined.

First of all, it should be noted that even at the beginning of the nineteenth century, the condor population was relatively small, and, among other reasons, presumably limited by a low reproduction rate rather than by an inadequate food supply. Low reproduction is a characteristic biological feature of the great scavengers and its regulatory function was not a serious handicap until the coming of man. A pair of condors raise only one young bird every two years which does not begin to breed until the age of five or six. Its longevity is remarkable, an age of 45 has been recorded in captivity and it can be assumed that in the wild, the bird may live at least 35 to 40 years. Under the most favourable conditions, the

female only produces some 15 young, of which two should breed to assure a stable population. Moreover, the data already cited, show that a maximum of five young could be produced each year for the total population of 60 individuals existing in 1952. According to the United States Fish and Wildlife Service, each year only two juveniles will live. If this reproductive deficit is confirmed, the species is doomed; one nesting failure and any natural or accidental death is of vital importance. Conservation of the condor, therefore, depends on nesting success as well as on lower mortality, at least for those deaths attributable to man.

Although this vulture is sociably inclined, its nests are solitary. It chooses an absolutely isolated site in a hole on a cliff face or between two boulders, where it settles as far into the interior as possible, sometimes as much as 27 feet from the entrance. The single egg is laid in February-March straight on to the sand or on a layer of detritus. The male and female condor share the incubation period lasting at least 42 days and perhaps more than 50 (56 days for the Andean condor). The nestling, fed by regurgitation, initially twice a day, then once, leaves the nest at about five months although only reaching full flying capacity much later. In spite of the fact that by the following spring it is able to find its own food, it is still fed by its parents until 10 or 12 months old. The unusually slow development period explains why the adults only breed every alternate year.

Throughout this period, because the adults are extremely shy, the greatest danger is disturbance by man. Koford reports that human presence at less than 500 yards from the eyrie at a critical time, even for a few minutes, causes the pair to desert the egg or prevents feeding of the young for a whole day. The alarm is already given at a distance of a mile. Disturbance can result in abandonment of the nest and later of the site. Successful breeding, therefore, depends on absolute solitude, not only for the seven-month nesting period, but throughout the year. The nesting birds must be left in peace. Only through strict control of the area can this requirement be met. Exclusion of wood-cutters, hunters, oil-prospectors and even bird-watchers and photographers should be assured. Attracted by the rarity of the species, photographers have time and again caused the nest to be abandoned by their eagerness for pictures and lack of precaution. In the vicinity of the nesting birds any road construction and, naturally, building projects should be avoided. All this in areas dominated by urban development and by the increase in human population.

Another important element in the condor's life is its roosting site, used also for rest during the daytime. In actual fact, it only flies for a part of the day, or in bad weather not at all, perching on the branch of a pine-tree or often in the cleft of a rock or in a sheltered spot on the cliff face. Up to 20 birds may use a familiar roosting site which is accessible from the air, located in a strategic position and protected from the wind and, finally, within easy reach of food and water for drinking and bathing purposes. Intruders who disturb the birds' peaceful everyday routine must be kept out of these areas.

A vital factor for the survival of the condor is its food supply. This has proved less of a problem than was originally believed. The condor is not fussy about the state of carrion and, like all vultures, will eat meat in any stage of decay. However, the carcass must be in the open, preferably on an expanse of mountain grassland where 20 birds or more can congregate undisturbed by man, eagles or coyotes.

Suspicion often holds them back from a corpse placed at their disposal. More than one photographer, after a long wait and in spite of the greatest care, has not been able to obtain a picture of them. The bait was not touched (at least not until after the photographer had left). Nevertheless, enough food seems available despite the need for security and space. In the condor's present territory, there appears to be enough choice of prey at its disposal. Koford believed that resources had dwindled and in winter the situation would be critical although he had not seen any starving birds. On the other hand, in 1958, McMillan estimated that the rate of mortality in the domestic herds was normal and supplied enough food. He pointed out also that since 1940, deer had increased because of the extermination of the coyote, cultivation of arid land and hunting restrictions; periodic death which balanced the increase in numbers had brought a food complement to the big scavenging birds. Therefore, it is neither necessary nor desirable to resort to artificial feeding.

In many countries on several continents, vultures have suffered from poisoned bait used to exterminate wolves and other predatory animals. In California, the wholesale destruction of the coyote and the ground squirrel was organized in this way; first with strychnine, later with thallium sulfate and, finally, with the even more virulent "compound 1080". Condors ate some of the bait and carcasses of poisoned animals, but they proved surprisingly resistant to the poison. However, they were not completely immune, McMillan cites five individuals at least which died of poison. This danger should be eliminated.

Guns were and still are perhaps the main cause for the species' declining numbers. Formerly, the condor was shot whenever possible without compunction, and in 1880, when the settlers began to arrive, it rapidly declined. Between 1890 and 1910, commercial interests were also responsible: in 1895, a skin was sold for $45, which clearly shows the influence of the collectors' trade. In 1917, a museum in California refused to give more than $200 for three specimens. As from 1920, this trade, as well as that of the egg-collectors, appears to have ceased, probably as much due to a change in fashion as to conservation measures. However, Koford cites six individuals killed between 1925 and 1944, and believes that on an average at least one is killed each year. A sheep farmer informed him that he shot at any condor which approached his flock! Amongst the thousands of deer hunters in the vulture's territory are those who, with total disregard of the law, will fire at any bird of prey: in their ignorance, will they spare this one? And, perhaps, its continued decline could be attributed to carefully hidden "mistakes".

Egg-collecting, so current during the last century and at the beginning of this one, is fortunately outdated. It caused considerable damage to an already dwindling population. The first nest was discovered only in 1859, but soon the egg had a high rarity value on the market. The demand led to a relentless hunt and nest robbing became more and more frequent. According to McMillan, in 1895, one of the most active traders advertised a purchase price of $250 per egg; he affirmed that his collectors had found nine of these precious objects. Koford states that 19 eggs were taken between 1900 and 1902. By 1920, the era of "scientific" collection was over, but private collectors and museums possess at least 60 eggs and 130 skins of the California condor.

These figures are ample proof that this harmless vulture was exploited by man and did not undergo a natural decline. Man has also tried to defend it. As early as 1869, Cronise requested that it be given legal protection. In 1890, Cooper mentioned the existence of a forgotten law. In 1908, several zoologists lodged a complaint and a hunter was fined $50 for shooting a condor near Pasadena, a unique case to date. Effective conservation measures were taken only many years later. Under the law of California, the condor is totally protected, any violation is liable to a maximum fine of $500 or six months imprisonment or both. Actual practical measures were taken only as the result of research by the University of California in Berkeley; especially by Carl B. Koford with the assistance of the National Audubon Society. By describing the conditions necessary for the condor's existence and conservation, this basic scientific effort aroused new interest without which there would have been no hope for the species.

The essential requirement was to stop all disturbance near the nesting and roosting sites by the creation of strictly guarded reserves in the critical areas. Already in 1937, as a result of the strong protest lodged by Robert E. Easton and the National Audubon Society against a road construction project in the Los Padres National Forest, the United States Forest Service closed an area of 1,200 acres around Sisquoc Falls in Santa Barbara County to automobile traffic and development. This condor sanctuary is now threatened by road construction. Around 1960, a development plan was considered, and in 1963, a public road was under construction on the Sierra Madre, less than five miles from the reserve.... What McMillan terms "bulldozer philosophy" has opened a beautiful wilderness district in California to human invasion.

In 1947, again in the Los Padres National Forest, which shelters the hydrographic resources of the Sierra Madre, the United States Forest Service created the Sespe Wildlife Reserve, on Koford's advice. This new condor sanctuary, covering more than 53,000 acres of magnificent hilly wilderness around the Sespe River, was closed to the public and to further development, with limited rights for fishing, breeding of livestock and oil prospection. It contains most of the eyries and winter roosting sites and may be considered the key area, for which total protection is vital to the condor's survival. However, even this beautiful reserve only narrowly escaped the bulldozer. Everexpanding Los Angeles needed additional water supplies and a dam and reservoir were planned on the Sespe, just above the reserve. An access road would have been built, going right through the nesting zone. This would have been the end of a long battle, a fatal blow to the condor and, in the long run so much wasted effort. An additional water supply would have led to further development, more building lots, creating new needs.... Strong opposition from conservation circles won support from the public and a vote rejected the project in 1966 and 1967.

Today, the pressure of industrial and political interests threaten the last refuge of the California condor in the Sierra Madre. It will be the subject of further controversy as long as influential business groups do not understand the need to maintain inviolate these wilderness areas. Conservation education of the public and authorities is now of primary importance to the future of the species.

Among other solutions, breeding in captivity has been suggested. In fact, the San Diego Zoo has managed to breed the Andean condor in captivity. However, capture of birds to the detriment of the wild population involves great risk for a highly problematic result. Even if the numbers could be increased in captivity, this would mean a population deprived of its natural habitat. Koford writes: "A condor in a cage is uninspiring, pitiful and ugly to one who has seen them soaring over the mountains." It may prove impossible to return a captive-bred bird to the wild and the experiment would be made only as a final desperate effort. As long as the California condor is able to survive in its natural habitat, the best solution is to reinforce conservation based on scientific investigations, and above all, to ensure the inviolability of its refuges. McMillan even believes that with such a programme, if it is carried out with the necessary authority and care, the species may increase in number. No more than with the whooping crane, discussed below, the battle for the condor has not yet been won. It is, indeed, a test for our civilization.

WHOOPING CRANE
Grus americana

At least five of the 14 different surviving species of crane are endangered: the Japanese crane *Grus japonensis*, the Siberian white crane *Grus leucogeranus*, the hooded crane *Grus monacha*, the black-necked crane *Grus nigricollis* in Asia and, finally, the whooping crane of North America. On this latter continent, two endangered subspecies of the sandhill crane *Grus canadensis*, should also be included.

Why do these long-legged birds, completely different from storks in spite of appearances, run the risk of becoming extinct? On the one hand, their reproduction rate is low, cranes lay only two eggs and often raise but one young bird each year. This low fertility is normally compensated for by quite a long life potential (about 40 years in captivity). On the other hand, the wide open spaces and marshes where they live are rapidly dwindling because of the expansion of agriculture. Finally, their large size makes them easy to see and destroy. The progress of civilization would, therefore, appear to condemn them to extinction in the long run, especially through the transformation of their natural habitat.

The history of the whooping crane can be summarized in three phases and presents a striking analogy with that of the Californian condor. First, this species seems to have been thriving and widespread over large areas of North America during the Pleistocene period. In prehistoric days, it withdrew from the east and west towards its central area which still seems to be that of its annual migrations. Finally, the decline rapidly increased during the last century after white colonization, thus causing almost complete extinction. At the last minute, strenuous protection efforts have kept the situation stationary, but it would be too soon to confirm that this superb bird is saved.

Dazzling white highlights the jet black of its remiges at the tip of its wings; the length of its legs and neck makes this crane as tall as a man when it stands upright. Its elegant and sober plumage has no ornaments other than a bright red naked skin on its head and cheeks and black moustaches. Armed with a beak like a pointed dagger, its small head bears a pair of sparkling eyes which have a wild and piercing look. Whether the whooping crane is strutting on the ground or beating the air with its large wings, neck outstretched towards its goal, its matchless grace is ever apparent. However, its beauty is only at its best in the vast open spaces.

Such areas still existed in wild America. The nesting couples dispersed in huge swamps, from the prairies of Illinois, from Iowa and probably from Nebraska to the northern wastes between the Mackenzie River, the Great Slave Lake and Hudson Bay; some birds spent the whole year in Louisiana. In the autumn, the cranes' calls resounded across the sky and the Red Indians listened to this signal from nature. The cranes wintered in the virgin marshes to be found along the coast between Florida and Mexico.

This species was first mentioned in 1722 by the English naturalist, Mark Catesby, followed by Linné who described and named it in 1758. In 1770, the explorer Samuel Hearne wrote: "This bird visits the Hudson Bay in the spring, though not in great numbers. They are generally seen only in pairs and that not very often. It is esteemed good eating. The wing-bones of this bird are so long and large that I have known them made into flutes." Following this, numerous accounts, including that of Audubon, who painted a picture of the crane in 1821, showed that it was being confused with the sandhill crane, which is just as noisy, but much more abundant and travels in far larger groups. Likewise, the biological facts concerning the species remained unknown for a long time.

The whooping crane cannot escape attention. As well as being visible at a considerable distance in the flat open treeless spaces, they also announce their presence by loud trumpeting calls; but extremely suspicious, and very sensitive to disturbance, they flee man and his work. Thanks to the National Audubon Society's expedition led by Robert Porter Allen in 1942, this species was thoroughly studied for the first time at their winter refuge in Aransas, Texas. From the moment they arrived in October/November, the groups of birds dispersed and each pair or family selected its territory in an area of 400 acres on an average and chased the neighbours away. These domains always seem to be occupied by the same birds. It is in these briny marshes composed of ponds, islets and mud-flats that they feed, amongst other things on blue crabs of which an ample supply is a vital part of their food. Occasionally, they also visit the cultivated fields for grain. At the end of December, the beautiful nuptial dances begin: side by side, the male and female flutter their wings, rush forward with graceful jumps, bend their necks on to their backs and arch them forward again, all this accompanied by ringing calls. This ritual takes place more and more frequently until the end of April.

The serial route of the whooping crane from their winter quarters is due north. Since time immemorial the River Platte in Nebraska seems to have been their favourite resting place: in groups of 10 to 20 and rarely more than 40 birds altogether, they used to spend the night on the sand-banks and in the morning they searched for frogs and grasshoppers in the grassy plains dotted with bison. Today, the surviving birds still stop there, but the bison are no longer on the plains. . . . In the afternoon, the cranes reassembled in a wonderful roundabout, gliding in higher and higher spirals before setting off for Canada.

When they still nested in the vast areas of the great prairies, the couples isolated themselves in the wetland hollows scattered with flooded marshes and small lakes—a paradise for aquatic fauna. At a distance of at least a mile from the firm banks, the nest was built, consisting of a pile of grasses, rushes and reeds, where, in May, the female laid two reddish eggs flecked with brown. At this stage, information handed down by the egg-collectors comes to an end . . . and it was only much later that the length of incubation, about 32 days, was known. The nestling has a reddish brown down and develops slowly under the watchful eye of its parents. The young bird follows its parents when they migrate and stays with them all through the autumn and winter. It does not reproduce in the following year, but, after the spring separation, it probably joins other immature birds to spend the summer apart.

To return to history, in the middle of the nineteenth century an unparalleled human expansion took place in the wild expanses of the west, from the Mississippi to the Rocky Mountains. After the pioneers, immigrants invaded the virgin lands to exploit them for agriculture and cattle-raising. This heroic invasion by man was a catastrophe for the native tribes, for the fauna and for the secular balance of nature. In half a century everything changed and the whooping crane, unable to adapt, a prisoner to set principles, could only perish or leave. The drainage and tillage of the land, the increased human population and, especially, the unrestricted hunting were all disastrous factors. According to Robert Porter Allen's estimate, 1,300 to 1,400 individuals existed between 1860 and 1870, but, by 1900, the population was reduced to one-tenth of this figure.

For the innumerable guns, from which the settlers were hardly ever separated, there was no game law and everything that came in sight was killed. The bison was the first animal to be massacred, but the cranes were also good targets, particularly in the migrating season. In Nebraska, during the last decade of the century, the hunt reaches its climax, stimulated by the increasing value of the trophy. McNulty related that in 1887 whooping crane skins were sold at $2.50 each or $2 if sold by the dozen. Only three years later they fetched between $8 and $18 according to their quality. In the beginning, the eggs could be bought at 50 cents a piece, but by 1890 they cost $2. The collectors' trade has too often accelerated the destruction of rare species, with little of scientific interest to it. However, several egg-collectors provided good descriptions of the birds' nests and behaviour.

During the same period the habitat of the fauna underwent profound transformation. In the northern territories, the vast treeless plains and marshes where the cranes nested were replaced by cultivated fields, farms, pastureland, buildings and railway lines. They, therefore, disappeared from Illinois towards 1880, from North Dakota in 1884, from Minnesota in 1889 and in 1896 the last nest in the United States was found by an egg-collector in Iowa near Eagle Lake. In turn, the Canadian prairie was also taken over by man and, consequently, the *Grus americana* declined. On May 28, 1922, a game-keeper discovered a pair of cranes nesting in Saskatchewan; he seized the nestling which had just been hatched and wrung its neck " to efficiently collect this uttermost nib of surviving offspring and give it immortality in the form of a tag with a number on it", Allen wrote. This specimen is conserved in the Royal Musuem of Toronto and was probably the last crane chick to be seen alive by man for more than 20 years.

Thus, from 1880 to 1922, the greater part of the nesting areas were abandoned. The winter quarters were also taken over for development. From 1880 onwards, with the introduction of rice cultivation, thousands of square miles in Louisiana were transformed into rice-fields. Only the coastal areas remained favourable to a few groups of cranes, but soon they also were eliminated from these regions by the onslaught of trappers resulting from the fashion for musk-rat fur in the 1920s. In Texas, drainage, crops and cattle-raising brought about the gradual drying-up of the wetland areas, especially in the region of the Rio Grande. Before long, very few areas of land remained intact from New Orleans to Mexico, due, in particular, to the oil rigs.

Chased away from everywhere, the whooping crane was doomed to extinction, but its tragic decline was only recognized at a late date. In 1912, the ornithologist E. H. Forbush declared that the species was doomed. However, false reports on the number of birds maintained deceptive optimism until about 1932. Robert Porter Allen dispelled this illusion by research and proved that in 1912 the actual total must have been between 80 and 100. In 1918, a farmer in Louisiana killed 12 whooping cranes which were pecking at the rice behind his threshing machine. After this date, only three groups of wintering birds remained, totalling 57 individuals. In 1938, only 29 were in existence.

During this period, the dramatic reality was recognized. Indeed, after the "Migratory Bird Treaty", ratified in 1916 by the United States and Great Britain (on behalf of Canada), it became illegal to shoot a whooping crane, but this protection proved insufficient: the guns still continued to reduce its numbers. Allen believed that in ten years, between 1948 and 1959, more than half of the 39 missing adults had fallen victim to poachers. An information campaign was necessary, but even more urgent was a greater protection of the remaining refuges. Already remorseful for having allowed the passenger pigeon to become extinct and for having almost lost the bison, the public was deeply moved by the anxiety of the naturalists. The damage to natural resources became evident and created a new interest in the conservation of wildlife which penetrated the political and administrative circles: financial aid was at last obtainable for research and concrete measures.

During the winter of 1936-1937, a biologist from the Bureau of Biological Survey spotted several cranes in Texas on a coastal peninsula and requested that this region be protected. Part of this land, amounting to 70 square miles, was bought for $463,500 and the act creating the Aransas National Refuge was signed by President Roosevelt on December 31st, 1937. Looking back, it can be confirmed that without this decision, the species would have definitely disappeared a few years later. In 1938-1939, the cranes were at their lowest level: only 14 individuals were counted.

Situated on the edge of the Mexican Gulf, 75 miles north of Corpus Christi, the Aransas refuge consists of salt-marshes bordering on lagoons which separate the flat islands from the sea. Its remoteness preserved it from agricultural assault. However, it was not completely protected, the seller having reserved the right to exploit the land for minerals. In 1940, the first oil rigs were introduced and army engineers began construction of a navigable canal cutting straight through the cranes' best habitat; in addition, the Air Force proposed installing a shooting and bombing range on one of the outer islands not far from the reserve . . . .

In the meantime, the small sedentary relic population which had been rediscovered in 1929 in the marshes of White Lake, Louisiana, was destroyed by a hurricane during the summer of 1940. Seven of the 13 known cranes probably disappeared through being killed or eaten by farmers in the vicinity. The others died one after the other, the last one living until 1947.

Twenty-six whooping cranes, of which five were juveniles, came back to spend the winter of 1940-1941 at Aransas. There were 34 individuals in 1949-1950, but they decreased to only 21 in 1952-1953 and 1954-1955. These alarming fluctuations in number were partly caused by the disappearance of several adults and, in some years, by the absence of young birds, easily recognized by their reddish-grey plumage. An information campaign, utilizing all modern means, allowed the authorities and the National Audubon Society to reduce considerably, if not suppress, the losses due to uninformed hunters. But, the hazards of reproduction could not be fully explained as the cranes' summer refuges remained unknown in spite of careful research. However, little by little it became apparent that they were to be found around the Great Slave Lake in northern Canada.

In July 1954, purely by chance, the crew of a forest survey helicopter came across a family of cranes in the marshes of Wood Buffalo Park to the south of the Great Slave Lake. This region is very wild and difficult to penetrate; 17,300 square miles were reserved in 1922 to protect the last herd of wood bison. In 1955, after numerous difficulties, an expedition arrived in this area, near the River Sass, where Robert Porter Allen was able to see his first nest of whooping cranes from the air. Once on the ground, he also had the opportunity to appreciate the problems of the swamp, where even the Indians never ventured: hemmed in by forests it is an appalling "muskeg", a labyrinth of treacherous peaty marshes, ponds and meandering streams amongst inextricable wetland undergrowth. Here at least the rare birds seemed safe: 11 adults and six juveniles were seen that year on a subsequent flight.

From then on, the two territories where the species existed, 2,200 miles apart as the crow flies, were recognized and it was believed, protected. However, in 1959, a railway line should have been built in the middle of Wood Buffalo Park in order to link up the zinc and lead mines near the Great Slave Lake. . . . A protection campaign was launched by the Canadian Audubon Society and two years later the Canadian Government decided on a longer and more expensive route to avoid this territory.

After the discovery of the nesting places, it was possible to carry out research on the irregularities of reproduction. It appeared that the variable climate of the north was one of the main limiting factors and, in particular, for the year-old juveniles which easily die during wet summers. In addition, the extreme conditions of dryness alternating with abundant rainfall seemed to be equally unfavourable at the Aransas refuge as this upset the delicate balance of the soft and salty waters and, in consequence, the food resources for the birds in winter.

Over the years, other threats menaced the Texan sanctuary. With the population explosion, the neighbouring land increased in value. The development of fishing, hunting and water sports brought about not only the parcelling out of the land, but also more and more

Gymnogyps californianus

CONDOR DE CALIFORNIE

CALIFORNIA CONDOR

Tympanuchus cupido attwateri

TÉTRAS CUPIDON D'ATTWATER

ATTWATER'S PRAIRIE CHICKEN

Spheniscus mendiculus

MANCHOT DES GALAPAGOS

GALAPAGOS PENGUIN

Grus americana

GRUE BLANCHE

WHOOPING CRANE

frequent disturbances. Private aeroplanes circled the refuge and the army carried out bombing and shooting exercises on Matagorda Island. The project for a new canal endangered the natural irrigation of soft water, oil drills created the danger of constant pollution, likewise the exploitation of the shell reefs for the cement industry . . . and thus at a time when the crane population was finally on the increase and more space was needed, the possibilities for expanding the Aransas refuge decreased. In 1965, a request to buy a further 5,000 acres was refused. Nevertheless, the number of wintering whooping cranes rose to 42 in 1964-1965 and to 50 at the end of December 1968 !

Due to the problems created by the protection of the wild population, attempts were made to breed in captivity at the Aransas refuge in 1946 and later at the New Orleans Zoo. A female invalid, "Josephine", the last survivor of the Louisiana group, was coupled with "Crip", an injured male which had been captured. After several unfruitful nestings, a young crane was finally hatched in 1957 and several others later on between numerous abortive attempts. Besides, as from 1961, biologists of the United States Wildlife Service undertook research on the sandhill crane and in 1964 succeeded in breeding young birds from the eggs taken from nests in the wild. After this success, they considered the same experiment with the whooping crane, with the cautious agreement of the Audubon Society. In June 1967, nine nests were localized in Wood Buffalo Park and six eggs transferred by air to the Patuxent Wildlife Research Centre, Maryland. It was there that, after artificial incubation, five nestlings were hatched and four young birds were raised. It should be noted that this operation was carried out with great care and in no way reduced the wild population. In fact, when one egg was taken from the nest, the parents continued to sit on the other one and it is a known fact that they generally only raise one young bird.

In 1968, all the eggs artificially incubated were hatched, but out of the nine nestlings, three died from disease or malformation which also frequently occurs in the wild state. In 1969,

the same number of eggs gave seven hatchlings and it is not yet known how many of these young birds survived. However, at the and of 1968, eighteen whooping cranes existed in captivity, some of which were at Patuxent and the others in the zoos at New Orleans and San Antonio; 15 of them were bred in captivity.

In time, the American and Canadian biologists hope to form ten adult couples, obtain reproduction and then set free their offspring. In the long run, this plan would no doubt facilitate the creation of a breeding stock which would enable the species to survive in captivity under scientific supervision. However, this idea is far from being realized, To date, the sandhill cranes bred at Patuxent have not yet produced an egg which has hatched, nor have the whooping cranes bred at New Orleans been successful in reproducing. Without going into details concerning the controversial aspects of these attempts, it is considered doubtful that it will be possible for these birds to return to the wild state after having been accustomed to man since birth. A leading article in the *Audubon Magazine* (September 1969), stated that "Hatching cranes in captivity is not conservation of wildlife if avaries and zoo pens are the end of the road. It is merely an exercise in producing a new kind of poultry."

To the dangers already mentioned should be added the fact that from 1964 the hunting of the sandhill crane was resumed in derogation from the Treaty of 1916 which abolished it. Under pressure from the farmers angered by the damage to their crops caused by the large migrating groups, the shooting of cranes was allowed in Saskatchewan, Colorado, New Mexico and Texas. In spite of warnings, misunderstandings could cost the lives of some whooping cranes and for the survival of this species, each bird is of inestimable value.

The progress is encouraging, since there were only 14 birds in 1939 ,whereas in December 1968, 68 existed. The future is far from assured as danger still threatens and the free spaces grow smaller. . . . But the history of *Grus americana* continues. Thanks to the work and devotion of everyone concerned, a lost cause has been replaced by new hope.

ATTWATER'S PRAIRIE CHICKEN

Tympanuchus cupido attwateri

The fate of the three races of prairie chicken illustrates in varying degrees the impact of the colonization of the United States on the fauna typical of the North American plains.

One of the nine species of tetraonidae of the northern hemisphere, the prairie chicken looks like a domestic hen, with its yellowish plumage striped and barred all over with dark brown. In its native grassland habitat, this sober neutral garb provides excellent camouflage for both male and female. The male bird differs from the female only by long tufts of dark feathers on the sides of the neck and by the uniform colour of its short rounded tail. But it is completely transformed during the nuptial parade.

Prairie chickens are known especially for their spring dances on traditional "arenas". Between February and June, at dawn and dusk, the cocks of the district assemble around an open rise on which the earth has been beaten by generations of birds. Sometimes as many as 30 or 40 individuals can be counted. A cock enters the arena, unrecognizable in the dawn light: the erectile feathers of his neck are raised to form a hornlike headdress, large yellow eyebrows bush out above his eyes and his whole being is possessed by a consuming fever. Head lowered, wings and tail raised, he rushes into the arena and stamps so hard that the earth resounds to the frenzied beating of his feet. Suddenly, two large orange-coloured bags, filled with air, balloon on the sides of his neck, and he empties them while emitting a resonant snoring sound on three rising notes: "whoo-doo-doo". He leaps, pirouettes, circles, stamps his feet, fans out his tail and challenges the other excited cocks capering wildly around him. A far-reaching clamour rises from the arena filled with dancers and, in the background, the females approach ready for mating.

In common with other tetraonidae, this fascinating group display has an important biological function; namely to stimulate and synchronize fecundation. Prolific reproduction is this game bird's only defence against a high rate of mortality. The hen lays 7 to 17 eggs, on an average about a dozen: after 23 days of incubation the chicks leave the nest which is hidden in the long grass. From that moment, the birds are in constant danger, as has been proved by the extinction of the eastern subspecies.

When the white man arrived on the North American continent, the heath hen *Tympanuchus c. cupido*, was probably widely distributed over the sandy plains between Massachusetts and the Potomac River. According to Nuttall, it was so plentiful in some places that on the site of present-day Boston, a contract between master and servant stipulated: "Not to have heath hen brought to the table oftener than a few times a week". ... The heath hen was so easy to shoot that it was rapidly wiped out.

By 1870, its last stronghold was on Martha's Vineyard, an island off the coast of Massachusetts. In 1890, William Brewster counted only 200 birds there. In 1896, there were less than 100 and, by 1908 about 50 were left. That same year, a reserve of 1,600 acres was created in the centre of the island and the population—carefully guarded—increased to 2,000 individuals by 1915. Confinement to one locality, however, was to prove fatal. In May 1916, fire destroyed most of the heath hen's island habitat. This was followed by an extremely severe winter which reduced its numbers to 150 individuals, mostly males. In 1920, when it had increased once more to 200 birds, disease struck the final blow;

there were too few survivors and the end was inevitable. In 1927, only 13 birds remained on Martha's Vineyard. In 1928, two, and the last one disappeared in 1932. The eastern subspecies had been annihilated.

Although farther west, in the Mississippi River Basin the *pinnatus* subspecies is still fairly abundant and is thriving in some areas, its decline is causing grave anxiety. Formerly, the greater prairie chicken was plentiful over a vast territory, extending from Canada to Texas. It even prospered from expending agriculture and land clearance, which, especially after 1860, brought it new resources and led to its establishment in deforested areas. There is no doubt that the hunting of this game bird attained fantastic proportions. In 1850, from a single county in Indiana, there were 20,000 individuals on the market. But this uncontrolled slaughter did not become really disastrous until the development of cereal farming reversed the hitherto favourable conditions created by prairie alternating with cultivated land. The loss of its natural habitat led to the bird's disappearance, first on the outskirts of its territory, precisely on the land most suited to it.

The species has now almost disappeared from Saskatchewan and the States of Iowa, Ohio, Kentucky, Tennessee and Arkansas. In Canada very few remain in Manitoba and Ontorio. It is seriously threatened in such highly developed States as Michigan and Wisconsin. In Indiana, where there were more than 100,000 in 1912, only 12 remained in 1966. In Illinois, the population dropped from 2,000 in 1955 to 300 in 1968. The western prairies, where the climate is less favourable, have also been affected by this decrease. In Kansas, for example, the bag was 80,000 in 1958 and only 4,000 in 1961 and 1962.

Concern for the fate of the greater prairie chicken has been shown not only by stricter hunting regulations, but, above all, by the creation of societies and foundations dedicated to the conservation of the last prairies inhabited by these birds in the States where they are most likely to disappear.

The third subspecies, found on the coastal plains of the south, have been even more seriously affected by agricultural development.

Smaller and darker than the races mentioned above, it was named *Tympanuchus cupido attwateri* by Charles E. Bendire in 1894, in honour of Professor Attwater. At the beginning of the century, about one million birds lived on a territory extending across south-west Louisiana to north-east Texas, in the vast, gently rolling plains covered with grass as far as the eye could see. This land was too fertile to escape the plough and was cultivated with wheat, cotton and rice. Smaller and smaller islands of the original plain remained. Heavily hunted, confined to increasingly small "pockets" of land, the Attwater's prairie chicken proportionately decreased. In 1937, a census found only 7,300 individuals in Texas, while the species had disappeared from Louisiana. In 1963, it was estimated that 1,335 remained: in 1965, barely 750. In 28 years a 90 per cent decrease had occurred and only isolated groups existed. The final outcome was inevitable if nothing was done to save the subspecies.

The only practical solution was to purchase enough suitable land. Already in 1941, the need to establish a sanctuary had been recognized. In 1963, on the advice of the biologists Val W. Lehmann and R. C. Mauermann, the first steps were taken to acquire 3,450 acres north of Eagle Lake in the county of Colorado.

In collaboration with the Nature Conservancy, the World Wildlife Fund financed this project with the help of a great many American donations totalling more than $434,000 by the end of 1968. In that year, the reserve was officially recognized as a Natural Landmark by the United States National Park Service.

This sanctuary is considered the best territory for the Attwater's prairie chicken on the Gulf of Mexico. It possesses about one-third of the existing population of this subspecies. The Soil Conservation Service and the University of Texas have undertaken an ecological survey to determine how the habitat can best be maintained and improved to obtain a maximum population, putting particular emphasis on cattle grazing and the burning of grass.

Since the creation of this sanctuary, the Attwater's prairie chicken has increased fourfold. There are estimated to have been 30 birds in 1936, 65 in 1964 and 100 at the end of 1966. At the beginning of 1968, there were 350 to 400 individuals, of which a hundred breeders remained after the spring dispersal, an encouraging sign. Furthermore, the ponds scattered over the plain make excellent winter quarters for waterfowl. The Eagle Lake Sanctuary is an achievement which may serve as an example; its creation has not only saved the southern race of the prairie chicken from extinction, but also preserves a natural environment of great interest.

To complete the story, mention must be made of the lesser prairie chicken, which many ornithologists consider to be a separate species *Tympanuchus pallidicinctus*, but which others count as a geographic subspecies of the prairie chicken. It occurs in New Mexico, Colorado, Kansas, Oklahoma and northern Texas. Although it does not appear to be in any immediate danger, its numbers have already substantially decreased. The conservation of its habitat should be considered while there is still time.

KIRTLAND'S WARBLER *Dendroica kirtlandii*

Almost all the species of songbirds threatened with extinction live on islands, where their decline, in common with other types of fauna, has been caused mainly by changes in their natural habitat and the introduction of foreign animals upsetting the ancient balance of nature. Some continental species appear to have been always numerically few and very limited in range, either because of a special preference for an ecologically restricted breeding area, or for unknown reasons, apparently unrelated to human influence. At least two examples belong to the large family of Parulids or American warblers.

The most incomprehensible case is the Bachman's warbler *Vermivore bachmanii*, discovered in 1833 in South Carolina and described by Audubon. Thereafter it was seen occasionally and isolated breeding reported from time to time in as many as ten different states, situated between Arkansas, Louisiana and Virginia. Some wintering birds were found also in Florida and Cuba.

The natural habitat of Bachman's Warbler is in swampy river edges, admittedly rapidly dwindling, but large areas are still to be found; even so, no stable population has yet been discovered. Nobody knows why this extraordinarily rare little bird makes such unpredictable and fitful appearances, nor how its tiny relic or surviving population still exists. The species is nearly extinct, wrapped in mystery and nothing can be done. . . .

On the other hand, the case history of the Kirtland's warbler has a happier ending. On May 13th, 1851, an unknown songbird was captured on the shores of Lake Erie, near Cleveland, Ohio, and given to the naturalist J. P. Kirtland. He, in turn, gave to it the name of *Sylvicola kirtlandii*, in honour of his friend. Later incorporated in the genus *Dendroica*, the new species was to remain a problem for more than half a century.

An amusing anecdote concerns the fact that a specimen had already been collected ten years earlier; in October 1841, Samuel Cabot, on an expedition to Yucatan, had picked it up on board his ship off the Bahamas. The specimen remained forgotten in a drawer of his collection until 1865. In the event, the winter quarters of this rare bird were discovered in the Bahamas in January, 1879.

Over the years, a certain number of migrating birds were recorded between the Great Lakes and Florida, but the breeding areas were unknown until 1903. In that year, E. H. Frothingham, of the University of Michigan, fishing for trout in the Au Sable River near Oscoda, was intrigued to hear an unknown song which led him to a small colony of Kirtland's warblers. Following his instructions, Norman A. Wood was able to find the first nest in a stand of jack pine in the vast forests of the lower peninsula of Michigan.

That these historical incidents are so few is surprising, because the bird is easily recognized in the spring by an experienced observer. It is one of the largest Parulids, 5 ¾ inches in length. Its plumage is bluish-grey above with black streaks on the back and lemon-yellow below; it has dark spots on the flanks and two white bars on the wings. Its habit of "wagging" its tail up and down is characteristic. Furthermore, the male's song, clear and lively cadances, attracts attention and the adult is not at all shy in its summer territory. Only the ecological needs and very limited range of its small population can explain why the mystery surrounding this bird has taken so long to clear up.

Today, complete information is available, thanks to the painstaking research of Josselyn van Tyne and the monograph by Harold Mayfield (1960). The Kirtland's warbler breeds only in the pine forests between Lake Michigan and Lake Huron, where all its colonies are grouped within a radius of 60 miles. In 1951, Mayfield and his colleagues organized a census and 432 singing males were counted. In the following year, the count was 502. The total population, therefore, is about a thousand individuals at the beginning of the breeding season, the numbers appearing to be fairly stable. However, for a continental migratory bird, this is an extremely low figure, the reason being that it depends upon a very special habitat which is constantly changing.

On their arrival in May, all the breeding pairs of *Dendroica kirtlandii* settle in dense groves of young jack pine *Pinus banksiana*, which must not be more than five to 18 feet high and six to 13 years old, with interlocking branches reaching to ground level, alternating with clearings of low vegetation. Finally, a dry, permeable soil, preferably sandy, is necessary. If all these requirements are met, the birds settle in loose colonies of six to 12 pairs, each occupying a territory of about eight and a half acres.

The nest is built on the ground, well hidden in the undergrowth. Four or five eggs are laid in June and incubation by the female lasts two weeks. Both parents raise the nestlings which are ready to leave after nine days. The production of a second clutch after the young birds have flown away is exceptional but if the first clutch is destroyed a second is normally produced. Autumn migration occurs between the end of August and mid-September. By then, however, the birds are a darker brown colour and more difficult to recognize. In the winter quarters on the Bahamas, the warblers are found on all the islands in the low scrub where they are scattered and inconspicuous.

The collectors who frequented these islands found the species fairly abundant between 1880 and 1900. This is no longer true today; a relatively large population which existed at the end of the last century has since decreased. Mayfield's study tends to prove that the population increase during the eighties and nineties was caused by the heavy lumbering operations in the Michigan forests and the species' subsequent decrease resulted from this practice being abandoned and also from the parasitism of the cowbird.

The cowbird *Molothrus ater*, was limited formerly to the vast bison prairies farther to the west, but settlement favoured its expansion in the forest regions cleared by the felling of trees and cattle breeding. This bird seems to have reached Michigan around 1840, and the north of the state towards 1870, at the same time as the wave of lumbermen and farmers. Some thirty years later, it was plentiful even in the forest clearings, where the Kirtland's warbler had just been discovered. It is known that, like the cuckoo, the cowbird lays its eggs separately in the nests of other songbirds for the young parasite to be incubated and raised by its foster parents. It instinctively pushes out the eggs and chicks which bother it, and, therefore, any nest adopted by the cowbird is lost for reproduction of its involuntary host. From 1900, this factor has certainly contributed to reducing the number of *Dendroica kirtlandii*. According to Mayfield's statistics, 55 per cent of the nests of this species are taken over by the cowbird and, if other natural factors of destruction are taken into account, it appears that less then 34 per cent of the warbler's eggs produce fledged young. His conclusion is that parasitism is the most important limiting factor for the species.

The natural habitat, described above, obviously plays a fundamental role. To put it briefly, the Kirtland's warbler depends on fire. In fact, since time immemorial, the dry forests have been ravaged by fires, caused by lightning or by the indigenous human inhabitants. Fires raged unchecked until extinguished by rain, changes in wind or water obstacles. If the flames ravaged great tracts of forest, they also prepared the way for regeneration, because only great heat can burst the tight cones of the jack pine and disperse the seed. After a few years, the burnt areas are covered with a thick carpet of young pines and the warblers settle in at once as soon as the trees are the right height, that is after six or seven years. As soon as the trees grow too high, the birds abandon the site and look for another one. Thus, the existence of the species has always been linked with forest regeneration in the aftermath of fire. The nesting sites are not destroyed, as the fires occur at the end of the summer, in the dry season.

If the jack pine is very widely distributed across Canada and extends to the south of the Great Lakes, it appears that only the north of the peninsula, between Lakes Michigan and Huron, satisfy the requirements of the Kirtland's warbler, as much by the type of soil as by the few natural fire breaks. According to Mayfield, this would account for the extremely limited territory of this bird. Furthermore, the jack pine plains offer ideal shelter for its nest and few enemies and competitors exist. In any other habitat, it would perhaps have been wiped out.

From about 1875 to 1900, lumbering operations developed considerably in Michigan. In the vast areas felled, the unwanted jack pine was usually burnt, and this practice certainly increased the regeneration favourable to the warbler. In any event, the increase in population observed during this period has been credited to this factor. Later on, the great felling operations ceased; fires, fought by the forest services, affected smaller areas and resulted in a decrease in numbers, intensified by the intervention of the cowbird. Mayfield writes, however, that during this century, the availability of breeding areas was not the factor limiting the population of the bird. Today, modern fire-control methods are becoming more and more effective, and, in the long run, could result in the disappearance of the Kirtland's warbler by depriving it of the habitat vital to its survival. On the other hand, the jack pine is used extensively for the pulp industry and replantings are probably less favourable than natural regeneration brought about by the great fires of earlier days. Finally, the jack pine stands are subject to variable economic conditions. The future of the species, therefore, now depends, above all, on man.

In 1950, ecological research and the almost nation-wide interest in this little bird encouraged the consideration of ways and means of maintaining the jack pine plains without sacrificing forestry interests. In collaboration with the local sections of the Audubon Society, as from 1957, the Michigan Department of Conservation set aside 4,010 acres as an experimental area for carrying out prescribed and controlled burning. This was a remarkable change in policy. In 1964, a block of approximately 500 acres of jack pine was felled, trees heavily loaded with cones were left standing (15 or so per acre), and controlled burning was then attempted. The natural regeneration proved successful, and it may be hoped that this area, especially prepared for the Kirtland's warbler, will be colonized by the birds as soon as the pines grow to the height required. Other blocks must be treated in the same way every five years, to create favourable jack pine plains in the Huron National Forest.

Along with these experiments, observers are continuing to study the population of the species, in particular by ringing the breeding birds. Their research also includes the parasitism of the cowbird and the method of controlling its numbers. Excellent co-operation between the authorities, societies and ornithologists offers a better future for this unassuming little songbird. Although it is of no economic significance the very rarity of the Kirtland's warbler ensures that it remains for the public a symbol that must not be allowed to disappear.

SYLVETTE DE KIRTLAND   *Dendroica kirtlandii*   KIRTLAND'S WARBLER

EUROPE

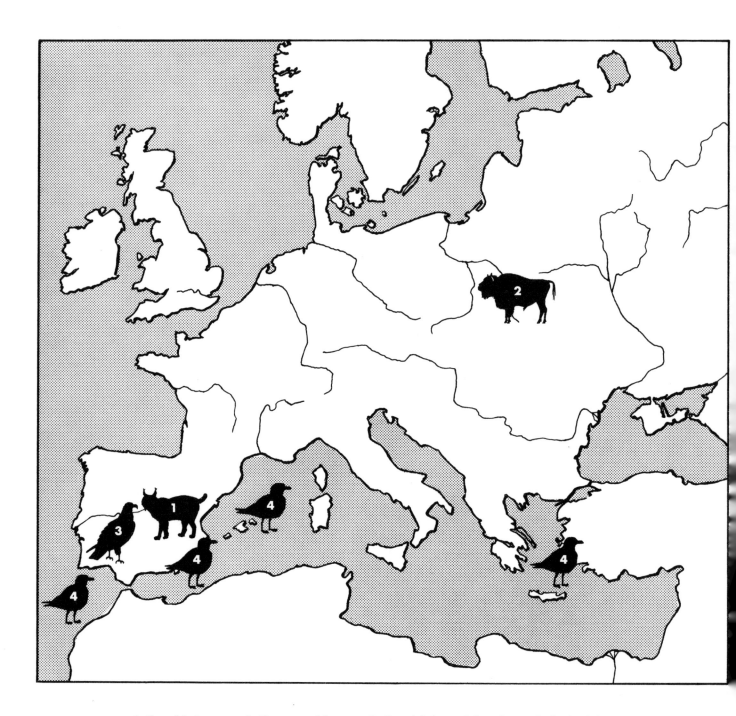

1, Spanish lynx — 2, European bison — 3, Spanish imperial eagle — 4, Audouin's gull

SPANISH LYNX

Felix lynx pardina

The lynx is a medium-sized member of the cat family, with long legs, short tail, and ears terminating in prominent black tufts. The general ground colour is light sandy-brown, with indistinct body markings.

The Spanish race (considered by some authors to be a distinct species, *Lynx pardina*) is smaller than the Eurasian forms, with shorter fur and more pronounced spots. The male is bigger and paler than the female, with larger head, neck and feet, as well as longer ear-tufts.

At one time the lynx was widely distributed throughout the forested parts of Europe, with the Spanish race occupying the greater part of the Iberian Peninsula, possibly as far north as the Pyrenees. It has gone from most of western Europe, apart from a few mountain regions. Farther east, however, it· still occurs in the Carpathians, the Soviet Union and elsewhere, while in Sweden it is reported to be gradually extending its range.

The lynx is known to exist in a few parts of the Pyrenees, but there has long been some doubt whether Pyrenean specimens are of the Spanish or the nominate race. This question was at least partially resolved when in 1965 Beaufort published particulars of his discovery of a skull in the vicinity of the Pic du Midi d'Ossau in the French Pyrenees, the first incontrovertible evidence ever to be obtained from this range of mountains which he established beyond doubt as belonging to the Central European race, *Felis lynx lynx*. Beaufort emphasizes, however, that the possibility of the two forms coexisting in the same region cannot be ruled out.

The lynx is essentially a forest-dweller (though the Spanish race has adapted itself to more open country). Widespread deforestation has destroyed much of its natural habitat, obliging it to retreat to less favourable regions. Although it appears to have no fear of man, it cannot tolerate living in close proximity to man, with the result that it will generally leave an area in which permanent settlement is established. This process has been accelerated by the relentless persecution to which the animal is invariably subjected because of the damage it sometimes inflicts on domestic livestock. For this reason it is understandably unpopular with shepherds; and, in some of the remoter parts of Europe, peasant myth and folk-lore credit the lynx with almost supernatural powers.

Today, the Spanish race is known with certainty only from the southern part of Spain where it is confined to some of the more inaccessible mountainous regions such as the Sierra Morena, the Sierra de Guadalupe and Montes de Toledo, as well as to certain controlled hunting blocks, or "cotos", in the delta of the Guadalquivir. Total numbers are not known, but Valverde (1967) estimates the lynx population in the *marismas*—which is believed to contain the bulk of the remaining population—at no more than fifteen pairs, about ten of which are in the Coto Doñana. It was in this region that he undertook his invaluable study of the Spanish lynx and its ecology, on which most of our present knowledge of the animal is based.

The lynx possesses keen vision as well as sharp hearing and an acute sense of smell. Despite its small size—an adult male recorded by Valverde weighed 59 pounds—it is extraordinarily powerful, and capable of attacking animals as large as a full-grown deer, though it usually restricts its activities to preying on the new-born young during the fawning season in May and June. Mountfort notes that "when young are being fed in the lair there is a sharp increase in attacks on fawns. A few years ago one pair of lynxes was known to have killed twenty-five fawns before their lair was found and the kittens destroyed."

Perhaps the only inhabitant of the Coto with little to fear from the lynx is the wild boar. An adult boar, or a sow with a sounder of piglets, is a formidable opponent. Normally, however, the lynx preys on smaller creatures, including birds and rodents, but above all rabbits; and, being indolent by nature, it prefers to attack those that are in poor physical condition, thus performing a useful service.

Valverde emphasizes the importance of the rabbit as the basic prey of the lynx. The 1955 outbreak of myxomatosis was a serious threat not only to the lynx but also to several other predatory mammals and birds of the Coto, as it practically wiped out the rabbit population. Since then, however, the threat has receded, and Mountfort states that the surviving rabbits "evidently bred immunity to the disease and are today as numerous as ever...".

Among the birds, the red-legged partridge (*Alectoris rufa*) is particularly common in the region and, to judge from the number of mutilated carcasses, probably figures prominently in the lynx's diet. Valverde relates an interesting report of a covey of partridges flying low over a bush under which a lynx was hidden from view. As the birds passed overhead, it leaped into the air and seized one in its paws. Mountfort mentions a similar incident.

The lynx needs space, and each individual occupies a large territory. According to Valverde, lynx territories in the Coto Doñana average from about 2 $\frac{1}{2}$ to 6 miles in diameter, and may be larger in winter. He cites an example of one animal which is known to have covered a distance of 12 to 19 miles in a single night.

Hunting generally takes place at night, but occasionally during the early morning and evening. The normal method involves stalking a rabbit from the cover of bushes, the lynx pressing itself to the ground in the manner of a cat, or, alternatively, lying in wait at the edge of a clearing where rabbits are grazing ready to pounce when one comes within reach. Valverde provides evidence to show that hunting may sometimes be done in pairs: "Justo Cuadros, head guard of Cazorla, told me that one winter's day he was drawn by the cries of a deer. When he came near he saw a lynx devouring the animal, while a second lynx stood nearby."

For the greater part of the year the lynx is inconspicuous and silent, but during the rutting season, which in the Coto Doñana is generally in January, or a little earlier, it becomes less cautious and is frequently heard at night. Valverde likens its howls to "a raucous catawauling similar to that made by a cat when the male bites its ears and neck at the climax of coupling. This cry of the rut is invariably emitted in the evening or at night, very rarely in the middle of the day. The two partners often answer each other when they are still some distance apart. Possibly its main function in these circumstances is to facilitate the meeting of the sexes."

The reproductive rate is low. Litters of up to four have been recorded in the Coto Doñana, but the average appears to be two. Cub mortality may be high. They mature rapidly, however, leaving the lair at the age of about four months and becoming independent of their parents a month or so later.

Lairs differ considerably according to the biotope. Favoured localities include dense thickets of briar or thorn in which "nests" are constructed of twigs and grass; hollow trees; burrows; and even old storks' nests, one of which was in a pine tree 30 or 40 feet from the ground.

The delta of the Guadalquivir comprises about 750 square miles of marshlands, and is one of only two major areas of unspoiled wetland remaining in western Europe, the other being the Camargue at the mouth of the Rhone. This extensive region is a haven for large numbers of birds, both resident and migratory, including many on passage to and from northern Europe and Africa. The *marismas* therefore has an importance which reaches far beyond its own boundaries.

For this reason the World Wildlife Fund gave high priority to the challenging task of raising the substantial sum of money required to purchase part of the area. After several years and with the collaboration of the Spanish Government (who contributed one third of the cost) this aim was achieved; and in June 1965 representatives of W.W.F. formally handed over the title deeds of the Coto Palacio de Doñana to the Spanish authorities, the Consejo Superior de Investigaciones Científicas (Higher Council for Scientific Research), who at once accorded it the status of a Nature Reserve. The area concerned is about half the Coto Doñana (25 out of a total of 50 sq. miles).

The Coto Doñana is essentially a spit of land approximately 25 miles in length and varying from about 1 to 8 miles wide, wedged between the Atlantic on the south-west and the Marismas de Guadalquivir on the east. The acquisition of

LYNX PARDELLE   *Felis lynx pardina*   SPANISH LYNX

this area is the World Wildlife Fund's most significant achievement in Europe to date, for it safeguards part of what is unquestionably one of the finest wildlife areas in western Europe. In addition to wildfowl, about half the species of birds occurring in Europe have been recorded from the Coto Doñana, among them the rare Spanish imperial eagle. The Coto Doñana is primarily of ornithological interest, but the establishment of a nature reserve is also of paramount importance to the preservation of the Spanish lynx, because although numbers have greatly diminished compared with half a century ago it is nevertheless believed to be more abundant there than on any other *coto*, from some of which it has already disappeared. Despite its rarity, the animal is moreover still officially listed as vermin, which entitles anyone to kill it on sight at all seasons; but this will no longer be permissible within the new reserve.

Management of the lynx will presumably be necessary within the context of an overall management plan for the reserve, but a difficulty arises in making proper provision for the animal until more is known of its biological and ecological requirements. In his capacity as Director of the reserve, Dr. Valverde intends to do everything possible to overcome this problem by continuing his studies of the animal.

This brief account would be incomplete without reference to Max Nicholson's brilliant sketch of the ecology of the Coto (in Mountfort, 1958) which bears out his assertion that it ranks as "one of the outstanding ecological demonstration areas in all Europe". The character and importance of the delta region as one of Europe's pre-eminent wilderness and wildlife areas are well summarized when he writes: "The dry habitats of the sandy coto and the wet habitats of the silty *marismas* are both rich in wild life, including red and fallow deer, wild boars, lynxes and many other mammals, reptiles, amphibians and invertebrates. . . . The different habitats . . . have their characteristic species, yet all are interlocked, and it is the broad series of differing opportunities for existence which make this delta so remarkable for its fauna and flora. But this is not all. Placed on the hinge between Europe and Africa, the region has been able to draw on an exceptionally wide range of species to build up its riches, and has not suffered the disastrous impoverishment of successive Ice Ages, or of geographical and climatic isolation. It has also, to a very rare degree, been shielded by vigilance and care over many generations from the damage inflicted almost universally in Europe by modern economic exploitation. It therefore forms a natural monument of outstanding importance and scientific interest, by the preservation of which from disturbance and development the present owners and Spain itself set an example to the world."

83

EUROPEAN BISON   *Bison bonasus*

As Kowalski has shown, the genus *Bison* originated in southern and eastern Asia during the Pliocene, and spread across Asia and into Europe during the Early Pleistocene. Later, in the Middle Pleistocene, it crossed the Bering Straits land connection into North America.

The genus is represented by two living species: *Bison bison*, the American bison, which until relatively recently was widely distributed in North America; and *B. bonasus*, the European bison, or wisent, which inhabited the deciduous forests of Europe. The latter is divided into two subspecies: the Lithuanian (or lowland) bison, *Bison bonasus bonasus;* and the more lightly built Caucasian (or mountain) bison, *Bison bonasus caucasius*.

The wisent stands higher at the shoulder than the American bison, and has longer legs, and a longer and less barrel-like body. Its head is smaller and carried higher. Its hindquarters are more powerfully built and better proportioned. Its mane is thinner, but the fur on its hindquarters heavier. The wisent has poor eyesight, but is keen of scent, and is a wilder and more wary animal than its American relative. It was much more difficult to hunt as it was said to be almost unapproachable. The American bison's heavy forequarters and weak hind legs placed it at a disadvantage when chased uphill; but the wisent's build meant that it could give an equally good performance on either steep or level ground.

The European bison is essentially a woodland animal and a browser. It causes surprisingly little damage to the forest, less than is caused by small game. The bark of the common sallow, poplar and European aspen is eaten, as well as the bark of broad-leaved trees such as lime, maple, and ash (although birch bark is scarcely touched). Young spruce and pine shoots are occasionally browsed, but acorns are the preferred food: during the season when the oaks shed their fruit the bison subsist exclusively on acorns. The American species, on the other hand, is primarily a creature of the open prairies and a grazer. This fact caused the American bison to undertake lengthy seasonal migrations in search of grazing, but the European species was relatively static. The depletion and, eventually, the almost total eradication of the indigenous forests of Europe was therefore the principal reason for the latter's decline. Hunting was a contributory factor, but of less significance than destruction of the forested habitat.

The original range of the species was known to have included western and southern Europe as far east as the Caucasus, and northward as far as the Lena River in Siberia. According to Hatt, "the wisent was well known to the people of early Mesopotamia and must have been an inhabitant of the fringing forested hills". By the beginning of the twentieth century, the only surviving wild herd of the nominate race was in the Bialowieza Forest in Poland, on the border with the U.S.S.R., which had been a royal hunting preserve since the eleventh century. The Polish kings stringently protected both the forest and the wisent. After the partition of Poland in 1803, the same policy was followed by the Russian tsars, the herd being maintained for the personal use of the Russian Imperial family. On rare occasions some were shot by privileged visiting sportsmen, and a few were presented to zoological gardens.

In 1914 there were 737 animals in the Bialowieza herd: but all were killed during the First World War and the Russo-Polish war of 1919-1921. The only survivors were about 45 animals of Bialowieza origin which some years before had been distributed among some of the zoological gardens of Europe, and the herd in the Pszczyna Forest (incorporated into Poland in 1923) on the Duke of Hochberg's estate in southwestern Upper Silesia. This reserve was established as a breeding centre in 1865 with a bull and three cows from Bialowieza presented by Tsar Alexander II. By 1921 the Pszczyna herd numbered more than 70: but only three specimens (a cow and two bulls) survived the political upheavals in Upper Silesia in that year.

These three, together with two cows purchased from Sweden and another bull from Germany,

BISON D'EUROPE   *Bison bonasus*   EUROPEAN BISON

were sent in 1929 to Poland, where they were kept under semi-captive conditions in a special 500 acre fenced enclosure in part of the Bialowieza Forest, of which 70 acres were cleared and sown to pasture grasses. These five animals formed the basis of the various herds which have since been re-established in the country.

In 1923 a proposal by the Polish zoologist Jan Sztolcman led to the founding of the International Society for the preservation of the wisent, under the chairmanship of Dr. Kurt Priemel, director of the Frankfurt Zoological Garden. This society made a very significant contribution to the rehabilitation of the species. Among other matters, it was responsible for compiling a stud book—the result of devoted work by Dr. Erna Mohr, Jan Zabinski, and others—containing particulars of all living pure-bred specimens of *B. bonasus*. The first *Pedigree Book of the European Bison* published in 1930 contained data on 40 individual animals. New editions of the stud book have subsequently appeared at irregular intervals.

By 1939 there were 30 animals in Poland and 35 in Germany, as well as a few others elsewhere in Europe. In spite of heavy losses, the Second World War was not as disastrous for the bison breeding centres as the First World War, and 46 animals were recorded as surviving in Poland in 1946. At that time no more than a dozen remained in Germany, in the Springe Reserve and at the Hellabrunn Zoo, Munich.

After the Second World War, Poland took the lead in the bison-breeding programme. Zabinski stated in 1949 that the basic material then available at the three Polish breeding centres comprised nine pure-bred cows of the nominate race at Pszczyna; three pure-bred cows at Bialowieza, together with a further three having a small admixture of Caucasian genes; and four cows at Niepolomice all containing Caucasian genes.

Zabinski adds that the Polish Ministry of Forestry proposed placing the hybrids "in a separate reservation and to interbreed them in order to maintain a possible accumulation of genes of the extinct race. . . . It is difficult to foresee whether it would be possible to reconstitute the Caucasian bison from this material,

as Bashkirov in the U.S.S.R. is planning to do. All the animals in question have a very low percentage of Caucasian blood, representing the fifth or sixth generation in relation to their only Caucasian ancestor, the bull Kaukasus. . .".

More recently the number of breeding centres in Poland has increased to five: Bialowieza, Pszczyna, Niepolomice, Smardzewice, and Borki.

Commencing in 1952, measures were taken to release wisent into the Bialowieza Forest. The

experiment involved liberating animals which had long been living in semi-captivity, and giving them the opportunity to become adapted to a wholly wild existence.

Insufficient time has elapsed to enable firm conclusions to be drawn; but initial results are encouraging. The free-ranging herd is in excellent condition—better than that of the semi-captive herd—and calves born in the wild state have developed well.

By the end of 1966 the free-living herd numbered 119, of which 98 had been born since the release. Krysiak estimates that 2,500 acres of forest will support two bison without damage to the habitat; but more recent studies suggest that the potential carrying capacity may be substantially greater.

The rehabilitation of the species calls for re-introductions on a larger scale. There are now enough specimens to achieve this aim, but the difficulty is that no suitable locality extensive enough for the purpose exists except in the Soviet Union. In the meantime, the Polish authorities are anxious to distribute the bison widely over the globe as an insurance against the possibility of catastrophic losses from disease or other causes.

The original range of the Caucasian race, *B. b. caucasius*, is not well known, partly because of confusion with the aurochs, *Bos primigenius*, and partly because it was not scientifically described until 1906, when it was already restricted to the Caucasus region. At that time the range embraced an area of about 2,000 square miles on the northern side of the Caucasus around the headwaters of the Bielaja and Malaja Laba rivers, both of which flow into the Kuban. At the end of the last century Prince Demidoff saw tracks in the snow at an altitude of 8,000 feet and heard reports of the animal's existence on the southern slopes of the Caucasus, from which he concluded that the wisent crossed over the main range.

This region remained outside proper administrative control until after the 1860s, when a system of protection was instituted which caused considerable resentment among the local Tcherkess people. In 1915 Van der Byl wrote: "Much ill-feeling has been created by making the natives vacate their grazing grounds, to which they have considered themselves entitled from time immemorial." Even the Grand Duke, in whom the local sporting rights were vested, was not permitted to kill a wisent without the Tsar's express authority, and in no circumstances were more than three kills allowed in any season.

Under these conditions the wisent flourished. There are wide differences of opinion on the size of the bison population in the Caucasus before the First World War. Some accounts state that the total was at least a thousand; but Filatow insists that there were "hardly less than 100,

but in no circumstances as many as 1,000". The truth will probably never be known. What is certain, however, is that when the gamekeepers were swept away by the Revolution, local herdsmen had ample opportunity to give vent to their pent-up feelings of resentment. Many bison were killed during hostilities in 1920, and by 1921 not more than about 50 survived. Fortunatov was of the opinion that by 1923 only about 15 to 20 remained alive.

In 1924 the Soviet Government accorded the species protection, and established the Kuban (Caucasus) Wisent Reserve (1,100 square miles), embracing the known range of the animal. Unfortunately, little was done to implement the decree; and three years later, when a team went to investigate the situation, they could find no living animals—but they did find evidence to indicate that deaths during the previous two to three years were not attributable to natural causes. It is generally believed that the last free-living wisent in the Caucasus was destroyed about 1925.

The only surviving representative of the subspecies at that time was a bull captured as a calf in May, 1907, and the following year presented by the Tsar to Karl Hagenbeck, the Hamburg animal dealer. This bull, named *Kaukasus*, sired several calves, but all out of cows of the nominate race originating from Bialowieza. He died on February 26th, 1925.

The recent history of the wisent in the Soviet Union followed a somewhat similar pattern: only a single pure-bred European bison survived the Second World War in the U.S.S.R. Between 1946 and 1951, 17 pure-bred specimens were obtained from Poland, and a comprehensive programme for the rehabilitation of the species was drawn up by Dr. Zablocki, which included the establishment of special stud farms.

By January 1966, numbers of pure-bred bison in the Soviet Union had reached 250, of which 69 were in the Bialowieza Forest, adjoining the Polish reserve of the same name, and 181 had been introduced into the Caucasus. This comprises more than a third of the total world population.

In addition to the pure-bred herd mentioned above, there is a further herd in the Caucasus

Aquila heliaca adalberti

AIGLE IMPÉRIAL D'ESPAGNE
SPANISH IMPERIAL EAGLE

National Park, containing a small admixture of American bison genes. American bison genes appear to have been introduced in a misguided attempt to improve the European stock. Zabinski records that in the 1920s there was thought to be "a decrease of vitality. . . and an almost unanimous expression of opinion even among responsible specialists . . . that the European bison was a degenerating species . . .". Mohr (1949) quotes a report to the effect that in 1928 at Saupark, Springe, American bison cows were put to a European bison bull. Of the resultant calves, all the males were slaughtered and the females retained for eventual mating with a bull of the European species. Under this system, the characteristics of the American bison were believed to have been eliminated by the third generation. This programme of cross-breeding ceased at Springe in 1934. The herd in the Caucasus National Park at present numbers 500 animals and occupies a range of 75,000 acres which the Russians extend each year by another 4,000 acres.

The aim of the Soviet authorities is not only to increase numbers, but also to re-establish the species under free-living conditions. More than a hundred wild-bred bison already exist in Central Russia.

In summary, the present position is that the Caucasian race, *B. b. caucasius*, is extinct; and pure-bred stock of the nominate race, *B. b. bonasus*, survives in modest but increasing numbers.

In addition there is a substantially larger number of European bison possessing genes of both races, and some with a small admixture of American bison genes. The world population of the species stood at approximately 926 in 1968.

THE IMPERIAL EAGLE (western subspecies) *Aquila heliaca adalberti*

One of the most urgent problems in conservation today is the future of the big birds of prey. In common with most endangered animals, large raptorial birds are threatened with direct extermination and with rapid deterioration of their habitat. Both factors depend upon man's approach to nature and the result is proportional to demographic expansion.

For example, the position of vultures, the lammergeier and eagles is becoming more and more critical almost everywhere in Europe. It is still possible to save them, however, if adequate protection measures can be taken. Confirmation of this is the golden eagle *Aquila chrysaëtos*, which has regained its normal population through total protection in Alpine areas—especially in Switzerland—and also through the animal wealth maintained by careful management of mountain wildlife. This should also be possible for the imperial eagle. The western race, confined to the Iberian Peninsula and reduced to very low proportions, is particularly worth saving from extinction.

The size of this magnificent bird of prey is approximately the same as that of the golden eagle, but it is much more massively built, with a larger head, broader wings and a slightly shorter, square tail, However, its weapons, talons and claws are weaker. Characteristic of the adult bird are white shoulder patches and cream-yellow feathers on the top of the head and neck in contrast to the brown-black of the rest of the plumage. The *adalberti* subspecies, described here, is distinguished by the large pure white zone on its shoulders and on the front edge of its wings which can clearly be seen when it is in flight. The young birds have a variegated juvenal plumage; first a pale russet colour with progressive molting adding spots, stripes, a medley of dark colours—an evolution that continues for five or six years until the bird becomes adult.

The imperial eagle is divided into two populations which separated in some distant age. The oriental subspecies extends from eastern Europe to northern India and central Asia.

Although heavily reduced in its European habitat, stretching as far as the Austro-Hungarian border, it has sufficient space to escape extermination. The western subspecies, described and named by Brehm in 1860, is confined to the Iberian Peninsula and north-western Morocco.

This, at least, is the distribution given in ornithological text-books; in actual fact, it is probable that the African branch has already disappeared or is in process of doing so. According to Malherbe and Loche, in the nineteenth century several imperial eagles still existed in Algeria. An eyrie and a clutch, seen by Tristram in 1860, may have belonged to this species, but, since then, nothing further has been reported. In Morocco, the territory of the Spanish population stretched from Tangier to the Mamora Forest where a female was killed on May 3rd, 1939. Since then, Sage saw two juveniles on April 18th, 1965 in the High Atlas at Tizi-n-Tichka and one on April 20th at Ouarzazate in the south. In 1967, he watched two individuals in the Riff Moutains, according to Lathbury (1970). However, this does not confirm that they are breeding, which was last proved to have occurred in Morocco in 1899 near Larache. There is very little hope that if the imperial eagle still exists on the African continent it will do so for much longer.

On the Iberian Peninsula the bird must have been fairly widely distributed beyond the high mountain zone, but its large size and predatory habits, especially where rabbits and partridges are concerned, marked it down for destruction by shooting and nest-robbing. Between 1865 and 1920, egg-collectors were also responsible for its decline in the lower Guadalquivir, where repeated collection of egg-clutches and shooting of adults reduced the marismas' eagles from a dozen pairs to a quarter of that number (two to four pairs), according to J. A. Valverde, Director of the Doñana Biological Station, the best-known expert on this species. Subsequent local protection has led to an increase in its numbers once again.

Furthermore, the clearance of land in the big domains has considerably reduced the eagle's habitat. The most optimistic estimate now possible is only 100 individuals or, at the most, about 30 adult pairs. Some are widely dispersed in central and western Spain, perhaps still in Portugal. Others in Andalusia, where the species was especially plentiful in the past from Cordoba to the Atlantic and from south of Cadix to lower Guadiana. Of this population, hardly 12 pairs remain in the Delta of the Guadalquivir and its immediate surroundings. It should be noted that these few birds are now the largest and most homogeneous group, also the best protected, thanks to the establishment of nature reserves in the marismas.

In 1964-65, the World Wildlife Fund in collaboration with the Spanish government, purchased 25 square miles of the famous Coto Doñana. Three pairs of eagles live in this first biological reserve. In 1969, the World Wildlife Fund also acquired 12 square miles of the Marismas of Guadiamar. Finally, the Spanish Government has just decreed the creation of a vast national park, comprising approximately 135 square miles and embracing both these areas. This major undertaking, conceived to protect the Delta's outstanding natural resources, offers the best chance of survival for the imperial eagle. Like other birds of prey, this species is now totally protected by Spanish law, which, however, will only be successful if scrupulously observed. Moreover protection of its habitat and food resources are vital to its future.

In general, this large bird of prey lives in partly-timbered savannas, in the plains and on the hills. Around the marismas it prefers the sandy areas dotted with superb cork oaks or pine trees and covered with short *Halimium* scrub, interspersed with grassy clearings and ponds. From there, it explores the edges of the flooded marshland. It is difficult to define the exact territorial limits of each hunting pair as they tend to overlap. Valverde noted that seven nests, occupied in 1959, were all situated within a ten by two mile area, which seems to be a maximum density and confirms the exceptional biological wealth of this region. Each pair is accustomed to spend the night in a thick tree near its eyrie. This is the centre of its territory, which it defends against intrusion by other birds of the same species, over a radius of half a mile to a mile. All around is the hunting territory which extends into the marismas. During the breeding season the eagles' range is extended and may exceed 12 miles.

In the early morning, adults remain on the watch, generally perched on the tops of trees. Later, until about 5 o'clock in the evening, they search for their prey which they may chase or seize by surprise attack. They then return to the look-out, lying in wait for rabbits to emerge in the dusk. The wild rabbit *Oryctolaqus cuniculus*, is in fact a basic food. In second place are medium-sized birds, fairly plentiful; partridges, ducks, water hens, and other water-fowl, sometimes grass snakes and big lizards. The grey-lag geese, wintering in large numbers in the marismas, are often attacked by the male and female eagle in unison. In fact, the Delta eagle is able to draw on a self-renewing plenti-tude of wildlife and seldom need fall back on the dead bodies of deer or other animals, which are quickly cleaned up by the vultures. The eagle by no means disdains carrion in other, less privi-leged areas where hunting is uncertain and its diet less varied.

The eyrie is built on the top of a tree, cork oak or pine, at a height varying from 25 to 64 feet. Its vast platform of sticks, more than three feet wide, is lined with green branches which are renewed all through the breeding season. From this belvedere, the birds overlook a wide area. The two to three whitish eggs, with or without reddish-brown spots, are laid between the end of February and mid-March. Both adults share the six-week incubation period, but the female assumes most of the responsibility as well as caring for the young birds. On hatching, the eaglet is clad in a pure white down and only after five weeks does it acquire its first full plumage. Its first flight takes place after 60 to 70 days. As a general rule, during the period of growth the male only pays brief visits to the eyrie with his plunder, whereas the female attentively looks after and feeds her young. This sharing of the work is customary with many birds of prey and I was able to watch it in practice during an observation visit to the Coto Doñana in June 1969.

In the late morning, I was shut into a hide on top of a metal pylon 54 feet high, overlooking a big cork oak and the eyrie where the eaglet was resting. On June 11th, he had almost all his plumage, a warm russet colour contrasting with his black remiges. The wind was blowing over the savanna ruffling the bushes, a few deer were feeding beside a lagoon nearby, to the west the immense green plain of the marismas extended to the horizon. Towards midday the eaglet stretched, fluffed his plumage, got up and beat his wings hard. Quickly tiring of these flying exercises facing the wind, he lay down again.

Suddenly at 12.35 the male appeared, dropped his prey into the nest, looked in all directions and left again. This visit lasted less than a minute. The young bird, left alone, began to tear up and eat the redshank he had received. He was resting again when the female arrived at 13.35; mightier than the male, with a more massive head, she was easily distinguishable by the extensive white zone on her wings. Purplish highlights shone on her almost black plumage, wet on the stomach; in her enormous yellow talons she held a dark-coloured bird that I later recognized as an adult coot.

She immediately began to tear it to bits, offering small pieces to the eaglet, bowing and even bending back her head to drop them into his beak. She kept the largest morsels for herself, especially the feet, which she swallowed whole. This family scene lasted 20 minutes, without a sound. Then the big bird unfolded her wings and perched on a neighbouring tree in the sun. A long moment followed for cleaning up and keeping a look-out. As for the eaglet, two meals had blown up his crop like a balloon and he lay down to sleep it off for almost an hour and a half. When he got up again to exercise his wings, I had to leave. (N. B. I have just heard that this young bird, ringed at the reserve, was killed a few months later to the north of the area. Further proof that legal protection has not abolished the danger threatening birds of prey.)

Most nests produce only one young bird, rarely two, probably because one of the eaglets kills and eats the other. But there are other rea-sons and, on an average, a pair only raises three young in four years, always at the Coto Doñana, according to Valverde. After the raising period, the juveniles disappear from the area, probably outside the adults' territory. As they only attain maturity after five years, this is a long and dangerous period for them. The death rate during adolescence is at present unknown, but it is probably high. The adult eagles appear to remain all the year round on their territory.

Survival of the Spanish imperial eagle essentially depends on man. The rational conservation of nature and respect for the birds themselves may ensure the future of this noble raptorial bird and perhaps lead to an increase in its population. It is most heartening to know that this work has already begun.

AUDOUIN'S GULL   *Larus audouinii*

Among the 78 existing species of the gull family, only one is considered to be in danger. Although the majority of sea-gulls, known as sociable birds and excellent flyers, have extensive areas of distribution and often expanding populations, the Audouin's gull is strictly confined to the Mediterranean where it is widely scattered and few in number.

Due to similarities of appearance, it has frequently been confused with the Mediterranean herring gull *(Larus argentatus michahellis)*. However, it is smaller, its silhouette slimmer, its flight lighter and the adults are distinguished be four principle features: the dark red bill, with a black bar and yellow tip; dark eyes and olive-grey feet and the wing-tip pattern. There are, therefore, two completely different species living side by side which do not appear to be rivals. How is it that one remains rare whereas the other enjoys almost arrogant well-being?

For a long time, information on the Audouin's gull was scarce and incomplete. Ever since the French naturalist, Payraudeau, published his description of this gull in 1826 and named it after a colleague, egg and skin collectors have eagerly sought it to secure specimens of high market value because of their rarity. This was not easy since access to the remote islands where it nests is extremely difficult.

Otmar Reiser who discovered this gull in the Sporades Islands on June 1st, 1894 can be cited as an example. He arrived on Melissa Island with his assistant in search of Eleonora's falcons and shot at two individuals but was unable to find their bodies. "For a moment, I stopped my search to contemplate the very rough sea and our little boat tossed by the storm. Suddenly, in a fit of rage, I aimed at the nearest gull and fired. The badly wounded bird flew on a moment and then fell into the waves. ... After half an hour on the island, we had to give in to the Greeks who were frantically urging us to leave, and we took our places in the dinghy to return to the sailing boat. I had almost forgotten the victim of my anger when the boatman told me to pick it up. On taking a closer look at the floating corpse, I found to my surprise that it was a superb specimen of *Larus audouinii*. There was then no question of my leaving ! I think I would have used force if the boatmen had not heeded my admonishments and taken us back to the reef, not without swearing abominably. In the meantime, a dozen gulls had re-assembled there and in no time we, Knotek and myself, each had our bird: we could leave the island content."

This account is typical of the period. An adventurous ornithologist with a gun. Fortunately, today, wildlife observation has replaced collection, allowing a better understanding of the Audouin's gull.

Its most evident peculiarity is to nest generally in small colonies, rarely consisting of more than 20 pairs and separated by considerable distances. However, two recent exceptions to this rule prove that the species may still form large colonies under favourable conditions. In 1963, Didier de Bournonville visited a colony of some 70 pairs on a group of islands off Corsica and, in 1966, Brosset and Olier discovered 1,000 birds on one of the Chafarinas Islands off eastern Morocco. Moreover, this gull always chooses very small islands, facing the open sea and often at a great distance from the mainland.

Information presently available mentions homogeneous colonies, with nests between 1 ½ feet and 11 yards apart, built on stony slopes with thin herbaceous vegetation and low bushes. These nests, which are usually in the open, greatly resemble those of the herring gull, as do the two to three eggs laid at the end of April or beginning of May. According to Makatsch, incubation lasts from 21 to 25 days with the male and female sitting in turns on the nest. Soon after they hatch, the chicks seek shelter under thistles and pistachio undergrowth. These basic reproduction features do not differ, therefore, from those observed amongst other gulls and, in particular, those of the herring gull. As the latter often settles nearby in much larger colonies, and is well-known to be a nest plunderer, the problem of relations between the two species arises. Is the proximity and well-being of the larger bird detrimental to the smaller? We have no proof nor any definite clue. Having studied an Aegean colony of Audouin's gull, Makatsch noted that the two gulls lived together peaceably and separately. He never witnessed a raid by the herring gull. In Corsica, Bournonville confirmed segregation and remarked on the vigilance of the Audouin's gulls: small groups chased away all the herring gulls that passed near their nests. No hostility exists between the two species; on the contrary, the somewhat later breeding season of the Audouin's gulls would rather prove that they seek the association of the herring gull.

On some of the islands, swarms of rats are the most threatening enemies, especially for the eggs and hatchlings, but we have no details of their predatory habits. Finally, the role of man should be considered. In the Mediterranean, the collection of gulls' eggs is carried out by fishermen, who, over the years, have certainly eliminated some colonies in this way and, by doing so, increased the rarity of the species. According to Makatsch, the collection of herring gulls' eggs takes place in the Sporades Islands in April, just after they have been laid, The collection does not affect the Audouin's gulls which lay their eggs later on. But, this exploitation may have more dangerous results. In 1966, Brosset and Olier reported that a systematic raid on gulls' eggs was organized in the Chafarinas Islands, for use in fancy cake making at Melilla ... and, naturally, there was no question of differentiating between the species. Finally, the egg-collectors and dealers should not be forgotten: they have carried out fairly regular raids in the known colonies and for them the Audouin's gulls represent a profit. Nevertheless, examination of the various predatory acts that could affect the species leaves the impression that these do not entirely explain its scarcity.

Could their numbers be regulated by the circumstances of feeding? Present research is still insufficient for forming an opinion on this question, especially since very little is known of the gull's life with the exception of the breeding period. According to Brosset, its basic food seems to be small fish, sprats and sardines, which it catches in the sea. Unlike the herring gull, the Audouin's gull spurns organic offal thrown back on the beaches; it does not follow boats, frequent the ports, or wait beside sewage outlets. Ignoring resources to which the large species owe its well-being, Audouin's gull has not adapted itself and only takes what nature provides.

In Majorca, Wallace observed birds fishing in flight, either above the breakers under rocky cliffs, or skimming over calm water and spearing prey with their beaks. They also attack shoals of fish accompanied by herring gulls and shearwaters. At the mouth of the Moulouya River, in eastern Morocco, Brosset saw them fishing with other gulls, but on the outskirts of the troup, like satellites. Audouin's gull, therefore, has individualistic tendencies and is apt to specialize; it remains at sea far more than the herring gull and rarely visits the coastal mainland. However, in autumn 1968, Allen saw a troup of about 120 individuals on the south coast of Spain, where the adults were twelve times as numerous as the juveniles. This detail is interesting: does it indicate a low reproduction rate, in the Chafarinas Islands for example?

Very little is known of the movements of this gull. Its wanderings at sea seem to be confined to the approaches to the colonies but without excluding visits to nearby shores. No real migration has been noted, although some of these gulls have been found outside the Mediterranean area, in the Gulf of Akaba in the Red Sea, near Agadir in south-west Morocco, and even on Lake Neuchâtel in Switzerland (a record sighting).

Estimation of the numbers of this species is complicated by the disparity of available information, especially attributable in particular to the difficulties of access to the breeding areas. The *Red Data Book* mentions that the total world population has been estimated at less than 200 individuals, but that more systematic research would yield a much higher figure. Bournonville reported that a total world population of 240 adult birds existed between 1960 and 1963. In 1966, however, Brosset and Olier were able to visit Isabella Island, in the Chafarinas Islands' group off the Moroccan coast, to which access had hitherto been forbidden by the Spanish military authorities. They were surprised to find the island inhabited by 1,000 Audouin's gulls, which explained the constant presence of 200 of these gulls at the mouth of the Moulouya River. Also in 1966 Makatsch studied a colony of 20 pairs in the North Sporades Islands which were formerly unknown. According to the data presently obtainable, we think, therefore, that the species numbers at least 1,200 adults and that, including juveniles, should amount to, if not exceed, 1,300 to 1,400 gulls.

In addition to the large Moroccan colony, at least one small one exists in the Balearic Islands, an important one off south-eastern Corsica, a fourth off north-western Sardinia—that of the Sporades—and one in north-western Cyprus. To these six certain and current breeding areas, others can probably be added in the Aegean and Tyrrhenian Seas, around Tunisia and Algeria, as well as perhaps at the Pityuses and the Columbretes. However, we lack up-to-date information on these regions. Finally, several localities mentioned in the past have been abandoned, for example: Nakl Island opposite Tripoli in the Lebanon, occupied in 1895, but taken over by tourism today, or again in the vicinity of Cape Saint-Vincent in Portugal, where the only known breeding areas outside the Mediterranean were situated.

Even if the Audouin's gull is not as rare as it feared, it is dependent on six small islands only, dispersed over a distance of about 2,000 miles and this fact is disquieting. Any interference on one or other of these colonies is an outrage—and, naturally, the collection of eggs for whatever motive is intolerable—but most serious threat of all, which weighs on all deserted islands, is the development for touristic and private interests. The protection of these six islets is, therefore, the most rational measure that can be taken for the preservation of this typical Mediterranean gull.

The opinion has been expressed that Audouin's gull is a residual species on the road to extinction, We believe that, on the contrary, limited by its ecological requirements, it has never been plentiful. Its numerical decline is not proven and fatality is not the reason for its abandonment of certain areas, but rather the result of plundering by man. Far from believing this species condemned, we feel that it is quite able to maintain its present strength, or even develop it, if its refuges are protected. This optimistic view is based on two encouraging examples: the net increase of the Corsican colony from 10 to 70 pairs between 1955 and 1963 and the unexpected wealth on the Chafarinas Islands. If the species can still successfully maintain such large colonies, it remains a vital force and need only be left in peace to survive.

GOÉLAND D'AUDOUIN   *Larus audouinii*   AUDOUIN'S GULL

ASIA

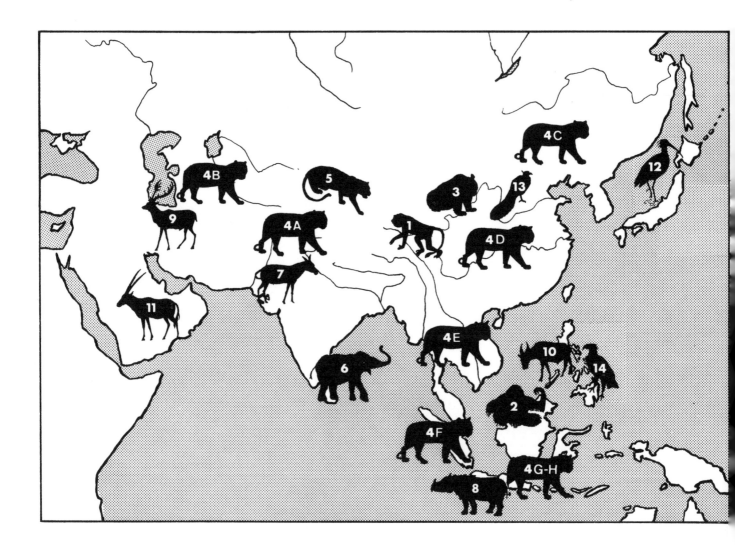

1, Snub-nosed monkey — 2, Orang-utan — 3, Giant panda — 4 A, Bengal tiger — 4 B, Caspian tiger — 4 C, Siberian tiger — 4 D, Chinese tiger — 4 E, Indo-Chinese tiger — 4 F, Sumatran tiger 4 G, Javan tiger — 4 H, Bali tiger — 5, Snow leopard — 6, Ceylon elephant — 7, Indian wild ass — 8, Javan rhinoceros — 9, Persian fallow deer — 10, Tamaraw — 11, Arabian oryx — 12, Japanese crested ibis — 13, Brown-eared pheasant — 14, Monkey-eating eagle

SNUB-NOSED MONKEY *Rhinopithecus roxellanae*

The snub-nosed (or golden) monkey is related to the langurs, but separated from them by an absence of cheek pouches and other anatomical differences. The species is distinguished by the thick-set body and sturdy limbs, with arms only a little shorter than the legs. The most distinctive external features are the long golden coat, which becomes denser and more brightly coloured with advancing age, and the bizarre snub-nose, which in adult males is so preposterously upturned that its tip reaches almost to the forehead.

The specific name commemorates Roxellana, favourite wife of Suleiman the Magnificent, who was abducted from Galicia by Turkish raiders in 1523. Her smile was so irresistible that she was known as "Khurrem", the laughing one; and although said to have been not especially beautiful, her unfailing charm, sparkling wit and infectious gaiety gained complete ascendancy over Suleiman.

The general range of the species extends from the high mountains of northern Szechwan, southern Kansu, Yunnan, and Kweichow in western China, into Tibet and possibly into Assam and Burma. Within this overall range the species occurs in three widely separated localities, each occupied by a different subspecies. A closely related species, and the only other member of the genus, is the Tonkin snub-nosed monkey, *Rhinopithecus avunculus*, which is found in the vicinity of the Song-koi River, in North Vietnam.

The nominate race occurs in the higher mountain ranges of western Szechwan and southern Kansu. The males are very strikingly coloured, the bare parts of the face around the nose and eyes being turquoise. The upper parts of the body from the tail along the back to the top of the head is brownish grey with long golden hairs. The under parts, the sides of the head, ears, forehead and throat, as well as the limbs, hands and feet vary from golden orange to buff in the male and pale yellow in the female.

R. r. bieti occurs in north-western Yunnan close to the frontier with Burma, along the high narrow ridge separating the Mekong and the Yangtze. Milne-Edwards stated that the animal occupied both slopes of the divide, but at different seasons. He believed that in summer it frequented the eastern-facing Chinese side, and in winter occupied the western, Tibetan, slope overlooking the Mekong Basin. This apparently is the southern extremity of distribution. Farther to the north-west, however, the range fringes Assam and penetrates some distance into the Chamdo region of eastern Tibet.

This race is larger than the nominate form and differently coloured. The back and outer sides of the limbs are black with long grey hairs, and there is white hair on the back of the thighs. The forehead is black, and the cheeks, whiskers and throat white; while the tail, limbs, hands and feet are black.

R. r. brelichi, is found in northern Kweichow, in Central China, to the south of the Yangtze River along the higher parts of the Kweichow/ Szechwan border region.

This is the biggest and most powerful of the three races, and, excepting the great apes, the largest primate known. Its back and outer limbs are dark grey, with a white patch between the shoulders. The upper arms are buff coloured and the back of the thighs yellow. The forehead, cheeks and throat are yellowish grey with black hairs. The ears are white; the tail black with a white tip, and more than a foot longer than those of the other races. On either side of the base of the tail is a yellow patch.

The snub-nosed monkey occurs farther north than any other species of leaf-eating monkey. It lives in the deciduous forest zone among dense rhododendron thickets, which is the dominant vegetation between the 8,000 and 10,000 feet levels.

Primates are generally associated with warm climatic conditions, but the terrain occupied by this species is under snow for about half the year, and, as Milne-Edwards remarked, the golden monkey has a greater resistance to cold than any other monkey. One of its vernacular names is in fact the "snow-monkey". It seldom leaves its mountain fastness and then only in winter when heavy snow compels it to descend to the valleys and foot-hills.

The species is mainly arboreal, seldom coming to the ground except to drink, and consuming young bamboo shoots as well as leaves, buds and fruit. It is said to live in large troops of a hundred or more, and is one of the few monkeys to have a definite breeding season, the young being born in the spring after approximately five months' gestation.

Little is known of the animal's natural history, and it remains largely unstudied in the wild state, but this is attributable, at least in part, to the remoteness and inaccessibility of its habitat which effectively discourage investigation and make observation difficult.

Apart from a solitary animal kept for a short while at the Zoological Gardens of London in 1939, no specimen has ever been exhibited outside China. The species is exceptionally difficult to maintain in captivity, partly because of its specialized diet; but within the last few years Chinese zoologists have successfully overcome the dietary problems and have established breeding groups at Peking, Shanghai, and Tsingtao zoos.

The golden monkey was one of the discoveries of the redoubtable French naturalist, Père Armand David, who obtained his original specimen in central Szechwan, in the district of Moupin. Szechwan is where the eastern extremity of the Himalayas meets the mountain ranges of western China, running down from the north. The confluence of these great mountain systems provides not only some of the world's most spectacular scenery, with colossal mountains and deep gorges, but the climatic variation, ranging from sub-tropical to arctic, results in wide environmental diversity, with a remarkably varied fauna adapted to the differing ecological conditions. For this reason Szechwan is one of the most interesting zoological regions in the world, containing more than a quarter of all the animal species in China.

The hunters employed by Père David informed him that the fur of the golden monkey has long been highly esteemed by the Chinese because of its alleged efficacy as a preventive against rheumatism.

Under the Manchu regime, cloaks made from its luxuriant fur were reserved exclusively for mandarin dignitaries. According to Milne-Edwards, this belief extended to the Tibetans also, and accounted for the difficulty of procuring specimens in that country.

The fur was regarded as the most valuable obtainable in Szechwan, the chief market being Chengtu, the capital, where it fetched high prices. Allen quotes a report that before the First World War a single skin with particularly long hair fetched the equivalent of £12 15s 0d.

The high price and heavy demand for the golden fur made hunting a lucrative proposition. The animal was relentlessly trapped and shot, and became so scarce that it was already rare by the time its existence was first made known to Europeans. In the 1930s, Sowerby included it among the Chinese fauna in danger of extinction. Today, it is legally protected by the Chinese authorities although Pfeffer states that he saw skins in several shops in Peking.

RHINOPITHÈQUE   *Rhinopithecus roxellanae*   SNUB-NOSED MONKEY

ORANG-UTAN

Pongo pygmaeus

The orang-utan is the only representative of the great apes now living outside central Africa. It is a large animal, the adult male being a little more than 4 feet tall, with remarkably human facial characteristics and with long shaggy, russet-brown hair. Its arms are extremely long, reaching almost to its ankles when it stands erect. Every night the animal constructs a simple "nest" or platform of branches in the fork of a tree, and there it sleeps.

Some authors recognize two subspecies: the Bornean race, *P. p. pygmaeus*; and the Sumatran race, *P. p. abelii*. The Sumatran form is said to be larger and more lightly coloured than the Bornean, but the differences are slight, and based on inadequate comparative material; for which reasons subspecific separation does not appear to be warranted.

Fossil and archaeological evidence indicates that at one time this primate had a much wider distribution. Remains have been discovered in such far-apart places on the Asian mainland as the Siwalik Hills of India and the provinces of Kwangsi, Kwangtung, and Yunnan in China; and fossil bones have been found in parts of Borneo and Sumatra beyond the present range, as well as in Java and Celebes. Teeth, all probably of fossil origin, have been sold in apothecaries' shops in Shanghai, Peking, Hong Kong, and Manila in the Philippines.

Distribution of the orang-utan is now restricted to parts of Sumatra and Borneo. It prefers the lowlands below about 2,500 feet, but may range up to 4,500 feet, and occasionally has been found much higher, as, for example, at 8,000 feet on Mount Kinabalu.

The largest surviving population is in Sabah, extending over the border into adjacent Kalimantan (Indonesian Borneo), where orangs are found in limited numbers in the north-east and west; they also occur in Sarawak, but have been exterminated in neighbouring Brunei.

No population estimates exist from before 1959, but it is known that numbers have declined drastically during the last century and particularly since the Second World War. The best available estimate indicates that the total population is now not more than 5,000 and continuing to decline. Of these, there are estimated to be about 2,000 in Sabah. Kalimantan and Sumatra each have approximately 1,000, and Sarawak about 700.

Carpenter, who visited Sumatra in 1937, showed that the orang was then widely distributed in about 50 per cent of the primary forests of Atjeh, the state in the north-western quarter of the island: the southern limit was "roughly a line drawn from Singkel on the West Coast to Pangkalan Brandan on the East Coast". Since the Second World War, however, its range has been greatly reduced, and the orang is now believed to be restricted to the Löser Reserve (which extends to about 1,700 sq. miles) and one or two smaller forested regions.

Carpenter noted that with the exception of the limited extension to the sea at Bakongan, the greater part of the Löser Reserve lies at an altitude of more than 2,500 feet; from which he concluded "that the Löser Reservation with its present boundaries is not and cannot be a satisfactory reservation for orang-utans, since there is a marked preference in these animals for altitudes below eight hundred meters". He therefore recommended that the reserve should be enlarged to incorporate several areas suitable for orangs and other primates. He also strongly recommended that an area near Meulaboh, on the coast north-west of the Löser Reserve, should be developed as a special orang-utan reserve; and that the Rafflesia Reserve should be considerably enlarged not only to protect the magnificent Rafflesia flower and other native flora, but also "that it may serve as a place for the protection of orang-utans, siamangs, gibbons, elephants and other indigenous fauna". The Second World War intervened before these recommendations could be put into effect.

Despite Carpenter's belief that the Löser Reserve was unsuitable for the orang, Milton, who visited Sumatra in 1963, concluded that this reserve contains almost all the orangs remaining in Sumatra. Most are in the north-eastern part of the reserve, in the relatively low-lying country on the inland side of the mountain range running through the centre of the reserve. "In addition, however, there is an area to the north which I was unable to visit, another area on the coast on the west slopes of the Löser, and a third area directly west of Medan, all of which are known to contain orang. . . . I do not believe there are any groups of any material size in Atjeh and North Sumatra east of an approximate line from Singkol to Pangkalan Brandan."

The general deterioration in the faunal situation in Sumatra in the last three decades has enhanced the importance of the Löser Reserve as potentially one of the key wildlife sanctuaries in Asia: yet, despite its importance, the reserve remains almost unknown. There is an evident need for a suitable person to visit the area and make an appraisal of the reserve and its fauna.

There are several reasons for the decline; these are applicable in greater of lesser degree to all the territories in which orangs exist.

For its survival the orang is dependent on a certain type of primary or old secondary forest, and it is doubtful whether it will ever adapt itself to any other type of habitat; but in recent years much of the suitable indigenous lowland forest has been exploited for commercial timber production. As a result, the orangs have been either destroyed or driven from their natural habitat and forced into regions, such as mountainous areas, that do not contain the rather specialized food (notably the fruit of the durian) on which they feed, or that are unsuitable for other reasons.

Widespread destruction of the habitat is probably the principal cause of decline; but an equally serious factor is the large illicit trade in young animals, which are smuggled into Singapore, Bangkok and other eastern ports and towns where they find a ready market. The high price paid for captive orangs is an irresistible temptation to smugglers to break the law.

Under favourable conditions, there seems to be no great difficulty in capturing orangs. Their movements are normally rather ponderous, which puts them at a disadvantage on the ground. Occasionally an immature animal may be isolated from its mother and captured, but the method most commonly employed involves shooting the mother; after that the young is easily taken. Shooting is a simple matter, as orangs normally show little fear of human beings and, animated by curiosity, do not flee when approached. In these circumstances a small-calibre rifle or shotgun is perfectly adequate, since it can be fired from close range. Larger animals may be driven into a suitable tree. The surrounding trees are felled and the creatures are left isolated, often for many days until forced to the ground by hunger and thirst; they are then so weak that their capture is easy. Sometimes the tree is felled and the animals caught as they crash to the ground. Sometimes the orangs are smoked out of cover.

Young orangs are delicate and especially prone to human infections. Many of those that have been caught are kept under primitive and unhygienic conditions; they are compelled to exist on an unnatural diet and die from malnutrition or disease. Only an estimated one in three survives the rigours of captivity.

Even in an undisturbed natural state the reproductive rate of the orang is slow. Mature females produce a single infant about every fourth year, but, because the infant mortality rate is about 40 per cent, the actual lifetime reproductive potential may be as low as two or three young per female.

Though the orang is a "protected" animal throughout the greater part of its range, generally speaking such protection is merely nominal. In Sumatra, for example, a relatively new factor in the situation is the presence of Indonesian soldiers who are reported to hunt orangs with rifles, and even with automatics for the high prices offered by smugglers.

The combination of deliberate slaughter and reduction of the habitat, both for logging and to provide areas of cultivation for the ever-expanding human population, is splitting the survivors into small, often isolated, groups. The more fragmented these groups, the more vulnerable they become in the struggle for survival.

Most of the orangs in Sarawak and Sabah occur in "forest reserves", a term implying that

ORANG-OUTAN   *Pongo pygmaeus*   ORANG-UTAN

the areas are protected. Unfortunately, the implication is misleading. The forest reserves are essentially areas that the Government has set aside for timber extraction, the work being undertaken by licensed contractors, with the Government deriving a return from royalties. Conservation of wildlife takes second place.

Because the orang depends on primary forest, the survival of the animal must surely require the creation of at least one large national park, or similar reserve, designed specifically for long-term protection of the species in Sarawak and Sabah, besides the one that already exists in Sumatra. This fact was recognized by Sarawak's Maias Protection Commission as long ago as 1959, and has since been advocated by several ecologists and naturalists, yet nothing has been done to carry out their advice.

The killing and capture of the orang for any purpose must be effectively prevented. Smuggling of young orangs will continue only as long as a market for them exists; and there is an urgent need to remove the legal loopholes that still leave smugglers free to carry on this traffic. Important progress in this direction has been the constructive action recently taken by the governments of Singapore and Hong Kong in prohibiting the import or export of orang utans.

The establishment by the I.U.C.N. Survival Service Commission of a specialist orang-utan committee under the chairmanship of Prof. T. H. Harrisson, has been of particular significance in improving the situation.

Strong action has also been taken by the International Union of Directors of Zoological Gardens by introducing stringent regulations prohibiting their members from purchasing orangs through illicit channels. This became necessary because of the many smuggled orangs which found their way through unscrupulous middle-men and dealers into the world's zoos. Unfortunately, many zoo managers remain outside this organization.

Measures are also being taken by several medical research organizations in the United States to try to establish their own captive breeding stocks of orangs and other primates, to reduce to the minimum the need for wild-caught animals.

All these measures are constructive and will undoubtedly help to arrest the decline, but the urgent need is to allocate certain areas for protection of the orang within the preferred natural range of the species, even though these areas may be desirable for commercial or agricultural purposes. This immediately sets the problem of choosing between the requirements of wildlife conservation and the needs of economic development. The ultimate solution lies squarely in the hands of the Governments of Indonesia, Sarawak, and Sabah. Unless they are prepared to set aside forest sanctuaries—adequate in extent and efficiently protected—to ensure the perpetuation of the species, it will be only a matter of time before Asia's sole great ape ceases to exist, except perhaps in captivity.

GIANT PANDA

Ailuropoda melanoleuca

The giant panda was first made known to the western world by the noted French naturalist Père Armand David. His original description was based on two female specimens, an adult and an immature, which his Chinese hunters obtained in 1869 from the mountains of the principality of Muping.

The specimen shot by Theodore and Kermit Roosevelt, in 1929, was the first to be personally collected by any westerner. Together with a second skin purchased locally, this was subsequently used for the Chicago History Museum's well-known habitat group. The ensuing publicity precipitated a series of expeditions to look for the animal, a search further stimulated when early in 1937 the Chicago Zoological Park obtained the first living example ever seen outside China. The sudden demand inspired local hunters to believe there was a ready market for skins, and resulted in many animals being needlessly slaughtered.

The Chinese have cause for pride in this remarkable animal which is unique to their country; and it is equally admired in many other parts of the world. Its universal popularity provides a link between East and West which transcends political and ideological differences. The giant panda can thus be regarded as symbolizing the activities and aspirations of international conservation, for which reason it has been chosen as the emblem of the World Wildlife Fund.

Television and other publicity have made the animal familiar to millions of people but, paradoxically, it remains little known in the wild state. It says much for Père David's ability that data on the species obtained during the century that has elapsed since the publication of his field notes have confirmed the accuracy of his original observations in almost every particular.

Adults may reach a length of six feet, excluding the stumpy tail, and weigh over 300 pounds. The thick, woolly coat is white, the legs, ears and patches around the eyes are black, and a black band reaches from the forelegs across the shoulders. The head is massive, and the skull provided with large ridges to which are attached the jaw muscles. These complement the powerful teeth required for chewing the tough fibrous material on which the animal feeds. The jaws and teeth are also used for defence, not the forearms and paws as with the bears. The fore paws have the unusual feature of specially modified pads which assist in clasping slender objects such as bamboo. Davis notes: "The skill and precision with which objects are grasped and manipulated by the fore feet is astonishing. I have observed animals in the Chicago Zoological Park pick up small items like single straws and handle them with the greatest precision."

Opinion has long been divided on the correct taxonomic position of *Ailuropoda*. Certain anatomical features appear to relate it to the lesser (or red) panda and the raccoons, and it has therefore been assigned by some authors to the family Procyonidae. The most recent contribution to this discussion is the authoritative study by Dwight Davis. He concludes that the giant panda is a highly specialized bear which warrants being assigned either to the family Ursidae or to a separate monotypic family.

Essentially, however, it is an aberrant bear— the only living representative of its genus—but distinguished from the true bears in numerous ways, not only physically but also in its behaviour and habits. It does not, for instance, go through a period of winter dormancy in the manner of the bears, although during periods of exceptionally cold weather it may shelter for short spells in caves or hollow trees. Sheldon frequently saw dens "under overhanging rocks in the midst of precipitous slopes of bamboos"; and he notes that nests are constructed from broken bamboo. On one occasion he saw "a well-used panda bed on the top of a large flat stump in an opening of the bamboo forests... natives say that it is in such places that the mother brings forth her young".

Little is known of the breeding habits of the giant panda in the wild state, although females are believed to bear only a single cub after a gestation period which captive specimens have shown to be about 148 days. Much useful information has been obtained from observations on captive animals, particularly from zoos in China where the majority of the twenty or so captive animals are located; above all by the Peking Zoo which, in September 1963, succeeded in breeding the species for the first time in captivity, a success which more recently has been emulated by the Shanghai Zoo.

Unlike the bears, which are omnivorous, the giant panda is strictly herbivorous. Its diet consists exclusively of the leaves, shoots and stalks of the dwarf bamboo, which is abundant throughout its range. As William Sheldon remarks: "It is no wonder that the muscular development of their jaws is so massive, and that their teeth have become so adapted for breaking the bamboo, which will defy the edge of the sharpest axe."

The quantity of bamboo required to sustain an animal the size of the giant panda is very great. It has a voracious appetite, and Sheldon estimates that ten to twelve hours a day would have to be spent feeding to obtain the amount sufficient for its needs. He also remarks on the

PANDA GÉANT   *Ailuropoda melanoleuca*   GIANT PANDA

extraordinarily numerous droppings, which have the appearance of being "completely undigested as though they had never passed through the stomach"; which led Brocklehurst to assume that they were "merely chewed and not swallowed". Sheldon followed one animal for two miles over freshly fallen snow and observed that it deposited one to three large droppings at intervals of about one hundred yards, which amounted to "a total of 70 excreted between very early morning and 9 a.m.".

Mention is made elsewhere (p. 120) of the diverse environmental and climatic conditions which, in combination with the geographical location, make the borderland between China and Tibet one of the richest faunal regions in the world. The giant panda is one of several interesting mammals indigenous to this region. It occurs only in the isolated mountainous regions of western Szechwan and eastern Sikang, where it is further restricted to the bamboo forests which grow within an altitudinal range of 5,000 to 13,000 feet. Above this height, where the bamboo gives way to rhododendron, it is not normally found, although Sheldon records "unmistakable panda droppings high on the Chen Lliang Shan range, 1,000 feet above the rhododendron forest, and probably 1,500 feet above the nearest bamboo". Generally speaking, however, the giant panda has little cause to leave the bamboo zone where it is surrounded by virtually inexhaustible quantities of its exclusive food.

The bamboo grows so densely that vision is limited to a few yards, and in most places a man has difficulty in getting through. It forms impenetrable thickets through which run game trails used not only by the giant panda but also by many other large mammals.

With the exception of the specimen obtained by Theodore and Kermit Roosevelt, which was taken at Yehli on the slopes of the Ta-liang Mountains, all records are from the Chuing-Lai Mountains, which gives the animal a very limited distribution. Sowerby believed it to be greater. From the evidence of Chinese hunters he defined the range as: "in more or less restricted localities from the Tsing Ling range of mountains in Southern Shensi southward

through Western Szechuan, the new province of Sikong and Eastern Tibet to Northern Yunnan".

More recently, Hung-shou Pen claims to have seen a giant panda on the open steppe of the Tibetan Plateau close to the upper source of the Yangtze River. He speculates that this may indicate an annual summer migration to the plateau with a reverse movement during the winter back to the less severe conditions in the mountains. If this claim is substantiated it represents an extension of the previously known range by a further 300 miles to the north.

The fossil record shows that within relatively recent geological times the distribution was far wider. Pleistocene remains have been found in the Northern Shan States in Burma, over 500 miles south-west of the limits of the present known range. Pliocene material has also been unearthed on the Yangtze in eastern Szechwan, some 250 miles to the east.

The status of the species is not known with any certainty. According to Roosevelt, the Lolo people considered the animal "excessively rare . . . in the nearest Chinese village, perhaps twenty-five miles distant, no one had ever heard of a giant panda, nor seen the skin of one. Other incidents of this nature continually confirmed our belief in the animal's scarcity."

No census has ever been attempted, and the nature of the habitat in summer would probably

make this difficult. Once snow has fallen, however, it should be possible to gain an indication of the density of the population, especially if Sheldon was correct in his belief that "a single animal probably confines its range to one main valley". His own observations provided "almost positive evidence that within 6 miles of Chengwei ... there were at least 6 different animals", which encouraged him to revise his earlier opinion and to conclude that "in this region the giant panda is not at all rare. In fact, for such a large animal of nomadic habits, I would say it is plentiful." This belief was strengthened by the "fairly fresh panda tracks on almost every slope that I hunted after snow had fallen".

When viewed within the context of the restricted range, however, it is difficult to avoid the conclusion that, even if the population is locally numerous, the overall total is unlikely to be large. At the same time, there is no evidence that the species is declining.

The animal is not heavily hunted, possibly because the skin, according to Sowerby, is of no commercial value. Allen states, however, that "in ancient times this animal was included in the tribute of Yu, from Liangchow, Szechwan, more than four thousand years ago. To this day the skins are said sometimes to be used as rugs in China ... [and] are occasionally [sold in Chengtu where they] command a high price."

A further factor, mentioned by Roosevelt, is that "the Lolo regards the beast as a semi-divinity, and does not attack it except in protection of his beehives. These the giant panda sometimes raids."

Some losses are caused by spear-traps set for other mammals, such as the takin. Brocklehurst describes the trap as a bamboo fence about 30 inches high erected "across a well-worn animal track, leaving a gap where the fence cuts the track. A spear, laid horizontally at one side of the gap, is attached to a bent sapling, which is operated by means of a trigger, and the spear driven with considerable force across the track."

Little is known of the extent to which the animal is subject to natural predation, or of losses from other factors. The mature giant panda probably has few enemies other than man; but leopard and wild dog inhabit the same general region, and it would be surprising if they did not prey on the young. But these and other questions must remain unanswered until a thorough field study of the species has been carried out.

In the meantime, there appears to be no reason for pessimism over the future of the giant panda. The establishment of a special reserve is considered unnecessary as the habitat is not being exploited; and the animal itself is stringently protected. Above all, the Chinese people are intensely proud of this superlative representative of the country's rich mammalian fauna; and the authorities have declared their intention of taking any measures that may be necessary for its protection.

TIGER   *Panthera tigris*

The historical range of the species is extensive, the northern limits stretching from the Causasus and Caspian regions through northern Iran and Afghanistan to the Aral Sea, eastwards to lakes Balkhash and Baikal, and the Maritime Provinces of the Soviet Far East. The tiger has colonized much of the area to the south of this line, notably China, the Indian subcontinent, South East Asia and Indonesia.

The reasons for the decline of the tiger are broadly similar throughout its range. They can be summarized as: loss or degradation of habitat; reduction of natural prey; and excessive killing by man.

Because of the tiger's incompatibility with human interests, its only prospect of survival lies in the establishment of firmly administered national parks and equivalent reserves embrac-

Panthera tigris

TIGRE DE MANDCHOURIE   TIGER

ing sizeable areas of suitable habitat, in combination with stringent enforcement of the game laws both within and without the reserves.

Opinions differ widely on the systematic status of the various races of the tiger, which is understandable in a species that varies from the massive, pale-coloured, long-haired animal of north-eastern Asia which has to endure winter conditions of arctic intensity, to the smaller, short-coated, darker-coloured animal of the humid tropical rain forests. Not only are the physical differences slight, but there is also great individual variation within each race, particularly of stripes and other markings. This account follows Mazak in recognizing eight races.

Six of the eight races are considered rare and endangered and are therefore listed in the *Red Data Book*. The Bengal and Indo-China races are not yet in that category, but are included here in an attempt to present a balanced picture of the whole species. This chapter sketches the current distribution and status of each race and, where possible, suggests measures to meet some of the situations described.

BENGAL TIGER   *P. t. tigris*

The Bengal tiger was formerly found from the Indus Valley along the southern slopes of the Himalayas through Nepal, Sikkim, Bhutan, and Assam into western Burma. Southwards it ranged throughout peninsular India, except for the desert regions. It has never occurred in Ceylon.

The tiger is still widely distributed in northern India but the habitat available to it has greatly diminished. As Schaller has shown, it occurs in most large tracts of forest, excepting the states of Gujarat, Punjab and Kashmir, but only sparsely.

The size of the population is exceptionally difficult to assess, not least because the tiger is nocturnal in habit and, unlike the lion, is known to wander great distances. Corbett was of the opinion that there were only 2,000 tigers in India at the end of the Second World War.

Gee (1964) estimated the total at 4,000, though he emphasized that this figure could be no more than a very rough approximation. Seshadri believes that the total in India "does not exceed 2,800". The Maharaja of Baroda considers this figure over-optimistic: he believes the present total to be nearer 2,000. These estimates must be viewed against the overall loss or despoilment of habitat, as exemplified by the Kumaon Hills in north-western Uttar Pradesh. Kumaon is part of the forested Himalayan foothills, which has long ranked among the finest wildlife areas in India, and became well known through Jim Corbett's exploits in hunting man-eating tigers and leopards. The huge forests of Corbett's day have been greatly reduced: some have been felled to make way for agricultural development or huge reservoirs for hydro-electric and irrigation schemes, and only a few sizeable tracts containing a small, widely dispersed tiger population now remain.

Furthermore, the tiger is represented in only a few northern sanctuaries, such as Kanha, Kaziranga and Corbett national parks. What is now the Corbett National Park was established in 1935 with the aim of safeguarding part of this superlative natural area in perpetuity, but this intention is being eroded by the construction of the Kalagarh Dam just outside the boundary which will inundate part of the park, and have ecological repercussions which will inevitably affect the wildlife.

The importance of the northern sanctuaries to the future of the Bengal tiger is accentuated by the heavy depletion in southern India where, even as recently as twenty years ago, it was quite common in some places. The tiger still occurs in the Nilgiri Hills, Orissa; the Bandipur Sanctuary, Mysore; and the Mudumalai Sanctuary, Madras; but in all these sanctuaries it is scarce.

Fortunately, the Himalayan fauna and flora is well represented in Nepal, where the tiger occurs in the Tappu Sanctuary near Biratnagar; the Rhino Sanctuary and the Mahendra National Park, both of which are in the Rapti Valley; and the Kanchanpur Sanctuary in the extreme south-west, where it is reported to be "very common". With the exception of the Mahendra

National Park, these sanctuaries are all situated in the *terai*, but Caughley warns that "wild life habitat is being destroyed at a rapid rate, particularly in the *terai*".

In the Kanchanpur Sanctuary, which Caughley considers potentially "one of the best in Asia", the chital *(Axis axis)* is the tiger's main source of food. Overgrazing by domestic livestock and burning are however having the effect of reducing the number of chital and lowering the amount of cover available to the tiger. If this continues unchecked the tiger must decline.

The tiger's status in Pakistan is precarious. It no longer occurs in West Pakistan, the last specimen in the Indus Valley having been shot in 1886 (Burton, 1952). In East Pakistan, according to Mountfort and Poore, it now occurs in the Sylhet region "only as a vagrant from Assam, though plentiful twenty years ago". They also report that very few specimens remain in the Chittagong Hill Tracts, and that "evidence obtained locally suggests that the total population in the Sundarbans does not exceed 100 and may be even smaller".

The Sundarbans had the reputation of being among the best tiger country in the subcontinent. It is a vast swampy region, forming the delta of the Ganges and Brahmaputra river systems, and covering several thousand square miles, the greater part of it in East Pakistan. The entire area is intersected by a series of large tidal rivers and criss-crossed by a labyrinth of channels. The area has long been a happy hunting ground for poachers; and, since 1947, much of it has been drained and cleared for human settlement, with the result that the once-abundant wildlife has been drastically reduced. This has caused the tiger to turn its attention to domestic livestock, and some have become man-eaters. Cases of a tiger turning stock-killer or man-eater are almost invariably due either to the animal being deprived of its natural prey or because of wounds or maiming caused by trapping or shooting. The depredations of the few have led the West Bengal Forest Department to classify all tigers as vermin and, since 1967, the department has issued free licences and other inducements in support of its policy of extermination.

Several bird sanctuaries have been established in the Indian sector of the Sundarbans, including Sajnakhali (140 sq. miles), Halliday Island (2.3 sq. miles), and Lothian Island (15 sq. miles), which may contain a few tiger, but in view of the official policy their prospects of survival are slight.

Before the war, the tiger was also common in the remoter parts of Assam, where Seshadri notes that deforestation is currently taking place on a large scale. This process is accompanied by wanton slaughter, including "the almost total destruction of wild animal and bird life in the Naga territory, which the authorities chose to overlook for political reasons".

The overall decline of the Bengal tiger is attributable to loss of habitat, the reduction of natural prey, and to excessive slaughter. In Schaller's words, "legal and illegal killing has been the major cause of the decline in tigers throughout the forested areas. Males, females and young are destroyed indiscriminately, although many states now have regulations which prohibit the shooting of tigers when accompanied by cubs. However, the shooting season is opened for the convenience of the hunters during the hot weather when the females are more likely to be pregnant or have small young hidden somewhere than at other times of the year."

Schaller indicates the extent of the decline when he writes: "In one of the most remote areas of peninsular India, the West Bastar District of Madhya Pradesh, thirty-four hours of walking along transect lines through a three hundred square mile tract of forest revealed only two fresh sets of tracks."

Because tigers are nomadic, they need space. One of the effects of large-scale deforestation has been to confine both tigers and the herbivores on which they prey to ever smaller areas, usually in proximity to agricultural and pastoral development, thus increasing the opportunities for wildlife to come into conflict with human interests and, simultaneously, reducing its chances of escaping the increasing pressure from human predation.

Cultivation and settlement have expanded to accommodate the rising human population, and village shikaris, now well-armed, take a heavy toll of wild animals in their own neighbourhoods. The post-war period has also seen the emergence of a new phenomenon, the jeep-borne hunter who roams the forests at night shooting at any living thing that appears in his spotlight.

Another relatively new menace arises from the indiscriminate use of pesticides. Spillett states that since 1955 endrine and folidol have been widely used in India to destroy wild carnivores. Kills are sprinkled with a small quantity of folidol, which is both odourless and tasteless, and which "the unsuspecting tiger would eat freely, and then travel anywhere from 15 yards to half a mile before dying an agonizing death.... The crux of the problem is the uncontrolled and free distribution of pesticides to agriculturalists by the Indian Department of Agriculture. . . . It is urgent that steps be taken as soon as possible to insure that toxic materials are not wantonly distributed throughout the nation, and that those to whom they are given use them only for the purpose for which they were originally intended. Otherwise much of India's already greatly diminished wild life may soon be brought to the verge of extinction."

The Bengal tiger is essentially a forest dwelling animal and its future is inextricably linked with that of India's forests. Schaller is of the opinion that some of the largest tracts of forest containing the best tiger populations are in Madhya Pradesh, where there would be no difficulty in preserving the animal if only firm measures were taken to stop poaching.

Another key region is the *terai* (or "moist land"), the narrow belt of marshy jungle situated between the lower Himalayan foothills and the plains, and extending from the Jumna in the west to the Brahmaputra, much of it in Nepal.

The *terai* is the home of many kinds of wild animals, among which are several rare and endangered forms, including the Asiatic buffalo *Bubalus bubalis*, the swamp deer *Cervus duvauceli*, the diminutive pygmy hog *Sus salvanius*, and the hispid hare *Caprolagus hispidus*. Each of these species has the dubious distinction of being listed in the *Red Data Book* because so much of their natural habitat has been swept away that survival is problematical. True, a number of sanctuaries have been established in the *terai*, but they are too few, too small, and too encumbered with domestic livestock to ensure the perpetuation of the wild fauna.

The *terai* is the last stronghold for a wide spectrum of India's fauna, but it is being rapidly destroyed. An evaluation of the *terai* is urgently needed to determine what unspoiled areas remain, as a basis for formulating detailed proposals for a comprehensive system of national parks and sanctuaries. Unless that is done it is only a matter of time before the Bengal tiger, and several other representatives of the Indian fauna, cease to exist.

CASPIAN TIGER   *P. t. virgata*

This is a medium-sized tiger, differing from the nominate race in having somewhat lighter and longer stripes that are less evenly and more thickly distributed.

The range of the Caspian tiger extends from Trans-Caucasia, Mount Ararat and the Caspian/Aral region through northern Iran and Afghanistan into Tadzhikistan, to lakes Issyk-Kul' and Balkhash and the Dzungarian Alatau, thence to lakes Bagrash Kol and Lob Nor in Sinkiang, and as far north as the Irtish Basin and the Altai. The Lob Nor (or Chinese Turkestan) race, *P. t. lecoqi*, is held by some authors to be subspecifically distinct. Mazak, however, regards it as synonymous with *P. t. virgata*. This animal was found in dense *tugai* vegetation along the Tarim River to Lob Nor, and along the Ili River and the swampy regions bounding the northern slopes of the Tien Shan, north across the Dzungarian lowlands to the Irtish River and the Altai. Theodore Roosevelt, writing in 1926 of the Tekes River region in the Tien Shan, stated that over a period of the previous ten or fifteen years, native hunters had been conducting a systematic poisoning campaign to annihilate the tiger. Its systematic position is only of academic interest, however, as it is now almost certainly extinct.

Until the end of the last century some of the best tiger country was in the valley of the Amu Dar'ya (Oxus), particularly the headwaters and the mouth where it enters the Aral Sea. This valley had extensive stands of *tugai* vegetation which supported an abundance of wild pig and other natural prey, including herds of Bactrian wapiti *(Cervus elaphus bactrianus)*, another rare and endangered mammal.

The tiger was fairly common along the Amu Dar'ya until the First World War, but within three decades it had almost vanished. The last was captured in 1947. Sporadic rumours of its reappearance persisted until 1951, since when there have been no further reports. The intensive propagation and commercialized cropping of the musk-rat in this region necessitates the year-round presence of large numbers of musk-rat hunters, who would certainly report any large carnivore.

The causes of decline have been broadly similar throughout the Soviet Union. Since the Russian Revolution, large-scale irrigation schemes and other agricultural and pastoral projects have been developed in many of the larger river valleys, as well as around the shores of the Caspian and other inland waters. These have involved the almost total eradication of the reed thickets and dense *tugai* * forests which provide both the tiger and its natural prey with protective cover. Destruction of this riverine vegetation by fire and plough was combined with the employment of parties of soldiers as "tiger extermination squads". Subsequently, numerous settlements sprang up along the middle reaches of the Amu Dar'ya, and the little *tugai* that remains in the Darganata District will shortly be inundated by the proposed Tuya-Murgan dam.

This has been the pattern throughout the animal's range; and there is little likelihood that a resident population of Caspian tigers now

exists anywhere in the Soviet Union. The very infrequent sighting reports invariably refer to vagrants from northern Iran or, more probably, from Afghanistan.

A similar situation has taken place in Iran, where the tiger inhabits forests on the northern side of the Elburz Mountains and along the Caspian littoral in the provinces of Mazandéran Gilan and Gorgan. The most optimistic estimate is that 15 to 20 tigers remain in Iran, but some recent reports question whether any have survived. Excessive hunting, both legal and illegal, has undoubtedly been a significant factor in the decline, which has been inadvertently hastened by the post-war malarial control programmes. These have effectively reduced the long-standing menace of malaria around the shores of the Caspian, and the human population has benefited enormously in improved health and vigour; but a less fortunate side-effect has been the steep rise in hunting pressure on the local fauna. At the same time, much of the magnificent indigenous forest has been felled.

In Afghanistan the tiger occupies a narrow strip across the extreme northern part of the country, from the headwaters of the Tedzhen River on the frontier with Iran, through the Murghab region into the Paropamisus Range, and along the length of the Amu Dar'ya and the Pyandzh, which together form the common frontier with the Soviet Union, as far as the western and north-western slopes of the Hindu Kush and the Pamirs, which provide an effective barrier to further easterly penetration.

It is possible that Afghanistan possesses the largest, perhaps the only, remaining resident population of the Caspian tiger. Whether or not that surmise is correct, the upper Amu Dar'ya/ Pyandzh basin unquestionably holds the key to the survival both of the Caspian tiger and of the Bactrian wapiti. This is the only place in which they have any reasonable prospect of survival, and it is there that efforts to conserve them should be concentrated.

Despite large-scale annual reed burning, the Afghan side of the River Pyandzh is one of the few regions where sizeable *tugai* forests remain. This is attributable to the absence of permanent Afghan settlement close to the frontier. On the

---

* *Tugai* can be briefly defined as riverine vegetation, comprising a variety of trees, shrubs and grasses, occurring on the seasonally inundated flood plains of certain rivers in the arid regions of Central Asia.

Soviet side however, extensive areas of pristine *tugai* are scarce, one of the few being on the lower Vakhsh from Dzhilikul to its confluence with the Pyandzh. Part of this area has been incorporated into the Tigrovaya Balka ("Tiger Valley") Reserve (101,300 acres). Farther west, the island of Aral-Paygambar (10,000 acres), situated in the Amu Dar'ya, has also been declared a reserve.

Both the Caspian tiger and the Bactrian wapiti are so dependent on the retention of adequate stands of *tugai* vegetation that, in the interests of both animals, it is urgently necessary to undertake a thorough evaluation of the remaining *tugai* areas as a first step in arranging for them to be accorded permanent protection. During the annual flooding of the Pyandzh and other tributaries of the Amu Dar'ya, there is regular movement of wapiti and tiger across the Soviet/Afghanistan frontier. It is therefore essential that protective measures should be closely co-ordinated on both sides of the border.

SIBERIAN TIGER   *P. t. altaica*

The Siberian tiger is the largest and most powerfully built of all the races, old males having a huge head and massive forequarters.

At one time it was widely distributed in the Soviet Far East from Lake Baikal and the upper reaches of the Lena River, through Trans-Baikalia to the Amur and Ussuri river systems, and south through Manchuria to Korea and the Liao-tung Peninsula.

It was abundant throughout the forested areas of Manchuria, being especially numerous in the Ussuri Valley and the Amur Province, particularly around the mouth of the Amur River. Sowerby states that when the western portion of the Chinese Eastern Railway was under construction tigers "became positive pests, killing and carrying off workmen, till a regiment of Cossacks had to be sent to cope with the situation".

The causes of decline are given by Bannikov who writes: "In the first half of the 20th century, drastic contraction of range and numbers occurred on two separate occasions: the first in 1905-1916 when human settlement was being intensified in the Far East. Deforestation and burning occurred on a large scale, and hunters accounted for large numbers of ungulates, especially the wild boar—the tiger's principal source of winter food. Massive destruction of wild boar and deer occurred also in 1914 due to the exceptionally harsh winter and deep snow, which was catastrophic for the tiger. By 1916 the animal survived in only a few places and in small numbers. . . .

"The second major set-back occurred in 1936-40 when intensive hunting took place and large numbers of cubs were captured. In 1939-40, according to A. G. Kaplanov (1948), only about 30 individual tiger remained in the entire Far Eastern territory, of which 10-12 were in the Sikhote-Alin National Park, which played an important role in safeguarding the species. Since then both the wild ungulates and the tiger have gradually multiplied, particularly in the Sikhote-Alin National Park; whence they have spread to other areas."

The present situation is summarized by Abramov, who states that in 1956 the tiger population in Khabarovsk and Primorye totalled 58. In that year a total ban on shooting and a partial ban on catching was imposed. This resulted in numbers increasing by 1959 to 60 to 65 in Primorye, 30 to 35 in Khabarovsk, and 10 in the Amur region; a total of 100 to 110 for the entire Soviet Far East. Since then, numbers have declined somewhat, notably in the upper reaches of the Iman and Bikin rivers, but this reduction has to some extent been offset by a slight increase in southern and south-eastern Primorye. Abramov considers that, on balance, the size of the tiger population in the Soviet Far East does not differ significantly from the 1959-60 figure. Mazak, however, believes that this estimate is too optimistic, and suggests that the total may be no more than 60 to 70.

In northern China, the tiger now occurs only in the Changpch Mountains and the Lesser Hingan Mountains in the provinces of Kirin and Heilungkiang, but it is possible that a few may have survived in the Kentai Alin and

Nadan-Khatala Alin Mountains near the Soviet border. Sludskii, who visited China in 1958, estimated that there may have been about two hundred tigers in northern China at that time. Since then, however, the total has undoubtedly diminished because, during the late 1950s, at least 50 tigers a year are known to have been killed by Chinese Army detachments who were directed to destroy these "blood-thirsty carnivores". No provision is made in China for the protection of the tiger, and any straying across the frontier from Russia are liable to be slain.

Once the tiger was distributed throughout Korea, but is now confined to the extreme northern part of the country, where a few still occur in the forested regions of Mount Baekdu and the neighbouring Machonryung and Rangrim mountains, close to the Chinese frontier. The remnant population is reported to number between 40 and 50, but this may be an optimistic estimate: Mazak quotes a reliable report that from 1957 to 1960 there were only five records of tiger in North Korea.

Not only is the splendid long-haired coat the most valuable of all tiger skins, but almost every part of the animal is used. Tiger-bone wine has long been the most highly esteemed of all Chinese medicines as a cure for rheumatism. The Chinese regard tiger's blood as an even more potent aphrodisiac than wapiti or sika horn. Sowerby writes: "The Chinese believe that the bones, blood, heart, and even the flesh of the tiger have medicinal properties brewed by the apothecary that contain such ingredients as powdered tiger's knee-cap or clotted tiger's blood. The heart of the tiger is supposed to impart to the consumer the courage and strength of the tiger itself."

This explains the persistent manner in which the animal has been hunted. The principal cause of decline, however, has been the widespread destruction of the vast Manchurian forests, thus depriving the tiger both of its habitat and of the herbivores which constitute its natural prey.

Despite being under legal protection in the U.S.S.R. since 1947-48, tigers are evidently still being killed. As in most countries, it is difficult to refute a claim that a carnivore has been killed in self-defence. Furthermore, the ban on hunting does not apply to catching them alive, and a few immature tigers are taken each year. Special licences are now obligatory for the capture of cubs, however, and no more than three are issued annually. Packs of trained dogs are used to bay the animal in deep snow, each hunter being equipped with a forked stick with which the quarry is pinned to the ground. The export of Siberian tigers is, of course, a profitable business and a useful source of foreign exchange. There have been regular sales to the U.S.A. and Western European countries in recent years, as, for example, the 15 cubs captured in the Iman-Bikin River system in the winter of 1963-64.

The most recent threat to the tiger's survival is the current build-up of substantial military forces along both sides of the Sino-Soviet border, which runs through some of the best remaining tiger habitat. The presence of large bodies of troops is never conducive to enforcement of the game laws.

The Soviet authorities have attempted to make provision for the tiger through the establishment of two reserves, the Sudzukhe (320,000 acres) and Sikhote Alin (250,000 acres). In addition to giving the animal legal protection, steps have been taken to protect its principal natural prey, including the wild boar. Unfortunately, however, the tiger's nomadic disposition causes it to wander immense distances, and the reserves do not therefore contain resident populations. For all these reasons the Siberian tiger continues gradually to decline.

CHINESE TIGER   *P. t. amoyensis*

The Chinese tiger differs from the nominate race in having a fuller coat, deeper colour and broader stripes. Until recently it was widely distributed in much of eastern, central and southern China, particularly along the larger river valleys, but it appears always to have been uncommon in the mountainous western parts of the country. The northern extremity of the range is about 38°-40° North, but Allen shows that before the Second World War the tiger was already "exceedingly rare" north of the Yangtze Valley.

Present distribution is not well documented but, so far as can be determined, the animal appears to be confined almost entirely to the Yangtze River valley westward as far as the Szechwan border, and to the province of Fukien. Elsewhere, so much of the country has been cleared for cultivation and settlement that the tiger's chances of survival are negligible.

Almost every part of the carnivore is highly prized by the Chinese for its alleged curative powers. Allen observes that the tiger's diet consists of various wild animals including occasional pangolins, and the "favourite lairs . . . are sometimes raided by the Chinese for the pangolin scales . . .", which are also esteemed as an aphrodisiac.

Despite attaching such value to the animal, the Chinese accord it no protection: on the contrary, it is ruthlessly hunted down and destroyed at every opportunity as a menace to human life and a hindrance to agricultural and pastoral progress.

So long as hunting was conducted with unsophisticated weapons—bamboo spears, poisoned arrows, traps, and the like—losses were at least tolerable. The widespread introduction of modern firearms intensified the pressure being exerted on the animal. This coincided with massive human expansion and the spread of cultivation and settlement into previously unoccupied areas, thus depriving the tiger of both cover and natural food. These factors in combination have brought the animal to the verge of extinction.

INDO-CHINESE TIGER *P. t. corbetti*

In 1968 Mazak founded a new race of tiger, the type-specimen, from Vietnam, distinguished from the nominate race by its smaller size, darker ground colour, and more numerous stripes, which are narrow and seldom bifurcated.

The range extends from the provinces of Yunnan, Kwangsi and Kwangtung in the extreme south of China, through eastern Burma, Thailand, Cambodia, Laos, Vietnam, and the Malay Peninsula, south to Singapore. Within this large region the tiger occupies a variety of habitats, from the mangrove swamps on the coast to the higher mountainous zones.

Until recently, the tiger was common throughout much of South East Asia, but developments since the end of the Second World War have proved detrimental to the animal. Here, as elsewhere, the rising human tide flooding into hitherto unoccupied areas has destroyed large tracts of indigenous forest. Deforestation, followed by cultivation, has reduced the tiger's natural cover and also its principal prey species.

Agricultural development has the incidental effect of attracting wild pig which serve to entice the tiger into the cultivated areas where it at once comes into conflict with man. As Kitchener points out, the tiger thus suffers when it is in fact performing a valuable service in keeping the wild pig in check.

The enormous numbers of firearms that have filtered into South East Asia since the Second World War, and are especially evident in rural areas, are the principal cause of decline. To this must be added the introduction of the wire snare and the increasingly indiscriminate use of poison, which together account for large numbers of wild animals of all kinds.

Information on the status of this race is so fragmentary that an evaluation of its current status is impossible. The most recent estimate for Malaya is given by Locke (1954), who assessed the total at about 3,000. In the ensuing fifteen years no further count has been attempted. The general consensus of opinion, however, is that the tiger has everywhere declined, but the extent of the decline is not known.

The Vietnam War has certainly had an adverse effect on the tiger, and much other wildlife besides, but in the absence of reliable data one can do no more than speculate. Elsewhere in South East Asia the tiger is still widely distributed and, although undoubtedly less abundant than twenty years ago, this race is probably in a stronger position than any other. That is only conjecture, however, and there is need for an up to date study of the tiger's current status and future prospects throughout South East Asia.

SUMATRAN TIGER   *P. t. sumatrae*

In common with the other insular races, the Sumatran tiger is small and dark coated. Mazak describes the ground colour as "reddish-dark-ochre". The paler parts of the coat are more cream-coloured than white, and much less conspicuous than in the nominate race. The stripes are very black, which accentuates the overall impression of dark coloration; usually long, broad, and bifurcated; and frequently consisting of a mass of small dark spots. The forequarters are strongly marked, and the forelegs regularly striped.

Sody provides abundant evidence that until less than a century ago the Sumatran tiger was very common. Burton quotes a report that "the number of people slain annually by tigers in Sumatra was almost incredible, whole villages being depopulated by the depredations of these animals. A writer in *The Field* in 1891 says that when he was on the north-west coast of Sumatra in 1885-68 the country swarmed with Tigers, which were more numerous about the tobacco plantations than in the jungle."

The tiger remained common and widespread until the Second World War, particularly in the

northern parts of the country and the mountainous regions in the south-west; and the report prepared by Heynsius-Viruly and Van Heurn in 1936 did not consider any special protective measures to be necessary.

Subsequently, the unsettled conditions that have been a feature of the post-war period resulted, in Milton's words, in "the cutting down of forested areas and the opening up of land for rural development and cultivation and, second, the ruthless poaching with firearms and motor transport". For these reasons the Sumatran tiger is believed to have undergone a marked decline, but, in the absence of any recent faunal survey, it is impossible to be certain of its current status.

JAVAN TIGER   *P. t. sondaica*

A century ago the tiger was widespread in Java also; indeed, right up to the 1930s it remained sufficiently plentiful to warrant no special protective measures. This situation can be better appreciated when considered against Hoogerwerf's statement that in pre-war Java "more than 60,000 hunting rifles were in circulation and every year about 9,000 licences were bought. . . ."

In 1921, the Netherlands Indies Government set aside the Udjung Kulon Peninsula, at the western tip of Java, as a reserve for the perpetuation of the Javan rhinoceros, the Banteng and the Javan tiger. Elsewhere, however, the animal was hunted avidly, partly for sport but primarily because tigers were looked upon as a menace to domestic livestock as well as a threat to human life.

By the time Talbot visited the country in 1955 the situation had deteriorated to the extent that no more than 20 to 25 tigers were estimated to remain in all Java, of which 10 to 12 were in Udjung Kulon.

The tiger no longer occurs in Udjung Kulon or in the Baluran Reserve in extreme north-eastern Java, though some reports suggest that a pair may survive in the latter. The position today can be stated briefly; the tiger is extinct in Java except for the south-eastern part of the country, much of which is too arid or rocky, or in some places too swampy, to be used for agricultural purposes. Within this general area, a few tigers are believed to occur on the lower slopes of the Semeru Volcano (to the south of the town of Malang), and along the Glidek River, as well as in the Blambangan Peninsula. Banteng and deer *(Cervus timorensis)* are still relatively plentiful here, especially on the Jang Plateau.

Within this large area the total tiger population probably does not exceed a dozen at most, the majority in the Betiri Forest Reserve (170,000 acres) in the South Djember District of East Java Province.

BALI TIGER *P. t. balica*

The Bali tiger is the easternmost representative of the species, and the smallest of all the races. Apart from size, it differs from the Javan race by being even darker in general colour and in having fewer stripes.

The validity of the Balinese race has been called into question by a number of authors who consider that the characters are not such as to warrant subspecific differentiation from the Javan. Some aver that this tiger was introduced into Bali from Java by human agency. But the opposite opinion has its advocates also, as, for example, Sody (1932), who states that "even a cursory examination showed that the differences between the 3 Sunda-races of the tiger were so obvious that, indeed, a single glance was sufficient to distinguish the races and to recognise the origin of the skins and skulls from their appearance!"

The tiger was once common in the western part of the island but is now believed extinct. The last reliable report indicated that it existed at least until 1952. The north-eastern part of Bali is densely forested and difficult of access even today, so it is possible that a few have contrived to survive. Occasional reports suggest that the animal may still occur in the two national parks in the western part of the island, but these reports have not been verified.

SNOW LEOPARD *Panthera uncia*

The snow leopard, or ounce,* is slightly smaller than the common leopard, and among the most attractive of all the great cats. In winter coat the fur, particularly on the lower parts, is unusually long, with thick woolly under-fur. This, in conjunction with the short muzzle, has the effect of making the head appear disproportionately small. The general ground colour is pale charcoal, faintly tinged with cream: the under parts up to the chin are milk white. The black rosettes are large, irregularly shaped, and randomly distributed. The markings on the head, along the spine, and on the upper part of the tail are well defined, but where the fur is

long they are somewhat blurred: the pattern is more distinct in summer coat. The tail is long and densely furred, with large rosettes on the upper surface, white beneath, and black-tipped.

The snow leopard is an inhabitant of the cold highland steppes of Central Asia, bounded by the Hindu Kush in the extreme north-east of Afghanistan; Gilgit, Hunza, Nagar in Pakistan; the Karakoram Range and the southern line of the Himalayas, through the northern parts of Kashmir, Nepal, Sikkim, and Bhutan. Gee reports a skin from Tawang in the north-eastern part of the North-East Frontier Agency, east of Bhutan.

In the west the range extends from the Hindu Kush into the mountains of Tadzhikistan, particularly the Darvaz, Gissar and Zeravshan mountains, and the Pamirs (principally the

* This name appears to have originated from a drawing of the snow leopard published by Buffon in 1761 and entitled *l'Once*.

western part). In Kirgiziya the animal occurs in the Chatkal Range, the Talass Alatau, and especially the Tien Shan. North of the Ili River, it has, been recorded from the Dzungarian Alatau, the Tarbagatay and Saur ranges, and even farther north-eastwards in the Altai and Tuva Autonomous Region (Tuvinskaya).

The Chinese sector of the range includes several points around the mountainous periphery of Sinkiang, notably the northern side of the central Tien Shan in the north; the Pamirs in the west; and the Astin Tagh in the south of the province. From the Astin Tagh the range reaches south across the Tibetan Plateau and east to the north-eastern part of Tsinghai Province as far as the Kilien Shan on the Tsinghai/Kansu border and the mountains of extreme western Szechwan.

There are numerous references in the early literature to the occurrence of the snow leopard in the Caucasus and even in southern Iran, but such reports almost certainly refer to pale-coloured specimens of the common leopard or the cheetah. Lay summarizes the evidence and concludes that "no *bona fide* specimen has ever been reported from any part of Iran. The nearest known localities on record are those from the Turkmen SSR. . . . The possibility that *F. uncia* occurs in the Iranian Kopet Dagh seems much more likely than does finding it in southern Iran."

Shou Chen Huang includes the Yin Shan, in Mongolia, within the range of the species, but it seems improbable that this claim could be substantiated. Similar reports from Manchuria and the Amur region are also of questionable validity.

The snow leopard's seasonal movements, like those of other carnivores, are largely governed by the distribution of prey species. Generally speaking, therefore, the summer is spent at the higher elevations, up to 13,000 feet (of the 23 specimens recorded by Dang, two were observed at 18,000 and 18,500 feet respectively), where the open alpine grasslands, just below the snow line, provide favourable environmental conditions for the herbivores on which it preys. These include the *bharal* (or blue sheep), wild goats, deer, gazelle, boar, serow, goral, takin, as well as many smaller mammals and birds.

As summer advances, the wild herds move higher into the mountains in the wake of the retreating snow. With the onset of winter they descend to the lower valleys, and the predators conform. This procedure is not inflexible, however, and in some areas, such as the Dzungarian Alatau, the snow leopard appears to stay at low altitude throughout the year: in others it is reputed to remain permanently at high altitude.

As both summer and winter ranges are used by constantly expanding herds of domestic livestock, the snow leopard inevitably falls foul of man through preying on domestic herds and flocks. Novikov states that in years of scarcity it will sometimes take up residence close to human habitation, and has even been known to attack cattle in their pens.

Few people have ever seen a snow leopard in the wild, and even fewer have witnessed one actually attacking its prey; but, in 1958, Dang was at a height of 12,000 feet in the Kumaon Himalayas "lying behind a boulder watching the *thar* climbing leisurely up the scree and the rock overhangs towards the north ridge of the Raj Ramba peak, when a flash of white and grey fur dived into the spread out herd, and rolled down some hundred feet, all the time hanging on to a young *thar* ewe. . . . The snow leopard, of course, vanished as soon as we rose to view. . . ."

The normal method of attack involves a gradual stalk, culminating in a sudden final rush to pull down the quarry. An alternative technique is to wait in ambush beside a game trail and spring upon a passing animal. The snow leopard combines great strength with extreme agility. According to Shou Chen-Huang, it is capable of clearing more than 30 feet in a single bound and of leaping to a height of 10 or 12 feet.

It seems probable that individual animals, or family groups, establish territories. Dang suggests that, "almost every major Himalayan valley has its pair of snow leopard"; and he advances the theory that they operate in "pairs working valleys in co-ordination, the prey, generally *bharal*, being chased from one part of the valley into the area where the other

LÉOPARD DES NEIGES　　　　　*Panthera uncia*　　　　　SNOW LEOPARD

animal of the pair hides in waiting . . .''. Very little is known of the snow leopard's life history and habits. Much of our ignorance is attributable to the remoteness and inaccessibility of the habitat and the severe climatic and environmental conditions under which the animal lives. These factors, in combination with the animal's nocturnal disposition, have effectively discouraged observation and study.

Births take place in the spring after a gestation period of about 99 days. The litter normally consists of two or three cubs, which remain with the mother throughout the following winter, hunting together as a group, until the birth of the subsequent litter.

The lair is usually a small cave or rock crevice in a secluded and inaccessible spot. Unless disturbed, an animal may occupy the same place continuously. Novikov makes the interesting observation that in the Kirgizian Alatau snow leopards have been known to utilize the huge nests of griffon vultures. Shou Chen-Huang describes a lair containing a solitary cub, which was discovered in 1955 on Chiu-meng Mountain in Szechwan. This was a cave about 4 feet square, the floor carpeted with moulted fur to a depth of about half an inch, and which through long use had acquired an almost blanket-like consistency.

The pelt of the snow leopard ranks among the most beautiful and valuable of all wild cat furs, for which reason the animal has been hunted assiduously. It is generally taken in winter when it descends to lower levels and can be more easily caught, usually by means of snares, traps and pitfalls. A method of capture recently adopted in China involves a stout net buried under the snow. The release mechanism is triggered by the weight of the animal which becomes entangled in the net, snatched clear of the ground, and thus taken without injury.

Referring to its status in Pakistan, Mountfort and Poore write: "Prices of up to Rs. 600 are currently being offered by fur traders in Rawalpindi and Peshawar for the raw skins of this species. Such a premium is sufficient to guarantee the extermination of the already rare snow leopard within the next few years unless the Government intervenes promptly."

Hunting has been particularly severe in Kashmir where the decline has been actively encouraged by an official policy which designates the species as vermin. A similar situation prevails in Mongolia where, as in other predominantly pastoral countries, there is an understandable lack of sympathy for any predator. Under Mongolian law, the snow leopard is placed in the same category as the wolf, lynx, badger, and various predatory birds which may be freely hunted at all times. Despite this permanent open season and the incentive of the valuable pelt, a revealing indication of the animal's scarcity is given by Hibbert's statement that only about 40 to 50 snow leopards are killed in Mongolia each year.

It is equally rare in the Soviet Union, where Gladkov and Nasimovich state that the total taken annually from 1961 to 1964 was between 24 and 60, and numbers are described as "sharply decreasing". The species is now accorded full legal protection throughout its range in the U.S.S.R., as well as being represented in the Aksu-Dzhabagly Reserve (185,000 acres) in Kazakhstan. This reserve, established in 1926, includes part of the Talass and Ugam ranges, and typifies the vegetation of the western Tien Shan.

In 1952 the Indian Board for Wild Life added the name of the snow leopard to the protected list. It is also included among the fauna of two Indian sanctuaries: Nanda Devi (250 sq. miles), and Tons (368 sq. miles). These are of doubtful value, however, as, in the absence of any attempt at supervision (for which reason neither is included in the U. N. List of National Parks and Equivalent Reserves), both sanctuaries could be more accurately described as poaching preserves.

The main hope for the species lies in stringent enforcement of the game laws, backed by deterrent sentences for infringement. The governments of both India and Pakistan have already prohibited the export of all wild cat skins, but this has not inhibited certain furriers from continuing to offer skins for sale. More effective control of the fur trade within these two countries is of paramount importance to the survival of the snow leopard.

CEYLON ELEPHANT

Elephas maximus maximus

The two living species of elephants—*Loxodonta africana* in africa, and *Elephas maximus* in Asia—are the only surviving descendants of a large family which was once widespread in the Northern Hemisphere.

The Asiatic and African elephants are easily distinguishable. The Asiatic species is the smaller; the curvature of its back is convex; its skin is smooth and marked with white or pink depigmentation spots, which become more numerous with age; its ears are small and triangular-shaped; its forehead is prominently domed; its trunk is tipped with only a single finger-like protruberance; the female is tuskless, or, more accurately, the tusks are so small that they do not protrude beyond the lips—and tuskless males are common. Deraniyagala estimates that only 11 per cent of male elephants of the Ceylon race carry tusks.

The African elephant, on the other hand, is a larger animal; the curvature of its back is concave; depigmentation marks are absent; its ears are large; its forehead is flat; its trunk has two protrusions at the tip; and it has large tusks which are present in both sexes.

The tusks are in fact the upper incisors. The jaw is also equipped with extremely powerful molars. As each molar becomes worn, it is replaced by another from behind, up to a maximum of six in each jaw, only one or two of which are functional at a time. These huge teeth, which may be almost a foot long, are capable of crushing and grinding the toughest vegetation.

Midway between the ear and the eye is the opening to the "musth" gland which, in mature Asiatic male elephants, exudes a dark oily substance at irregular intervals. The exact function of this gland is not well understood, but is believed to be connected with sexual activity. When in "musth", elephants are abnormally aggressive; captive animals become dangerous and uncontrollable and so the mating of captive elephants is usually discouraged.

There is much confusion over the classification of the Asiatic elephants. Many races have been described, but most are of question-able validity. Generally, however, four races are recognized: the Indian elephant *E. m. indicus*, which inhabits parts of India, South East Asia, and Borneo (where it is believed to have been introduced by human agency); the Sumatran elephant, *E. m. sumatranus ;* and two other races, both of which live in Ceylon: *E. m. vilaliya*, a large tuskless form, with relatively smooth, light-coloured skin which is restricted to the flood plains of a few rivers in the Eastern Province; and *E. m. maximus*, the smaller, darker, typical Ceylon form.

The elephant has long played a prominent part in the culture and economy of many Asiatic countries; so long indeed that the origins of the practice of capturing and training it are older than recorded history. The animal was particularly valued for military purposes. Porus's army, for instance, included a contingent of elephants, which strongly contested Alexander the Great's advance into India in the third century B. C. In Ceylon, according to Norris, "the Sinhalese in the 16th century employed war-elephants against the Portuguese; in the siege of Colombo, which took place in 1587, it is recorded that 2,200 animals were used".

In many South East Asian countries the elephant was also trained as a work animal. A force of several thousand elephants was said to have been employed over a period of many years in the construction of Cambodia's renowned temple of Angkor Wat. Even today, the elephant is indispensable to forestry in Burma.

A ruler's power and prestige were considerably enhanced by the number of elephants at his command. The elephant thus became the symbol of power and royal splendour: it also served as an important adjunct to court and temple display. Ornately caparisoned elephants are still a familiar sight in India and other Asiatic countries during religious processions and on ceremonial occasions.

The Ceylon elephant has long been credited with possessing the finest qualities of all the Asiatic elephants. It was regarded as superior in size, strength, intelligence, and courage, for which reason it was much in demand at the court of the Moghul emperors of India and elsewhere. During their occupation of Ceylon, the Portuguese, and later the Dutch, captured and trained elephants for export, in the course of which they devised and developed the *keddah* (or *Kraal*) system of capturing elephants by driving a herd into a stout enclosure, in place of the traditional Sinhalese method of capturing them in foot-nooses.

Although Asiatic elephants have for centuries been used in the service of man, there appear to be no records of successful captive breeding in Ceylon, where it is considered easier and more profitable to acquire replacements from wild-caught stocks. A different policy is followed in Burma and in the Indian States of Mysore, Madras and Assam, which are the only places where domesticated elephants are bred.

The gestation period is usually regarded as about 22 months, but Kurt shows that it can vary from 18 to 25 months. If the calf survives and remains with its mother, she will again give birth after 4 years. If, on the other hand, the calf dies at or shortly after birth, the interval between births will be shorter. Kurt concludes that theoretically a female could continue to bear young for thirty years, during which time she would give birth to about eight calves.

A single calf is normal, although twin and triple births have been recorded. The newborn calf is covered with thick hair, which reduces with age. The pair of mammary glands is situated between the mother's forelegs. The calf suckles with its mouth, not with its trunk as was at one time supposed. It starts to eat green food at the age of a few months, and is weaned after about two years. Calf mortality is high; Kurt estimates that fewer than 50 per cent reach maturity.

Calf rearing is an exacting and time-consuming occupation, and, as Kurt remarks, "for the successful raising of a young wild elephant more than one adult is required. To look after a baby is an exhausting 24-hour task. As an adult elephant normally feeds during 18 hours in 24, it is essential that the job of looking after babies is shared amongst various members of the herd . . . who not only take upon themselves the task of protecting and looking after the baby, but also assist in its feeding by preparing grass and breaking branches. . . . Babies are usually grouped together in what might be termed a nursery. The nursery is in charge of one adult animal, which is relieved from time to time by others. Water holes are pivotal points in the life of elephants, and it is at these points that the young are handed over from the mother to the nursery and vice versa; it is at water holes that herds usually close up into a compact gathering, and this as much as the presence of water makes water holes of such great importance to elephants."

At the age of six or seven years, the male calves begin to move away from the herds, but they maintain a loose association until, at the age of about ten, they sever connection with the females and establish disparate male groups.

Asiatic elephants live in small herds, which are essentially female family units, and normally contain only mature females and young of both sexes. Adult males are usually solitary animals; they join the herds only briefly when they are in "musth" and a female comes on heat.

Kurt states that occasionally "a number of family groups and single elephants may join together into large concentrations of over 100 animals during periods of drought or under other uncommon conditions (such as floods, shortage or abundance of food). In concentrations of up to about 40 animals, the leadership is taken over by various elders who jointly decide on the group's movements. Still greater concentrations become unwieldy and are no longer under the direction of individuals or groups; the concentration then moves along traditional routes or remains stationary. Within concentrations individual herds retain their identity and cohesion; they do not mix, and remain in close direct contact. This cohesion of family groups within a large concentration was clearly demonstrated at last year's *keddah* in Mysore when throughout the great excitement and disturbance caused by the driving and capturing operations, the family groups remained compact until all animals were roped and forcibly separated, and even then they kept vocal contact with one another. The bonds within the family group are, therefore, enormously strong, and there is further no doubt that individuals recognise one another by voice."

Elephants were once widely distributed in Ceylon and sufficiently numerous to cause considerable damage to plantations and crops. Their depredations became so serious that in 1831 the government introduced a bounty scheme to encourage their reduction. Initially, the bounty was ten shillings for every elephant killed, but later it was reduced to seven shillings on the ground, as Sir Samuel Baker explains, that "the number killed was so great that the Government imagine that they cannot afford the annual outlay". An indication of the scale of the slaughter can be gauged from de Silva's statement that Major Rogers, a celebrated elephant hunter who lived during the first half of the nineteenth century, "is credited with having slain over 1,400 elephants; a Captain Gallwey with over 700; and Major Skinner almost as many".

The shooting of wild elephants is now prohibited in Ceylon, except for rogue elephants which become a danger to life or property. Some elephants are also killed in the course of crop protection. Elephants are particularly fond of sugar cane and a herd can cause extensive damage to a sugar plantation in the course of a night.

The freedom with which elephants once moved throughout the island can be seen from the evidence of numerous long-established elephant paths. The spread of peasant cultivation in the lowlands was later followed by intensive development of the highlands, at first for coffee and later for tea production. The establishment of plantations in the high-rainfall areas severed the elephant trek-routes, thus dispossessing the herds of their traditional foraging grounds, and forcing them to move into more arid regions where dry-season food is scarce.

Concern at the apparent decline of the elephant led the Wild Life Protection Society of Ceylon to undertake a preliminary survey of the animal. The results of this survey, published in 1959, showed that the elephant population is largely confined to the eastern half of the island. Although numbers were more or less stable during the previous ten years, the survey revealed that the status of the elephant was likely to deteriorate. This was chiefly because

the proposed Heda-Oya sugar development project, sited between the Gal Oya and the Ruhuna (Yala) reserves, would have the effect of forcing more elephants into these reserves than could be maintained in them. The two reserves, which were established specifically to protect the species, are about 60 miles apart, and situated in the drier part of the island, for which reason they are unable to sustain the elephant population throughout the year. Shortage of food and fresh water compels the herds to move out of the reserves early in the dry season; they do not return until the commencement of the rains three or four months later.

This preliminary survey was followed in 1967 by a more extensive three-year study undertaken by a team of scientists working under the auspices of the Smithsonian Institution, and supported by the World Wildlife Fund. The Smithsonian Elephant Survey is designed to provide detailed information on numbers, distribution, daily and seasonal movements, ecological requirements, individual and group behaviour, and reproduction; it will thus provide the data on which a comprehensive long-range conservation programme can be based. It will complement similar studies on the African elephant which have already been started.

The problem of ensuring the elephant's survival in Ceylon is complex. Preliminary estimates show that there are approximately 2,500 elephants on the island, most of them living either in areas which have been earmarked for future cultivation or in the national parks and reserves. As agricultural development reduces the remaining areas of natural forest, these wildlife sanctuaries become correspondingly more important to the elephant. The animal's future is therefore becoming increasingly dependent on the reserves. But the system of reserves is inadequate for the task.

If the reserves were ecologically self-sufficient there would be no need for the herds to move outside their boundaries. The only satisfactory permanent solution lies in adjusting the boundaries to make them if possible perennially viable. This would involve assessing the numbers of elephants each reserve can carry, and devising methods of limiting the population to that figure.

Elephas maximus maximus

ÉLÉPHANT DE CEYLAN

CEYLON ELEPHANT

INDIAN WILD ASS

Equus hemionus khur

The Asiatic wild ass, *Equus hemionus*, includes five subspecies: *E. h. hemionus*, the Mongolian wild ass, or kulan; *E. h. onager*, the Persian wild ass, or onager; *E. h. khur*, the Indian wild ass, or ghor-khar; *E. h. kiang*, the Tibetan wild ass, or kiang; and *E. h. hemippus*, the Syrian wild ass, which is probably extinct.* All are rare and thus listed in the *Red Data Book*.

The Indian race is a medium-sized form, its average height being about 4 feet at the shoulder. Its upper parts are a bright sandy colour, which Spillett describes as "almost a palamino colour", grading into white on its hind quarters and underside. Its mane is dark, its ears short and dark-tipped. A relatively broad chestnut-coloured line extends along the full length of its back from its mane to the root of its black-tufted tail. It has no hoof-rings.

This subspecies originally ranged into the more arid parts of north-western India, West Pakistan, and south-eastern Iran, where it inter-graded with the Persian wild ass. The contraction of range is very recent: Talbot in 1954 "talked with Pakistanis in Karachi who remembered its occurrence in the deserts near there in earlier years".

Harper's careful review of the evidence shows that the decline of the Indian wild ass was directly attributable to destruction by man. Since historical times the animal has been widely used as a substitute for the horse, both for purposes of war and as a draught animal for agricultural and other work. It is still occasionally used by the Indian Army for breeding what Talbot calls "super mules".

For many centuries, therefore, the wild ass has been a valuable animal in the service of man. The Baluchis and others made a regular and profitable business of capturing foals for sale,

usually by riding them down during the foaling season. Full-grown asses—excepting gravid females—are too swift for mounted men to catch, though relays of horses and riders are sometimes used to wear them down. Others are caught in pitfalls or shot. Wild ass meat is greatly esteemed; and various parts of the animal are valued for reputed medicinal properties, particularly the testes which are considered a potent aphrodisiac.

The combination of uncontrolled slaughter and competition from ever-increasing herds of domestic livestock led to the gradual elimination of the Indian wild ass from most of its range, with the exception of the princely state of Kutch, where it was rigorously protected by the ruler. There it is almost entirely confined to the Little Rann of Kutch, which now forms part of the state of Gujarat, on the Indian side of the frontier with Pakistan.

For many years little was known about the status of the Indian wild ass; until in 1962, following reports of heavy losses from disease, the I.U.C.N. Survival Service Commission sponsored a visit by E. P. Gee to the Little Rann of Kutch to carry out a preliminary appraisal. His travelling expenses were paid by the World Wildlife Fund. Gee's report confirmed that numbers had been seriously depleted, and made several far-reaching conservation proposals.

The Little Rann of Kutch is described by Gee as being an area of about 1,000 square miles of "salt-impregnated, flat waste, only a foot or two above sea level. It is sometimes described as dried up from about November to June when motor vehicles can travel over most of the surface quite easily, avoiding the darker patches which might be soft. During the monsoon months from July to September, the discharge from the rivers Banas, Rupen and others, together with sea water blown up from the Gulf of Kutch in the south-west by the strong monsoon winds, covers the area with 1 or 2 feet of water and renders it impassable. As this flat area is salt-impregnated, no vegetation of

* The systematic arrangement of the wild asses remains in dispute. Groves and Mazak (1967) place both the Asiatic and the African wild asses in the genus *Asinus*. They divide the Asiatic forms into two species: *A. hemionus* (the onagers), with six subspecies; and *A. kiang* (the kiangs, or Tibetan wild asses), with three subspecies.

any kind can grow on it. In the Little Rann there are several small islands or *bets* of higher ground, on which there is some sparse tree and grass vegetation. The wild asses graze on the *bets* and on the 'shores' of the mainland which borders the Rann."

Spillett states that the largest of these *bets* is "the somewhat centrally located 18 to 20-square-mile Pung Bet. Salim Ali considered

this *bet* as the 'headquarters' for the Indian wild ass during his 1946 expedition. However, he also stated that the relatively small *bets* of Vachda and Jhilandan were probably the only source of perennial water within the Rann and and the asses shifted to them from Pung Bet about the middle of March. Other *bets* include Nanda, Mardakh, Kesmari and Zilanand or Jalander, as well as a number of smaller 'islands'. Rainfall in this region is only 5 to 15 inches per year."

Wild asses in the Little Rann are in competition for the sparse grazing with large numbers of domestic livestock. Spillett frequently encountered big herds of cattle along the fringes of the Rann, "as well as flocks of sheep, goats, and donkeys. With very few exceptions, all the areas which we visited were severely overgrazed. A lack of forage was already evidenced by the condition of most of the animals and it was

difficult to imagine what would sustain them during the next six months until the monsoon rains. Mesquite appeared to be the only plant species relatively unaffected by the abuse of too much domestic livestock."

The wild ass is the dominant wild mammal in the Little Rann. Other species, such as blackbuck, chinkara, and nilgai were once commonly found around the periphery of the area; Spillett observed "no blackbuck, but saw two chinkara and four nilgai in the Rann north-west of Tikar. However, we witnessed the ruthless gunning down of one of these by some 'sportsmen' in a jeep and had the unpleasant task of apprehending the culprits. Except for wild asses, no other wild mammals were observed within the vicinity of the Little Rann."

The Indian wild ass undoubtedly owes its survival in the Little Rann of Kutch to the unusually tolerant attitude of the local people; all of whom, in Gee's words, are Gujarati-speaking vegetarians who "do not harm the wild asses or other wild life. In fact some of them are reputed to be so 'orthodox' that they are very reluctant to kill the locusts which devour their crops, but wish only to drive them away. One village, I was informed, does not allow even eggs to be eaten by others in the vicinity of their village."

Spillett relates that a wealthy land-owner living in Ahmedabad, but with extensive holdings near Kharaghoda and Patadi, petitioned the Government in the spring of 1966 to reduce the number of wild asses because of crop depredations. However, Forest Department personnel reported that when the local Divisional Forest Officer met this man and explained the importance and need for protecting this unique species, he withdrew his petition".

Such tolerance is the more remarkable in view of the ass's addiction to crop-raiding. The herds spend the day in the desert, but at night they enter the cultivated areas around the edge of the Little Rann. The local people try to discourage these visits by attempting to drive the asses away; some animals are occasionally lamed by stones, but they are not otherwise molested.

The wild ass is highly susceptible to certain diseases, particularly *surra* and African horse

HÉMIONE DE L'INDE   *Equus hemionus khur*   INDIAN WILD ASS

sickness, which are transmitted by domestic livestock. Spillett refers to an occasion in 1964 when a forest guard found "about 100 asses between Jesda and Malvan". Recurrent outbreaks of these two diseases during the 1960s have caused heavy losses among the wild ass herds. Spillett suggests that "coupled with poaching and habitat destruction, disease [including rinderpest and anthrax] may be the 'coup de grace' for species such as blackbuck, chinkara and nilgai".

In 1961 the Government instituted and financed an annual vaccination programme. This well-conceived measure has not been entirely successful, however, as several owners have refused to allow their horses to be treated on the specious ground that they cannot afford to have them idle for the week or fortnight's rest that the treatment requires. Clearly this constructive programme cannot hope to achieve its purpose unless vaccination is made obligatory.

The rapid decline of the Indian wild ass since the end of the Second World War is shown by the series of population estimates made over a period of twenty-five years. When Salim Ali visited the Little Rann in 1946 he estimated the total number of wild asses at between 3,000 and 5,000. The population appears to have remained at about the same level during the ensuing decade: Wynter-Blyth estimated the total at about 4,000 in 1956, including several herds of more than 200 animals. Within a few years, however, more than three-quarters of the population had been destroyed, presumably by disease. Gee's careful census showed that by 1962 the total had dropped to about 870. Events during the Indo-Pakistan war resulted in the wild ass population again being halved: an aerial census carried out by Dharmakumarsinhji in October 1969 revealed that the total has been reduced to about 400 animals.

Gee could find no evidence of wild asses in the Great Rann of Kutch except for "a few stragglers". More recently, however, Mountfort has reported a group of about 20 to 30 asses which are said to be permanently resident in part of the Great Rann near Nagar Parkar. Several were shot during the Indo-Pakistan war, and others have since been either killed or captured.

These figures reveal both the extent and the speed of the decline; and underline the need to establish a legally constituted sanctuary, primarily for the wild ass and other relict native fauna, but, not least, to safeguard an unusually interesting desert environment. This should be done while the land is still available. There is also a need for a thorough ecological study of the wild ass and its habitat to provide the essential foundation on which to develop a programme for the proper management of the sanctuary.

JAVAN RHINOCEROS   *Rhinoceros sondaicus*

A century ago the Javan rhinoceros was widely distributed in South East Asia; but because all three species of Asiatic rhinoceroses occurred in the same general region, and early reports failed to distinguish between them, it is impossible to be certain of the precise historical range. It is known, however, that the Javan form occurred as far west as the Sundarbans in Bengal, whence it extended along the Brahmaputra Valley into Assam. Authentic records from Burma are limited to Tenasserim, but the range included south-western China, thence along the Mekong and other large river valleys into Laos, Vietnam, Cambodia, Thailand, Malaya, as well as Sumatra and Java.

Much of the uncertainty in early reports arose from the similarity between the Javan and Great Indian rhinoceroses which for many years were regarded as the same animal, and the fact that the ranges of the Javan and Sumatran species largely coincided. It is easy to see how this confusion arose. The Great Indian rhinoceros is only a little larger than the Javan (though its head is noticeably heavier); and both have prominent folds in the hide. The skin folds in fact differ slightly, notably on the neck and shoulders, while the skin of the Javan rhinoceros lacks the tubercles that are so conspicuous in the Indian species. Most accounts state that the horn of the male Javan is invariably about half the length of the Indian, and that Javan females have the distinction, unique among the five rhinoceros species, of being hornless or of having only a token horn in the form of a small horny boss. But Schenkel refutes this belief. His observations have shown that although some Indian rhinoceros bulls have longer horns than the Javan, the converse is sometimes true. "Furthermore, all the females which we have seen and which the guards saw during our presence in Udjung Kulon have horns quite similar to those of bulls."

An indication of the animal's former abundance in northern India is given by Pollock who spent seven years in Assam during the 1860s: "I never shot the lesser rhinoceros on the right bank of the Brahmaputra but I have no doubt that it exists; but it is fairly plentiful on the left bank south of Goalparah, where I have killed it. . . . I may here mention about them in Assam that I shot there 44 to my own gun, and probably saw some 60 others slain, and lost wounded fully as many as I killed."

Blyth, writing in 1862, said that the rhinoceros was still common in the Sundarbans at that time, a statement that is corroborated by several other authors. The species is known to have been there until 1892 when Edmond de Poncins found three or four individuals, but, as poaching was rife at the time, the species is unlikely to have survived for many more years.

The last specimen to be taken in Burma was shot in 1920, and in 1933 Peacock wrote: "It is extremely doubtful whether there are now more than half a dozen specimens of *R. sondaicus* in existence in Burma, and it is unlikely that they will survive." The last Malayan specimen was shot in 1932.

Occasional reports of the continued existence of a few individual animals in Tenasserim still persist but these are unconfirmed, and probably refer to the Sumatran species. Guggisberg alludes to a report that rhinoceroses, possibly *Rh. sondaicus*, may have survived into the 1960s in the mountainous part of Laos north of the Srepok River. This is a large and little-known region of extensive jungle and swamps.

As long ago as 1885 Neumann was saying that the rhinoceros had been hunted to excess in Sumatra and had become scarce. Sody, who undertook a comprehensive appraisal of the animal in Sumatra and Java, showed that it remained relatively abundant in Sumatra until the turn of the century, after which the decline was rapid. The last specimen of *Rh. sondaicus* in South Palembang was shot in 1928, according to Heynsius-Viruly and Van Heurn, who stated that the species still survived, though only sporadically, "in the plateaus and mountain swamps of Atjeh, especially in the Gajo and Alas districts, in the extensive forests in the hinterland of Langkat, at the salt springs on Sumatra's East Coast, at Indragiri (between Taloek and the P.R.I.), in Riouw, Djambi as well as N. W. Palembang (Benarat). On the western coast they are still found in the Barisan Mountains, though in small numbers." In 1933, however, de Voogt warned that the species was practically extinct in South Sumatra.

In the 1930s the Netherlands Commission for International Nature Protection (founded in 1925) expressed hopes that the establishment of a system of reserves might remove the danger of extermination and also ensure the long-term protection of both the rhinoceros and other indigenous fauna. Among the 68 fauna and nature reserves in Sumatra two were of particular importance to the rhinoceros: the Löser Reserve (1,030,000 acres) in North Sumatra, established in 1934; and the South Sumatra Reserve (881,000 acres) in the Benkoelen/Lampongs districts, gazetted shortly before war broke out in the Pacific. Heynsius-Viruly and Van Heurn provide evidence which suggests that both the Javan and Sumatran species may have occurred in the Löser Reserve. Both species were reputed to have co-existed in the Lampongs also.

Talbot, writing in 1955, stated that the Javan rhinoceros "has been presumed extinct in Sumatra for at least two decades. I have found no evidence to the contrary." This is borne out by Hoogerwerf's belief that "there is nothing to contradict the findings of some observers before the war that this rhinoceros had disappeared from Sumatra. It seems indeed the truth that the last specimens outside Java were shot by a European hunter in the southern part of Sumatra about 1934." It appears, however, that the species survived in Sumatra at least until 1959, in which year two immature specimens were said to have been captured. Sody, who records this information, unfortunately gives no details.

Sody also shows that the species was once abundant and widely distributed in western Java from the coast into even the highest mountains, confirming Horsfield's * and Neumann's earlier observations that the species occurred both "in the plains as well as on the highest and most impassable mountains".

The last free-ranging rhinoceros in Java was shot by Franck in 1934, since when the species has been restricted to Udjung Kulon, although Heynsius-Viruly and Van Heurn mention "the presence of a single rhinoceros in the district Karangnoengal ... also a few specimens in the Garoet Mountains as well as near Pameungpeuk and to the west of Lake Kinder."

The decline of the species in Java has coincided with the eruption of the human population, which Talbot shows to have risen from an estimated 3 to 4 million in 1800 to 11 million in 1850; 28 million in 1900; 41 million in 1930 and 57 million in 1958. As Schenkel has shown, the preferred habitat of the Javan rhinoceros is secondary vegetation. The animal was therefore naturally attracted to the man-made clearings, temporarily cultivated and then abandoned, which accompanied the spread of human settlement; which at once brought it into conflict with man. As Talbot states: "with the tremendous population growth in Java the rhinos would have been excluded from most of the island by agriculture, even if they had not been hunted to death for their horns".

It is impossible to shake the firmly held belief, prevalent throughout the East, in the infallibility of rhino horn as a powerful aphro-

* The English physician who at the time of the Napoleonic Wars worked closely with Sir Stamford Raffles in studying the flors and fauna of Java.

disiac; and most Asians will go to any length and pay almost any price to obtain it. Not only the horn but every part of the animal is utilized by Chinese pharmacists, including the blood, bones, various organs, flesh and hide: even the urine is considered efficacious.

Thom states: "The blood especially, if drawn straight from the heart, is valuable. It is dried slowly in bamboos over a fire and sold for almost its weight in gold. The horn again is more valuable than the blood as it is ground down, mixed with other drugs and used as an aphrodisiac and as a sovereign remedy for all sorts of ills. The Javan and Sumatran rhinoceros are considered of particular value for medical purposes by the Chinese and Burmese. The Chinese seem to know more than any other race about the uses to which the blood and horn of a rhinoceros can be put to." Peacock notes that the horn and blood of the Javan rhinoceros were considered more valuable than those of the Sumatran.

The horn trade has been the principal reason for the eradication of the rhinoceros throughout virtually its entire range with the exception of the Udjung Kulon Peninsula at the westernmost tip of Java. This reserve, which extends to 130 sq. miles, is the species' last stronghold, and contains about two dozen animals.

The Netherlands Indies Society for the Protection of Nature, a private organization founded in 1912, was the initial driving force behind the development of conservation in the Dutch East Indies. It was largely at the Society's instigation that the Government introduced game laws and regulations and inaugurated a system of reserves, among them Udjung Kulon.

The peninsula was set aside as a Nature Monument in 1921, with the particular aim of protecting the Javan rhinoceros, the Javan

tiger, and the banteng. Protection was only nominal, however, and poaching was of regular occurrence. In 1937 the status of the area was upgraded to that of a Nature Reserve, from which all human settlement was excluded.

But law enforcement remained difficult in Java, particularly in the outlying districts. "We have even been informed that natives were secretly shooting some of the few remaining rhinoceros in the Nature Monument Oedjoeng Koelon. Dr. Charles Bernard, Director of the Department of Agriculture, Commerce and Trade, who is in charge of Nature Protection, had to complain that a Chinese, caught in the act of shooting rhinoceros, had been freed by the Judge" (Kies).

The Society repeatedly urged the "Volksraad" to appoint an officer with specific responsibility for fauna protection, but this proposal was resisted for financial reasons. Eventually, in 1935, the Government created the new post of Nature Protection Officer, a position occupied with distinction by Mr. Andries Hoogerwerf until Indonesian independence.

In general the reserves were well maintained during the Second World War, and we have it on Hoogerwerf's authority that "during the whole of the Japanese occupation the guards remained at their posts, [but elsewhere] all efforts to induce the [Japanese] to take measures against poaching had no or only a very small result". Despite the total prohibition on possession of firearms by non-Japanese nationals, intensive poaching took place outside the reserves, and illegal clearance of forests occurred on a large scale. It was only after the Japanese withdrawal, and particularly from 1945 to 1949, that the reserves themselves were ravaged.

In the chaotic conditions prevailing immediately after the war, bands of insurgents armed with modern automatic weapons overran the reserves and devastated the fauna. They had a compelling motive for killing the rhinoceros because of their belief, as Hoogerwerf tells us, that "certain parts of a rhino give invulnerability to the bearer (so-called *Djimat*)".

In 1955 Talbot visited Udjung Kulon during the course of a mission to investigate the status of rare and endangered species in different parts of the world. His report drew attention to the plight of the Javan rhinoceros and recommended an ecological study of the reserve to assess the animal's status and future needs, as the basis for a proper management plan.

From 1946 to 1951 at least ten Javan rhinoceroses were known to have been killed in and around Udjung Kulon (Hoogerwerf). In 1963-64 a further seven were killed in the reserve, and in the conditions then prevailing there was no likelihood of the poachers being apprehended. This situation was a matter for grave international concern, and caused the I.U.C.N. Survival Service Commission and the World Wildlife Fund to send special advisers to collaborate with the Government of Indonesia in safeguarding the remnant population. Preliminary visits by Talbot (1964) and Verschuren (1966) were followed by the mission of Rudolf and Lotte Schenkel, commencing in 1967, which aimed: "Firstly to study the Javan rhino, the size and reproductive capacity of its population, and the suitability of Udjung Kulon as a habitat; secondly to assist the Indonesian authorities in their effort to save the species."

This important work was further advanced and placed on a more permanent footing when, in January 1968, in close conjunction with the University of Basle, the World Wildlife Fund established the "Basle Patronage Committee for Udjung Kulon", under the chairmanship of Professor R. Geigy, Director of the Swiss Tropical Institute, Basle. The committee was formed with the object of giving practical help to the Indonesian authorities, above all in ensuring continuity of the work of studying the rhinoceros population and its ecology.

The salient fact is that the future of *Rh. sondaicus* is inseparably bound up with Udjung Kulon — the only place in the world where there is a known population with any prospect of survival under natural conditions. Since the eruption of Krakatau * in 1883 the reserve has

---

* Schenkel (*pers. comm.*) remarks that up to the time of the Krakatau eruption there was human settlement in Udjung Kulon, mainly on the north coast. The ensuing tidal wave wiped out all settlement, as well as destroying most of the lowland primary forest.

Rhinoceros sondaicus

RHINOCÉROS DE JAVA

JAVAN RHINOCEROS

not been modified by man, except for small clearings along the coast, made during the Japanese occupation, where artificial grasslands were established to improve grazing for the banteng *(Bos javanicus)* and the Javan deer *(Cervus timorensis)*.

The survival of the Javan rhinoceros is entirely dependent on maintaining an efficient guard system to prevent poaching. The World Wildlife Fund has therefore provided practical assistance in the form of a boat and a Land Rover (including running costs) and the construction of guard-posts, as well as by giving money to provide the rangers with regular wages, uniforms and medicaments.

But, even assuming that poaching can be successfully contained, the rehabilitation of the species is certain to be protracted. The reproductive rate is naturally low. A single calf is born after a prolonged gestation of about 16 months, the calf remaining with the mother for up to two years; and even under ideal conditions mature females probably do not breed more often than every third year or so. Concern has been expressed that the population has reached such a low level that adequate reproduction might no longer occur, in which connection it is interesting to note Thom's statement that "during the 49 years I have been in Burma I have never seen either a young rhinoceros or tracks of one". These fears, however, have been dispelled by Schenkel who saw immature rhinoceroses on four separate occasions, three of them accompanied by their mothers. He also came across numerous juvenile footprints.

Schenkel makes the important observation that Udjung Kulon does not contain large stands of the saplings and plants that comprise the rhinoceros's diet: these are scattered and scarce, and in many parts of the reserve have been replaced by unfavourable plant species. As the rhinoceros population increases it will therefore be essential to develop a programme for managing the habitat in a way that will be most beneficial to the rhinoceros.

Continued protection, research, and management are the essential requirements for Udjung Kulon. The Indonesian Government recognizes that the future of the reserve depends primarily on their own efforts, but because of the depressed economic situation their most effective contribution, at this stage, consists of good will and support for those scientists and others who are prepared to provide practical help.

PERSIAN FALLOW DEER *Dama dama mesopotamica*

The fallow deer originated in the Mediterranean region and Asia Minor but has been widely introduced into many parts of western Europe where it has become successfully established in numerous forests and deer parks. The common European fallow deer is abundant and in no danger, but its close relative, the Persian race, is one of the rarest mammals in the world.

The Persian form is substantially larger than the common fallow deer and the antlers, which are present only in the male, are conspicuously different. Those of the nominate race are terminally flattened whereas those of the Persian race normally terminate in three principal tines, the extremity of the antler being either not at all or only slightly palmated. The brow tines of the latter are much less prominent.

The Persian form is also more brightly coloured. The ground colour of males in summer coat is light brown, darkening to red-brown in winter. The upper part of the body is flecked with prominent white spots which along the spine fuse together to form a continuous stripe. The lower parts are lighter, becoming whitish on the belly and chest. Females are smaller than males with a darker ground colour and whiter spots.

The original range extended from south and south-west Iran through Mesopotamia into

Syria, Jordan, the Lebanon, and Israel (where abundant fossilized remains have been found in Pleistocene deposits).

The Babylonian, Assyrian and other ancient Mesopotamian civilizations were well acquainted with the fallow deer, and there are numerous references in the literature to representations of the animal on pottery and sculpture. Reed gives an exceptionally interesting account of the Sassanian cliff carvings at Taki-Bustan, near Kermanshah, dating back to the fifth or seventh centuries A. D., with bas-reliefs depicting scenes from a royal hunt. The unmistakable antlers enable the stags to be positively identified as fallow deer.

For more than a thousand years after the end of the Sassanian Dynasty (A.D. 226-641) the Persian fallow deer remained unknown. In 1875 Sir Victor Brooke revealed its existence, basing his description on material—a skin and skull with antlers in velvet—sent to the Zoological Society of London by the British Vice-Consul at Basra. Yet within about half a century of its rediscovery the animal was thought to be extinct.

According to Ellerman and Morrison-Scott, the last record from northern Iraq was of a male taken in 1917 at Zakho. Aharoni states that the species existed along the Euphrates until as recently as the late 1920s, but his evidence is inconclusive. It is possible, however, that some may have survived in Iraq even longer. When Talbot visited the country in 1955 "fallow deer were reported as still living in a valley between Maidan and Halabja, near the Persian border, perhaps thirty miles (48 km.) airline north of where the Baghdad-Tehran highway crosses the border. They are in a spot allegedly shunned by man because of the malarious swamps in the Sirwan River."

Talbot also mentions the possibility of fallow deer occurring as recently as 1940 in the Alawit region, to the north of Latakia, in northern Syria, but he could obtain no verification of the report. In any event, the fallow deer of the Taurus and other parts of Turkey are of the nominate race, and any specimens that may have survived immediately south of the Turkish border are likely to be of the common form.

The head of a stag from the Upper Karun River (into which the Dez flows) was presented to the British Museum by Captain Heinicke in 1893; and what Ellerman and Morrison-Scott describe as "the last recorded specimen from the Luristan district appears to have been one seen in the upper reaches of the River Diz (sic), about 1906". The same authors record another "from the Juanrud district, north of Kermanshah, Western Persia", but when Misonne visited that area in 1954 the local people were unable to tell him anything about the animal.

In 1946 Pocock stated that "inquiries over several years have failed to elicit any positive information about it", and the animal was generally assumed to be extinct.

In 1955, during the course of a mission on behalf of the I.U.C.N. Survival Service Commission, Lee M. Talbot obtained information that small numbers of fallow deer were to be found in Khuzistan, south-western Iran.

The following year Werner Trense visited the region and succeeded in locating the subspecies. Subsequently, Haltenorth, who had consistently supported and encouraged Trense's work, undertook a detailed study of the animal and of its habitat.

The fallow deer was found to have survived in only two small areas of poplar, tamarisk and acacia gallery forest, each about 2,500 acres in extent, along the Dez and Karkheh rivers. The nature of the habitat made any census difficult. Trense initially estimated that no more than 20 or 30 deer were present in the two areas. Haltenorth gave a substantially higher figure of between 200 and 400, but he appears to have based his estimate on reports from local people and his assessment was unquestionably over-optimistic. Krämer (1963) considered that "at most there are 100 to 150".

A survey conducted by the Iran Game and Fish Department in November 1968 revealed that probably no more than 30 Persian fallow deer remain in the wild state. Almost all of them are believed to be along the Dez River, the Karkheh population having been reduced to a tiny remnant of about half a dozen animals.

The Persian fallow deer had disappeared from the greater part of its ancestral range long

DAIM DE MÉSOPOTAMIE   *Dama dama mesopotamica*   PERSIAN FALLOW DEER

before the introduction of modern firearms. The principal reason for its decline is attributable to the widespread destruction of the forests which constituted the animal's natural habitat, the process being accelerated in the later stages by excessive hunting.

The relict population along the Dez and Karkheh rivers owes its survival to the dense riverine vegetation which is so impenetrable that it deters even the most ardent sportsman or hunter, and thus provides a secure refuge for the animals. But although man himself is unable to penetrate this last stronghold, it is being slowly whittled down by the gradual intrusion of mounting numbers of domestic livestock, including camels, water buffalos, cattle and goats, as well as by villagers cutting wood for fuel and other purposes.

The area occupied by the deer is potentially valuable agricultural land, and pressure from the rising human population means that it will be increasingly converted to man's use. Reed summarizes the situation when he declares:

"The basic factor assuredly dooming the deer in Khuzistan is that the pressure of a poor and growing populace lies heavy upon the land. With modernization of the area proceeding rapidly, by way of dams, irrigation, electric power and machine agriculture, that pressure will be increased and, simply, the habitat available to the deer must inexorably disappear.

"Even without the planned modernization of Khuzistan, which is destined to be the granary of Iran again as it was in the time of Darius, the deer's environment would disappear. The patches of pasture and ploughed fields grow larger; woodchoppers and charcoal burners, simple men intent on wresting a livelihood from an inhospitable environment, penetrate daily deeper into the jungle patches, opening the way to herd-boys with buffalo, dromedaries, cattle and goats."

The Iranian authorities are concerned at the drastic decline of the fallow deer and conscious of the need to take effective action to safeguard what they rightly regard as their national animal.

Since 1963, the Iran Game and Fish Department has embarked on a rehabilitation pro-gramme involving the capture of some of the remaining wild fallow deer. This operation is performed by driving them into nets about a mile in length, several hundred beaters being engaged for the purpose. The captured animals are then transferred to the Dasht-e-Naz Park (136 acres), some 16 miles north of Sari, the capital of Mazandaran. This reserve is thickly forested and fully fenced, and a permanent staff has been engaged to man it. In 1969 the park contained eleven deer (five males and six females), and breeding appears to be proceeding satisfactorily.

The programme envisages building up the Sari herd until numbers are sufficient to permit some to be introduced into the Mohammed Reza Shah Wildlife Park (227,060 acres). This park is located in north-eastern Iran and about 65 miles east of Gonbad-e-Qabus; a substantial part of it consists of unspoiled forest.

In addition to imposing a total ban on hunting the animal, the Iran Game and Fish Department declared the remaining woodlands along the Dez and Karkheh rivers protected areas, but this measure was not as effective as had been hoped owing to the difficulty of law enforcement. More recently, an area of 27,000 acres along the Dez River near Haft Tappeh, has been designated a "Wildlife Park". The Game and Fish Department intends to ring-fence the area, except for one end which will be left open to facilitate movement of deer into and out of the park. Domestic livestock are barred from the park and the cutting of wood is prohibited.

Despite the small number of deer and the discontinuous nature of the habitat along the Dez River, this park is of great value as it is one of the few sizeable areas of relatively unspoiled riverine woodland that remains. Its newly strengthened status will help discourage encroachment and development and thus buy time for the deer to multiply. This is of vital importance in the light of proposals which have already been made for large scale irrigation and other agricultural development schemes in the region.

The rehabilitation of the subspecies has been stimulated and enhanced by the personal interest of Dr. Georg von Opel. At his "Freigehege", near Kronberg, a programme is being developed for the establishment of a captive breeding herd of Persian fallow deer.

The original pair was imported from Iran in the early 1960s, but the male was accidentally killed after siring only two female fawns. Several years elapsed before a replacement could be found, and it was not until 1965 that another male could be obtained from Iran. The total number of pure-bred Persian fallow deer at Kronberg has gradually increased and now stands at four males and seven females. In a few years' time when the herd has sufficiently increased it is planned to establish additional captive breeding groups in other zoos, thus minimizing the risk of loss through disease or other factors. These captive stocks constitute a reservoir of fallow deer as an insurance against the future.

TAMARAW   *Anoa mindorensis*

The tamaraw is one of the smallest of the wild cattle, standing about $3\frac{1}{2}$ feet at the shoulder, with short thick-set horns, slightly incurved at the tips; and in general appearance resembling a diminutive water buffalo. It is stockily built, however, and its courage and ferocity more than compensate for its small stature.

The species is endemic to the island of Mindoro, and has never been recorded from any other place within historical times. Early reports indicate that before the exploitation of Mindoro's forests, when the human population was still sparse, the tamaraw was widely distributed throughout the island: it appears to have been most abundant in the lowlands, in the vicinity of swamps and marshlands.

During the late 1920s an outbreak of rinderpest among the introduced domestic buffalo, many of which were living wild in the forests, also infected the tamaraw. No details are available, but it can be assumed that losses were substantial, possibly as heavy as among the African buffalo at the time of the great rinderpest epidemic in the 1890s. In Kenya, for example, at least 90 per cent of the buffalo succumbed to the disease, but losses were subsequently matched by the extraordinary recuperative powers of the species. In less than a decade numbers had been restored to a satisfactory level. It can be reasonably inferred that the pattern was probably repeated with the hardy and fast-breeding tamaraw, which still enjoyed the security of undisturbed natural environment.

Mindoro's wetlands were extensive and provided the tamaraw with extremely thorough protection. The efficacy of this natural refuge was enhanced through being the breeding ground for mosquitoes that were vectors of a particularly virulent form of malaria, thus effectively discouraging human settlement. This situation prevailed until the early 1950s when a malaria control programme, undertaken by the Foreign Operations Administration of the United States, systematically eradicated the menace of malaria, and thereby opened the way to settlement. Thousands of settlers poured in, and within a surprisingly short time the swamps had been drained, the forests felled, the land cleared and cultivated, and the tamaraw compelled to retreat to the higher, colder regions, extending in places to over 6,000 feet, and covered with dense rain forests, where environmental conditions were substantially less suitable.

The pace of human expansion was so rapid that within a few years the tamaraw had been completely displaced from the lowlands, and reduced from abundance to a state of critical depletion. Pressure on the land has become increasingly intensive, particularly since 1960, when many thousands of new settlers began moving into Mindoro from other parts of the Philippines.

Although most of this human development was concentrated in the lowlands, its effects were felt in the highlands also. Sawmilling and

TAMARAO   *Anoa mindorensis*   TAMARAW

mining companies gradually extended their operations deeper into the central mountain range, where a number of large cattle ranches have also been established. Not only have these activities destroyed or altered much of the natural habitat but, in the process, many mine, mill and ranch employees have taken to hunting.

The indigenous hill people, the pagan Mangyans and Batangans, have always hunted the tamaraw whenever opportunity occurred. This type of subsistence hunting did no harm, the effects being limited not only by the primitive methods employed—pit-falls, spear-traps, and the like—but also by the aboriginals' fear of the animal, which generally discouraged them from hunting it very actively.

The techniques used by the sophisticated Filipino hunter are in an altogether different category, however, and the impact of present-day hunting needs to be viewed against the background of the Second World War and its aftermath, when large quantities of firearms of all kinds were introduced into the country. More recently, the supply has continued through Vietnam. The result of this massive inflow of assorted weapons caused Talbot to describe the Philippines as having probably "one of the highest percentages of actively armed, non-military citizenry of any country in the world. It also has a numerous well-armed military and a variety of law enforcement groups, and considerable numbers of U.S. military personnel stationed in the country. In addition to firearms, dogs and traps of all kinds are very widely used in hunting. Most present 'big game hunting' is done at night with spotlights."

Perhaps the most sophisticated innovation has been the recent enthusiasm for hunting from helicopters, which has introduced a new potential for slaughter, and has opened even the most inaccessible areas to the hunter. Harrisson cites "one helicopter party working in liaison with a ground party burning off the grass and scrub cover at the driest period (February) and credited with killing 70 deer, pig and tamaraw in one place. Some of the carcasses were left to rot; only the heads were collected as trophies."

Talbot also graphically describes the technique of hunting and its effect on the tamaraw population: "Hunting is clearly the major limiting factor. Cattlemen on all the ranches from which we were able to obtain information shoot tamarau whenever they have the opportunity for food. Ranch owners and their friends fly in from Manila or other cities for sport hunts. When fires are lit during the dry season it is reported that any animal that is seen fleeing

from the fire is shot. Everyone in this area is armed. Outside of the ubiquitous sidearms, there is an amazing variety of sporting, defence, and ex-military weapons, ranging from fine sporting rifles and .22 caliber target rifles to full automatic military carbines and Thompson submachine guns. With the armory available, precision shooting is apparently not necessary. We spoke to one cattleman who told us of the last tamarau he had helped kill with a group of cattlemen armed with a variety of weapons, mostly automatic. The animal had been shot 167 times."

The tamaraw has been legally protected since 1936, but there appears to be no instance of the law ever having been invoked. Even if it had, a legal loop-hole permits the animal to be killed in defence of life or property.

The first reserve for the protection of the tamaraw was established on Mt. Calavite in 1920, and embraced an area of 100,000 acres, but it existed only on paper and no attempt appears to have been made to administer it.

A second reserve, the Mt. Iglit Game Refuge, of 20,000 acres, was established in 1961, but its boundaries have never been properly determined and its purpose was to some extent frustrated when, shortly before its establishment, a substantial area in the centre of the reserve was allotted to the Korienoff Ranch.

Lack of any attempt at law enforcement completely nullified the effectiveness of the reserves: indeed, the tamaraw is chiefly hunted in the very areas which were set aside specifically for its protection; and as much hunting is done by influential people who are above the law, the purpose of the reserves has been stultified.

The effectiveness of the reserves can be gauged from Manuel's statement that, "there are more tamaraws killed in Mt. Calavite and in Mt. Iglit than in other ranges combined. Mt. Calavite preserve can be reached within 10 hours from Manila by automobile, motor boat and a short hike ... people prominent in their respective communities and who can afford expensive hunting parties organize these parties to hunt the tamaraw for its meat, its hide, its horns, or just for fun."

Early in 1969, the I.U.C.N. Survival Service Commission and the World Wildlife Fund jointly sponsored a visit to Mindoro by Prof. Tom Harrisson and General Charles A. Lindbergh, with the aim of evaluating the situation at first hand and of ascertaining what practical measures required to be taken to prevent the extinction of the tamaraw.

The conclusion reached was that the species has been reduced to three small but probably viable populations, totalling approximately a hundred animals, two of them in the Iglit and Calavite reserves respectively. The third population occurs in the vicinity of the Sablayon Penal Settlement and its survival is attributable to the reflected notoriety of the inmates. Their reputation is such that a considerable area surrounding the prison has become a sort of no-man's-land, shunned by all law-abiding folk, for fear of encountering bands of escaped thugs and murderers. These fortuitous circumstances have given rise to a situation which is the exact reverse of that already mentioned in connection with the official reserves: a sanctuary has been constituted, in fact but not in name, where the tamaraw enjoys more effective protection under the patronage of the convicts than it has ever received under the law.

The most important result of the I.U.C.N./ W.W.F. Mission has been the establishment of the Philippine Wildlife Conservation Association by a small group of the country's most influential citizens, representing the timber, mining, banking, sugar and ranching interests. President Marcos has shown great interest and, as a result of his personal intervention, the hunting of tamaraw has now been outlawed. The Constabulary and the Air Force are collaborating with the Parks and Wildlife Service in giving effect to the presidential proclamation. Moreover, President Marcos has issued instructions that all intrusions into the Calavite and Iglit reserves shall cease and that all "titles" to land within the reserves shall be cancelled.

These developments have done much to stimulate local interest in the need to conserve the country's wildlife. The Philippine Wildlife Conservation Association is giving active consideration to the overriding question of maintaining protection at an effective level and on a continuing basis. Part of this programme includes the establishment of a small research station on Mt. Iglit where studies can be taken by graduates of the University of the Philippines, an important development for ensuring continuity.

Not since the age-long custodianship of the malarial mosquito was extinguished has there been such good prospect of the Filipinos themselves taking positive action to bring back from the brink of extinction an animal that is not only unique to the Philippines but also symbolizes admirably those qualities of indomitable courage, unconquerable spirit and rugged independence that are so representative of the national character.

ARABIAN ORYX

Oryx leucoryx

The Arabian oryx stands about 35 inches at the shoulder, and is thus the smallest of the three species which together constitute the genus. It is a fairly heavily built animal, with a slight but distinct shoulder hump. The general coloration is white, with prominent black markings on the head and neck, and sometimes a flank stripe. The tail terminates in a black tuft, and the legs are dark brown. There is considerable individual variation in both the colour and the intensity of the markings. The hooves are broader and rounder than those of other oryx. Both sexes have horns which are almost straight, diverging gradually from the base, and with a slight backward curvature. The record horns, 29 inches in length, are those of a female.

Arabian oryx are generally found in small groups, from one to fifteen being the usual number. The herds include both males and females, usually under the leadership of an elderly female. But larger congregations have been seen, particularly following sudden rain. Oryx have the ability to sense rainfall at a distance, and quickly converge where a shower has induced a sudden flush of grazing.

The diet consists mainly of various kinds of grasses, but certain types of herbs, roots and fruit are also eaten on occasion. Oryx cover substantial distances during their constant search for grazing, a revealing instance being given by members of the 1962 expedition. The cars tracking an oryx—which was unaware that it was being followed—recorded the distance travelled as 58 miles in less than 18 hours.

The oryx generally keeps to the *jol*, the flat plain of gravel and stones interspersed with occasional low hills and sand dunes that fringes the desert proper. The *jol* is cooler than the sands and affords greater security as well as more food; but the animal may move into the sands when alarmed or to take advantage of a sudden flush of herbage following rain. In summer, however, the heat in the sands is too great even for the oryx.

During the heat of the day, hooves and horns are sometimes used to scrape out a shallow depression under a bush or some other suitable place, partly for shade and possibly as a measure of concealment. The animal blends well with its environment and even from short range is surprisingly difficult to see.

The original range included the greater part of the Arabian Peninsula, extending from the Sinai Peninsula in the west to Mesopotamia. It is known to have occurred in Iraq from the time of the early Mesopotamian civilizations, but there is no firm evidence that it ever existed east of the Euphrates. Hatt quotes a report that the last specimen to have been taken in Iraq was shot in 1914. The northern limits of the range have never been satisfactorily determined, but the range is known to have included parts of Israel and Jordan and the Syrian Desert.

By the turn of the century, both numbers and range had been heavily reduced and, except for occasional stragglers, the species survived in only two sectors of the Arabian Peninsula. In the north it was confined to the area known as the Great Nafud, and in the south to the Rub al Khali. By the early 1950s the Great Nafud population had been wiped out, and the southern herds greatly depleted.

The traditional method of stalking an animal as wary as the oryx was a protracted and arduous undertaking for poorly armed Bedu hunting on foot or with camels. Loyd describes the technique used by a Bedu armed with an ancient Martini-Henry carbine and employing his camel as a stalking horse: "When he sights an oryx he circles widely to get downwind. He dismounts, unsaddles his camel and walks it towards the oryx. He walks directly behind his camel in step with its hindlegs until he is close enough to shoot, firing along the flanks of his camel."

The difficulties were such that, in Grimwood's words, "it became a distinction to be a successful oryx hunter, even though a man might kill no more than one or two in his whole lifetime. Unfortunately, the distinction persisted after the motor car had removed all the difficulties, making it possible to kill a dozen animals in a day by running them down and slaughtering them as they stood exhausted and helpless."

Almost every part of the animal is utilized. The flesh is greatly esteemed and fetches a high price not only as a delicacy but because it is reputed to impart strength, courage and endurance; the hide makes valuable leather; the fat is used for a variety of disorders, a mixture of fat and blood being regarded as a cure for snake-bite. Even the gastric juices are consumed and the stomach contents given to the camels.

Hunting also involves patient tracking, and Bedu proficiency is described by Grimwood: "Tomatum and Mabkhout gave a foretaste of the uncanny skill in tracking they were afterwards to display on many occasions. In the Landrover moving at 20 miles an hour they could follow a spoor which was so lightly imprinted, or so far to flank, as to be quite invisible to Europeans. Such a demonstration also served to show how helpless the Arabian oryx is against motorized hunters."

Stewart writes: "when they judged that they were within a few miles of the animal they would sometimes, depending on the direction of the wind, make a wide detour and lie up ahead of the oryx in order to ambush it. Often such a hunt would occupy as much as two weeks, and comparatively few animals were obtained each year in this way. . . . The advent of the motor car and the availability of modern weapons as a result of World War II has resulted in a tremendous increase in the number of oryxes shot each year. Oil companies, soldiers, and local citizens have all joined in the slaughter. . . ."

In Grimwood's words: "The Arabian oryx is, by its vigilance and ability to travel great distances, more than a match for the Beduin hunting on foot or camel back. . . . But the oryx is helpless against motorized hunting parties, for on the *jol* 99 per cent of the country carries a good spoor and 95 per cent of it can be traversed by car. It is therefore simply a matter of following up an animal till it is sighted—spooring at speeds of 20 miles per hour being possible—and then running it to a standstill."

An indication of the scale of motorized hunting operations is given by Talbot who states that 40 to 60 vehicles normally take part, but sometimes this figure can be as high as 300, some of them hunting cars, the remainder used for carrying the expedition's supplies and servants. "The hunting cars fan out into a sort of skirmish line, driving down and shooting virtually everything that moves. Repeating shotguns are used more than rifles, and often the animals are run until they drop from exhaustion and their throats are cut by servants. St. John Philby told me of riding with the late King Saud when the king personally shot over a hundred gazelles in a day. Between January and April 1955, in a royal goodwill tour around northern Saudi Arabia the retinue numbered 482 cars at one point. Hunting was a part of this excursion and the vast army of vehicles spread out, crossing the desert, and shooting everything. As a result of the incredible blood lust of the past 20 years, virtually all of the abundant wildlife of Arabia has been extirpated from areas accessible to automobiles. In the last eight years the Arabs have been also using airplanes for hunting. It is hard to see how any animal can survive this attack. The Arabian ostrich has been exterminated, the bustards greatly diminished, three species of gazelle (once present in vast herds) reduced to the danger point, the cheetah almost exterminated and the oryx reduced to one or two hundred individuals."

In recent years oil company prospectors and their escorting soldiers—who, according to Talbot, are Arabs "over whom by government decree the companies have little control"—have gradually but persistently expanded their operations into remote areas which hitherto were a secure refuge for the oryx.

The publication in 1960 of Talbot's *A Look at Threatened Species* did much to focus attention on the plight of the Arabian oryx. His assessment of the situation led him to conclude that "the only way to assure survival of this interesting species is to transfer some specimens to a safer habitat. . . . This should be done as soon as possible, to be assured of finding enough animals."

The accuracy of Talbot's appraisal and the timeliness of his warning were quickly affirmed by the destruction of the last remaining oryx in

ORYX D'ARABIE   *Oryx leucoryx*   ARABIAN ORYX

the Aden Protectorate. The story of the three populations which were known to have existed in the Aden Protectorate until the 1950s is recorded by Grimwood: "The last oryx was seen in the western, Subatain, area in 1947 and the last record from Khusham-al-Jebel is the killing of one animal in 1951. The eastern, or Mitan, population had, however, existed successfully up to 1959 when the Fauna Preservation Society's attention was drawn to it by Mr. M. A. Crouch, then Assistant Adviser, Northern Deserts, Eastern Aden Protectorate. At that time its numbers were estimated to be between eighty and one hundred. The reason for its survival was the remoteness of the area, which was used by only a few Beduin, who can have killed no more than four or five animals a year. In December, 1960, however, a party of armed raiders from outside the Aden Protectorate prepared a motorized expedition and having apparently crossed the whole of the Rub-al-Khali from the north, arrived at the Ramlat Mitan, in which vicinity they remained and hunted for several weeks. This party, hunting from cars, is known to have killed at least forty-eight oryx."

A year later the raiders returned to the Wadi Mitan and killed another thirteen oryx. Grimwood's field party subsequently concluded that only eleven animals had survived the raid, "of which five had left the area before our arrival and travelled so far east into the neighbouring state of Oman that it was politically impossible for us to follow them. Four others, three males and one female, we tracked down and caught, killing one of the males in the process, while the other two, which we never saw, alarmed either by our spotter aircraft or the vehicles, escaped into the sand sea, where we could not go, and from which they did not emerge again while we were in the area."

In 1960, the available evidence endorsed Talbot's belief that the situation was so precarious that the only hope for the survival of the species was to capture sufficient individual animals to enable a breeding group to be established in captivity, before the wild stocks ceased to exist. The remaining herds were believed to be confined to the south-eastern part of the peninsula, along the southern and possibly the eastern fringes of the Rub al Khali. The eastern part of this zone, which is in Muscat and Oman, was virtually unknown territory.

The Fauna Preservation Society, in conjunction with the I.U.C.N. Survival Service Commission, and with the support of the World Wildlife Fund, therefore undertook to insure against the possibility of the species' imminent extinction by sending a capturing expedition to the Eastern Aden Protectorate. This decision led to the mounting of "Operation Oryx", which aroused widespread public interest and received the active support of several governments, conservation organizations, air lines, oil companies, zoos, and many private persons.

In May 1962, an expedition led by Ian Grimwood, at that time Chief Game Warden of Kenya, and equipped with a spotter aircraft provided by the East African Wild Life Society, succeeded in capturing three oryx (two males and one female). These were flown to Kenya by the Royal Air Force, the journey from Sanau—the last outpost of the Hadhrami Beduin Legion—to Nairobi being accomplished in less than thirteen hours. Their arrival unfortunately coincided with an outbreak of foot-and-mouth disease which delayed their onward journey to Isiolo for six weeks. This setback was overcome by Mr. John Seago, who constructed emergency accommodation for the animals, and by the East African Power and Lighting Co. which ran a special line and ransacked its own show rooms to instal heaters in the pens as protection against the unaccustomed cold of the Kenya Highlands.

After a period at Isiolo in northern Kenya, the three animals were flown to the Phoenix Zoo, Arizona, in June 1963. The cost of constructing the specially-designed compound at Phoenix and of transporting the animals to it was met jointly by the World Wildlife Fund and the Shikar Safari Club. The herd was subsequently increased by other animals generously donated by Sheikh Jabir Abdullah al Sabah of Kuwait, and by King Saud of Saudi Arabia, as well as by another from the London Zoo.

The Phoenix herd has thrived. Breeding has occurred regularly and satisfactorily, and at the end of 1968 numbers stood at ten males and six females. A second herd has meanwhile been established at the Los Angeles Zoo, and others exist at Riyadh in Saudi Arabia, and at Slamy in Qatar.

The second stage of "Operation Oryx" involves building up numbers in captivity with the aim of establishing several captive herds as a precaution against losses from disease or other factors. This phase is under the control of a board of trustees, and the breeding programme is facilitated by an official stud book.

Having ensured the survival of the species in this way, and when captive stocks are sufficiently numerous for the purpose, the ultimate aim of "Operation Oryx" is the reintroduction of small but viable herds into parts of their ancestral range where they no longer occur but where prospects of survival are good.

"Operation Oryx" had the incidental but important effect of arousing widespread interest in the species, as a result of which sighting reports and other data began coming in from the little-known eastern part of the range, thus enabling a more comprehensive appraisal to be made of the remaining wild stocks than hitherto.

Much of this information came from British officers seconded to the Sultan of Muscat and Oman's Armed Forces, the Trucial Oman Scouts, the Hadhrami Beduin Legion, the Desert Locust Survey, as well as from oil company geologists. In 1963 and 1964, while serving in the Sultanate of Muscat and Oman, Loyd discovered oryx in the Jiddat al Harasis, a remote and little-known region along the southeastern edge of the Rub al Khali. From his own observations and information derived from Bedu of the Harasis tribe, Loyd concluded that the oryx population can probably be numbered in the low hundreds.

The position today is that oryx are generally confined to the Jiddat, the territory controlled by the Sheikh of the Harasis, although there are occasional reports of individual animals or small groups outside this area, notably in the Duru and Wahiba country to the east of the sand sea. Loyd shows that oryx do not occur north of the Jiddat, which he describes as a waterless region which "can therefore only be occupied by Bedu for short periods in winter or after heavy rains. Oryx probably owe their continued survival to the absence of resident Bedu".

The Sultan of Muscat and Oman has shown personal interest in the species, and has issued instructions prohibiting the hunting of oryx from motor vehicles. There remains the almost insoluble problem of border violations by highly mobile and well-armed raiding parties from neighbouring territories who owe no allegiance to the Sultan and who strike and are gone before any counter-measures can be taken, but Loyd hopes that "the remoteness of their habitat and political restrictions will probably continue to protect the oryx from such incursions".

THE BROWN EARED PHEASANT

Crossoptilon mantchuricum

Of the 49 known species of pheasants, all except one are Asiastic. These superb birds— among which should be included the peacock and the jungle-fowl, ancestors of the domesticated fowl races—have always attracted man, first of all for their flesh and feathers and then by their decorative splendour. It is on this latter characteristic the chances of survival of several of these species depend.

In their wild state, the pheasant population have suffered greatly from hunting and deforestation, the effects of which have been accentuated by the demographic explosion in southern Asia. Their situation would be still more precarious if it were not for aviculture. For a long time these gallinaceous birds have attracted wealthy collectors who have endeavoured to maintain and increase in captivity the rare or spectacular species. Today, scientific breeding has become more important by far than the interests of collectors or dealers: for several species, it is the only hope of their avoiding extinction and being reintegrated in their original habitat.

Take the example of Swinhoe's pheasant, *Lophura swinhoei*, whose numbers in the mountainous forests of Formosa have been reduced to a critical level, while more than 600 birds bred in captivity are kept in zoos and private collections in various parts of the world. A successful attempt at breeding them in England has enabled the Ornamental Pheasant Trust and its originator, Philip Wayre, assisted by the World Wildlife Fund, to attempt reintroducing these birds into Formosa as from 1967.

A similar move cannot be envisaged as yet for the brown eared pheasant. This pheasant belongs to a small group of three species found in China and Tibet which are particularly distinctive because of tufts of white feathers protruding upright on either side of the head, like pointed ears, in conjunction with the identical appearance of the two sexes. In contrast with the uniformly dark-brown body plumage, this brown eared pheasant has another ornamental feature: a magnificent trailing tail of a silvery white colour, in which the median feathers with fine loose sprays separate and rise gracefully. Including the tail, the total length of this bird is about three feet. In spite of the Latin name given to this species by Swinhoe in 1862, on the basis of erroneous information, it has never been found in Manchuria. Its habitat is limited, in fact, to the mountains and high plateaux situated to the west of Peking and the plains of China.

The French missionary, Armand David, to whom we owe so many zoological discoveries, published a list of Chinese birds in 1867 in which he writes "This bird known to Pallas and to the missionaires even before that great expert visited Siberia, was rediscovered by us in 1862 and hunted in the wooded mountains beyond San-Yu where it has become very rare. . . . The Chinese call this bird Ho-ki." Even at that period, therefore, the numbers of this bird had been appreciably reduced and it must be assumed formerly to have been far more widespread. According to Vaurie (1965), the brown

eared pheasant or hoki lives in the mountains of southern Chahar in Inner Mongolia, perhaps going as far as eastern Suiyuan, as several specimens have been found about 44 miles west of Changkiakow (formerly known as Kalgan). Its area extends to the north and north-west of Hopeh and the north of Shansi, and to the south as far as the Yangku region. However, it seems to have abandoned parts of this region: according to Chen Tso-Hsin (1963), the species is practically extinct in the Province of Hopeh. There is reason to fear a considerable decline, if not an almost complete disappearance, in other areas. We do not know if the protection afforded by Chinese law has been able to arrest the general decline of this beautiful bird.

Between 1909 and 1911, during the expeditions which enabled him to write his splendid monograph on pheasants, William Beebe had the opportunity to observe the hoki in its natural habitat in Shansi. "A bleak and rolling country, diversified by irregular mountains and in places with deep valleys cut well down to the lower level of the outlying plains. Much of the country is barren and rocky, and here the vegetation consists of low woody shrubs and coarse grass. But wherever the soil and the shelter of a southern exposure permits, sparse woods can be found, or occasional dense growths of pine and white birch seldom higher than 15 or 20 feet. Scrub oak is also common—seven to ten feet high and very gnarled and rugged. From competent observers I learned that the Brown eared pheasants are resident in regions such as these throughout the entire year, rambling in flocks of ten to thirty birds during the winter. . . ."

Beebe also notes that the hokis do not fly very readily. On the other hand, they run rapidly, even over uneven ground. When alerted by the presence of an enemy on the ground, they quickly make off up the hillside and if they do not go down the other side on foot, they take to the air from the crest and glide across the valley. At the sight of a bird of prey, they crouch down or rush to the shelter of a thicket. When they are in search of food, however, they move slowly, elegantly lifting their train of floating feathers and stopping to scratch and explore the ground. David observes that the stomachs of the birds killed in winter often contain tubercles or orchids and other succulents, as well as seeds, leaves, roots and insects: three specimens examined in July had been eating Cytisus leaves. Beebe found the crop of one bird full of acorns; sometimes, near a village or hamlet, these pheasants also forage after corn crops or millet, They are therefore omnivorous, which gives them a good resistance against hard winters in the mountains, without their having to resort to seasonal migration.

Very little is known of their breeding in the wild state. In spring, the flocks break up into pairs, for monogamy is the rule. It is at this time that the cocks emit resounding cries, morning and evening, their rolling croak lasting sometimes for an entire minute. The nest, hidden on the ground in vegetation, usually contains six to eight eggs (whereas in captivity the hen lays as many as 16 eggs), and incubation lasts 28 to 30 days. Their settled and sociable disposition and their lack of shyness has proved a major handicap to the hokis. Although they stand up well to the harsh climate and know how to escape from their natural enemies, they too easily fall victim to hunters who massacre entire groups.

Being also very attached to their familiar haunts, they are rapidly decimated or exterminated there, as soon as the hunters set out to pursue and trap them. Beebe writes that their mediocre flesh, tough and stringy, was not thought much of, but the scarcity of meat has led the Chinese to slaughter them indiscriminately. The demand for hides and decorative feathers has also encouraged hunting. Finally, the habitat itself has suffered extensive damage, felling of trees, the scourge of the country, has not spared the mountain forests. This has proved to be a decisive factor in facilitating hunting and hindering normal breeding.

It is not surprising, therefore, that this species has been reduced gradually to a residual population with an uncertain future. At the present time, it is in captivity that the brown eared pheasant can be most sure to survive. As Père David wrote a century ago: "Its gentle and calm character seems to make it a bird of the poultry-yard and I do not doubt that the few pairs sent to France could become the progenitors of a new and beautiful domestic bird." However, after some encouraging success, the breeding enclosures were ravaged by disease after 1870 and numbers have remained limited. The aggregate of brown eared pheasants in public and private zoos in Europe and North America probably does not amount to more than 120, all of these being descendants of the first pheasants to be imported. To this total should be added the birds raised in China or elsewhere, the exact number of which is not available. Despite the inevitable inbreeding resulting from these circumstances, it should at least be possible thus to ensure the continuation of the species.

JAPANESE CRESTED IBIS *Nipponia nippon*

It is not a mere coincidence surely, that two large birds living in the same regions of the Far East are simultaneously affected by what appears to be an inexorable decline. The demographic explosion in China and Japan, wars and the extensive damage which resulted, have had disastrous repercussions on the fauna of these countries. It is difficult to assess its scope, owing to the lack of precise information concerning vast regions. However, it is evident that a number of species are in serious danger.

One of these is the Japanese white stork *Ciconia boyciana*, considered by most authors to be a subspecies of the white stork, well known in Europe and Africa, but which Vaurie, for example, considers as a separate species distinguished by its big black bill and larger size. Formerly widespread in Ussuri, Manchuria, Korea and Japan, they have become extremely rare in less than a century. The Japanese population was reduced to nine individuals in 1965 and it is probable that, if there are some survivors in Russian territory, the Korean and Manchurian breeders have disappeared.

At the same time, the Japanese crested ibis also became very rare. Like the 23 other species of ibis in the world, it has a long, down-curved beak, adapted to pick up food on the ground, in the mud and in water. It is fairly small, 27 to 31 inches in total length including the bill which measures between six and eight inches. It has a beautiful plumage; adults are completely white, with rosy-orange tints on the wings and tail; a grey phase was noted by Père David (Oustalet 1872). The naked facial skin gives it a vermilion red mask and a crest of plumes falls elegantly from the nape of the neck: the red feet and black bill, tipped with red, completes the picture. The juveniles have a grey plumage, still lacking the salmon-coloured shades, and brownish wing-tips.

The natural habitat of the Japanese crested ibis is divided into two elements: they need wetlands such as marshes, rice-fields, streams, ponds or lakes and, nearby, clumps of large trees for roosting and resting in small colonies. According to Cheng, the birds search for food during the day and pick up crabs, frogs, small fish, snails, insects and other invertebrates; in the evening, they return to their usual nocturnal roosting areas in the tall pines and chestnut trees. It should be noted that they like to live in mountainous regions with a harsh climate. For example, Père David writes that "several pink ibis can be seen at Suen Hou Fou during the coldest days of winter . . ." But birds nesting farther north migrate, whereas those in Japan appear to be non-migratory.

Judging by information originating from China, persecution makes this ibis very shy and its preference for forest regions also makes observation difficult. It has a resonant croaking cry. As for nesting, we know that it builds a platform of sticks in tall trees, 16 to 33 feet high, where the female lays only two or three greeny-blue eggs with brown spots. It has a very low reproduction potential, to be taken into account when considering the catastrophic drop in numbers in the space of a century.

Although possible regression had already reduced its habitat before 1850, the Japanese crested ibis was still widespread over a vast area at that time. According to Vaurie, in China it used to extend south to Chekiang and Anwhei and west to southern Shensi and southern Kansu (where breeding was proved in 1925). It also nested in eastern Manchuria and in the Ussuri basin, especially around Lake Khanka, as well as in Korea. In Japan it was plentiful on the large islands of Hokkaido, Honshu and Kyushu. The migrating birds spent the winter in south-eastern China, as far south as Hainan; long ago some stragglers were even noted on the islands of Formosa and Ryukyu. Although few in number, they were thriving.

The history of the continental population and the reasons for its downfall is still vague. The lack of up-to-date information does not help in localizing and assessing the surviving groups. If reference is made to Cheng (1963), this ibis is now rare, a victim of deforestation. He says that according to the villagers of Hu-Hsien, in the Shensi region, the ibis was "recently" still numerous and nested in the tall white poplar trees in the vicinity; these trees were felled and, as children destroyed its nests, the birds continued to decrease. He also mentions three individuals collected in Shensi for the Peking Museum, one on November 30th, 1956, at Sian, and the other two on June 13th, 1957, at Yang-Hsien. We can, therefore, hope that a colony still exists in this province, whereas we know nothing of the ibis in Kansu, nor in the Chekiang Valley where Père David appears to have found it fairly abundant in 1870 and 1871.

There is no recent information about the Japanese crested ibis in Manchuria and Ussuri, where, in 1951, Spangenberg was unable to find the birds which formerly nested by Lake Khanka and on the banks of the Lefu River. However, as a few individuals were noted near Vladivostok in the 1950s and on the Amur, to the south of Khabarovsk on August 27th, 1949, it is quite possible that an unknown colony exists in these areas, its most northerly habitat. This is all the more likely in that the ibis has been observed four times in Korea since 1950, ten birds were seen in March 1965 in the northern area and three in February 1966 at Panmunjom; they had disappeared from this country as breeding birds before the end of the nineteenth century.

In Japan, its history has been resumed by Yamashina as follows: "It is a regrettable fact that the Japanese crested ibis, as well at the storks and cranes, were almost wiped out in about 20 years, between 1870 and 1890, when the game laws were abolished shortly after the general upheaval which followed the Restoration in 1868. As a result, this species was believed for some time to be completely extinct. In 1930, however, a few birds were found to have survived and were breeding on the Noto Peninsula in central Honshu facing the Sea of Japan, as well as on Sado Island in the Niigata prefecture also on the western shores of Honshu." In 1934, the government classified the species as a "National Natural Monument": and since then they have been protected by law. According to findings at that time, 50 existed, 30 on Sado Island and 20 on the Noto Peninsula.

In spite of this decision, the two surviving groups gradually diminished. On Sado Island, 27 birds were counted in 1941, 21 in 1952, 14 in 1953 and 12 in 1954. The Noto colony consisted of only five birds in 1956 and two young ones were raised. But in 1960, the total was only 12 for both these localities. In 1962, Yamashina explained the main reason for this rapid decline over a period of 20 years: it was "the reckless deforestation and felling of trees in the vicinity of the breeding grounds imposed during and after World War II. In the ensuing period of great shortages, almost all the tall trees suitable for nesting were cut down, so that these unfortunate birds were driven away or killed." (A cold snowy winter cycle would also have been fatal to them. Thus, the severe winter of 1960-1961, with heavy falls of snow, and ice on the fishing grounds, compelled the starving ibis to search for food on the mainland, where two birds were found dead near Niigata.) Since then, annual statistics show little variation, and the death rate is more or less compensated for by regular breeding. At the end of 1968, the total number in Japan was ten, nine on Sado Island plus one that has survived since 1964 on the Noto Peninsula.

These numbers prove that the Japanese ornithologists have followed developments closely and have also attempted to improve matters with the help of the authorities. These efforts have been concentrated on Sado Island, the last refuge of the ibis. In 1962, the government bought 740,000 acres of beech-tree forest on the island to establish a sanctuary: in hilly countryside at the southern foot of Mount Kunimi, the small colony lives in complete security from spring to autumn and two or three young birds are raised each year. In winter, they move to the woods of sugi *Cryptomeria japonica* and pine near the village of Niiho. For commercial reasons the local authorities intended to cut down these trees and they had to be persuaded to sell part of the land to the State. In 1965, on the recommendation of the Japanese section of the I.C.B.P., the State purchased 124,000 acres of these woods as a winter refuge.

For Dr. Yamashina and the Sado Association for the Conservation of the Japanese Crested Ibis, the main problem since has been to improve food resources for the winter season. With financial help from the government and the World Wildlife Fund (W.W.F.), artificial ponds to breed fish were constructed in 1967 at Shimizu-daira, on the edge of the forest, and thus sufficient food for the birds is guaranteed. In addition, an aviary was built and breeding attempted, so far without success. Two permanent keepers are responsible for the management and observation of the ibis. In the meantime, examination of dead birds has revealed two new hazards, parasite nematode worms causing internal haemorrhage, and contamination by mercurial pesticides used in the rice-fields and ingested with food. Although the deadly effects have not been proved, it is evident that they are a new danger and a feeding place has been organized to avoid possible risk.

Today, through care and attention on a scientific basis, efforts are being made to preserve the last survivors of the ibis in Japan. There is still hope as long as the young birds are raised by their parents in the forest reserved for them. There is a possibility also, that other colonies will continue to perpetuate the species in remote parts of China and in the Ussuri basin area.

MONKEY-EATING EAGLE   *Pithecophaga jefferyi*

One of the finest and most powerful raptorial birds of Asia, and also the rarest, is the monkey-eating eagle which is endemic to the Philippines. Like the harpy-eagle and some other tropical eagles with strong predatory habits, it has huge talons, comparatively short, broad wings and the fairly long tail typical of the forest hunter.

The monkey-eating eagle of the Philippines has a striking appearance with a superb "mane" of long tapering feathers covering its head and the nape of its neck, which it bushes out or raises at will and which, when excited, it wears like a warlike head-dress. Its bluish eyes and enormous curved beak, flattened on the sides, gives it an expression of extreme ferocity. The two sexes are alike, clad in dark brown plumage, striped with paler edges and whitish on the upper part. Also remarkable is its great size. Brown and Amadon refer to a male weighing nine pounds, even heavier than the golden eagle.

The eagle lives in thick mountainous forests on the big islands up to an altitude of about 3,900 feet. It is occasionally seen flying at this height, but it usually hunts silently under the tall trees, gliding from one perch to another. It would be difficult to find if its sudden appearance did not provoke a major disturbance; monkeys screech the alarm and, above all, the hornbills detest it. Gonzales reports that they harass it in groups and even peck its head with their big beaks; in spite of its terrible appearance the eagle seems unable to retaliate. Its favourite prey are medium-sized tree-living mammals, particularly monkeys and squirrels. However, at the eyrie studied by Gonzales in 1963-1964, out of 48 prey, flying lemurs, *Cynocephalus volans*, made up more than 90 per cent, and monkeys, *Macaca philippinensis*, only 6 per cent.

The eagle, probably finds it expedient, therefore, when hunting alone to concentrate on small animals which are easy to catch, whereas monkeys can be more readily taken by a pair hunting in unison. While the islanders complain that chickens and piglets are sometimes stolen by the eagle, this behaviour seems out of character.

Like all big birds of prey, it has a very low reproduction potential. It is uncertain that even one eaglet it raised each year. The eyrie mentioned above was built on a branch of a giant tree, on the slope of a wooded hill from where the birds overlooked a vast tract of forest. The single egg was laid on November 13th or 14th, incubation lasted about 60 days, and the young bird left the nest when three and a half months old.

Originally the eagle was to be found on four of the islands in the Philippines. It has since disappeared from Samar, where Ogilvie-Grant described and named it in 1897, and also from Leyte. On Luzon, where it was believed to be extinct, two individuals were killed in 1963 and 1964 and some others have subsequently been sighted. There is probably a residual population with a very uncertain future on this island. Mindanao is practically the last stronghold of the species, but it is rapidly disappearing there as well. In 1964, the Talbots estimated that fewer than 100 birds remained. In February 1969, Tom Harrisson wrote to the World Wildlife Fund saying that the number was much less and the last figure obtained from research carried out by Alvarez, and passed on by General Charles A. Lindbergh in October of that year, indicated about 40 eagles on Mindanao. No doubt it is very difficult, if not impossible, to carry out an exact count of this bird in a steep, heavily wooded area of such vast dimensions. But even allowing for the inevitable margin of error, the monkey-eating eagle of the Philippines must be regarded as nearly extinct.

Although information on its decline since the beginning of the century is lacking, particularly in Samar, Leyte and Luzon, shooting is certainly the cause. With respect to the tamaraw, Noel Simon alluded to the incredible increase of firearms in the Philippines since the Second World War and the disastrous effect on the fauna; the monkey-eating eagle has not been spared either. According to Talbot, it has become a highly-prized trophy: "A mounted specimen is a prestige item and there is competition to

see who can bag the largest one." An article in *The Philippines Today*, vol. 10, No. 2, described a recent capture at Isabela: "The largest eagle ever shot in recent times." Perhaps it is as well to say that the bird was killed in the Aurora Memorial Park on Luzon by a game-keeper, in defiance of the law protecting this species. It is true that until lately, legal protection was of no use whatsoever, the worst offenders being the persons who should have enforced it: thus impunity was assured to trophy hunters, who were often important people.

The monkey-eating eagle of the Philippines has been captured and its nests robbed because it is a desirable acquisition for zoological gardens which are all anxious to show off this rare and spectacular bird of prey. For example, six individuals were exported in July 1963. Once again a profitable trade which is greatly to blame for the decline of this species.

Another, more insidious, danger stems from the demographic expansion; human penetration in the forests, lumbering, agriculture and temporary land clearance have reduced the species' habitat. Gonzales' study gives significant data on this aspect. In 1967, in the Kibawalan area where the 1963-1964 eyrie was located, a new road had been built, bringing settlers, and the big trees had been felled. Deprived of their land, the local inhabitants have had to move to more remote, less accessible regions, where they are beginning to degrade the forest. On a slope of the hill occupied three years before by the eagles, the trees had been cut down.

About 100 yards from the abandoned eyrie, a family had settled and made a clearing; other attempts at cultivation were apparent, no doubt abortive on the stony ground ... the pair of eagles had been obliged to seek another territory. This typical situation has been made worse by the present availability of guns.

Once the status of this superb bird of prey was recognized, the International Union for Conservation of Nature and Natural Resources (I.U.C.N.) and the World Wildlife Fund, have made the species, with the tamaraw, their main concern in the Philippines. Research in the field, indispensable as a basis for effective conservation measures, is already well under way. In collaboration with the I.C.B.P., the W.W.F. has helped to finance the study led by Assistant Professor Rodolfo B. Gonzales of Silliman University. In 1969, with the assistance of a student, Jesus Alvarez, he carried out an enquiry on the distribution and numbers of the species on Mindanso Island, to identify areas where conservation efforts should be organized. A vehicle will be required for an effective guard system and the lumbering companies encouraged to spare the areas surrounding the eyries. The missions carried out on behalf of the I.U.C.N. and W.W.F. by General Lindbergh and Professor Tom Harrisson of Cornell University have already obtained an assurance from the President of the Republic of the Philippines that legal protection will be reinforced. These missions have also encouraged research and overall nature conservation.

The present situation urgently requires an information campaign to discredit the hunt for trophies and effective sanctions to deter violations. Finally, the sale and export of birds, dead or alive, should be forbidden, and even their possession should be subject to special authorization. At the same time, all zoos overseas must give up importing this eagle, which has never reproduced in captivity.

This is a vast programme, extremely difficult to carry out, but it is the only one which will keep the famous monkey-eating eagle alive in its natural habitat. The responsibility for safeguarding it is in the hands of the people and the government of the Philippines.

Crossoptilon mantchuricum

HOKI BRUN
BROWN-EARED PHEASANT

Nipponia nippon

IBIS NIPPON
JAPANESE CRESTED IBIS

Pithecophaga jefferyi

AIGLE DES SINGES
MONKEY-EATING EAGLE

AFRICA

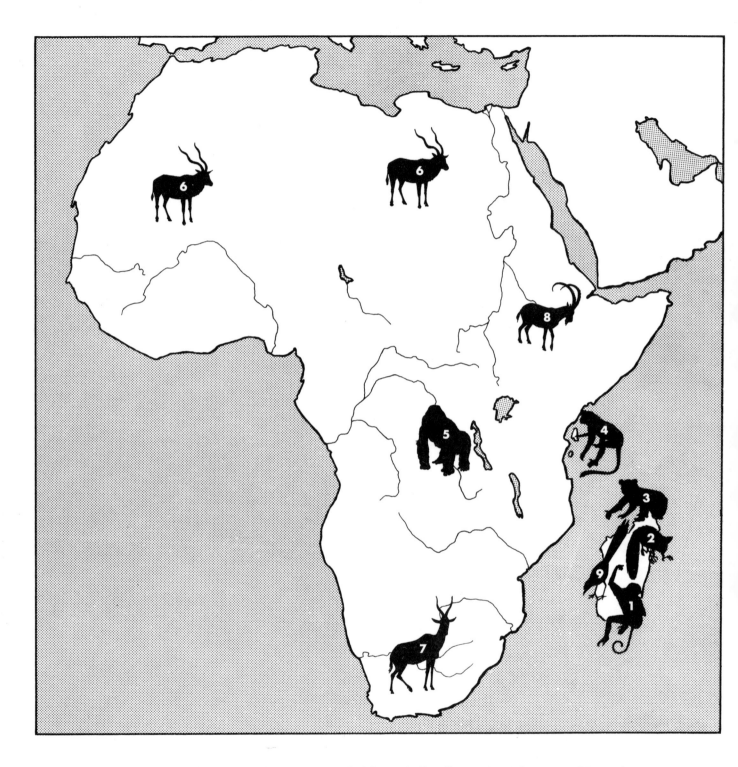

1, Crowned sifaka — 2, Aye-aye — 3, Indris — 4, Zanzibar red colobus — 5, Mountain gorilla — 6, Addax — 7, Bontebok — 8, Walia ibex — 9, Long-tailed ground roller

VERREAUX'S SIFAKA

Propithecus verreauxi

The genus *Propithecus* comprises two species. Taken together, their distribution covers almost every forested region in Madagascar; *P. diadema*, the diademed sifaka, inhabiting the eastern part of the country, and *P. verreauxi* the west and south. The latter species is divided into five subspecies, with widely differing colour patterns.

The general colour of Verreaux's sifaka, *P. v. verreauxi*, is principally white tinged with yellow. The crown of its head is either black or dark brown, and separated from the black face by a white band across the forehead. This race is restricted to the south and south-west of Madagascar. It is represented in two reserves; the Tsingy de Bemaraha (370,000 acres) and Lake Tsimanampetsotsa (43,000 acres), and possibly also in the Massif d'Andohahela Reserve (176,000 acres).

Coquerel's sifaka, *P. v. coquereli*, is a very distinctive pure-white race with a black face, and maroon patches on parts of the arms and legs. Its hands and feet are white, with black palms and soles. This form lives in north-west Madagascar, in the vicinity of the Bay of Mahajama. It is protected in the Ankarafantsika Reserve (165,000 acres).

Decken's sifaka, *P. v. deckenii*, is an almost entirely albinistic form—except for the face, ears, palms and soles, all of which are black—the white is tinged with yellow or ash-grey on the neck and front parts of its limbs, and its chest is washed with red. It lives in north-west Madagascar, and is represented in the Tsingy de Namoroka Reserve (14,200 acres).

The upper parts of the body of the crowned sifaka, *P. v. coronatus*, are a dirty white, except for a fringe of dark hairs around its face; its arms, legs, and base of tail are all tinged with rust. The under parts from throat to abdomen are a rich mahogany colour. Within this general colour pattern there is a wide range of individual variation. This race is confined to the region west of the Mahavavy River.

Forsyth-Major's sifaka, *P. v. majori*, is a partially melanistic race with the crown of its head and the back of its neck black, and its black face framed by a broad band of long white hairs. Parts of its back and shoulders have white or brown markings. Its limbs are white, but with large expanses of chocolate colour. Its under parts are dark brown, and its tail white. It lives in the Sakaraha Forest in south-western Madagascar.

Surprise has sometimes been expressed that the various races, living under superficially similar environmental conditions, should show such marked differences in coloration. But, apart from differences arising among populations long isolated by impassable natural barriers such as rivers and discontinuous areas of forest, Petter has shown that the habitats of the various races also differ greatly both topographically and climatically. Furthermore, each race does not necessarily occupy the same ecological niche, as indicated by the fact that both *P. v. verreauxi* and *P. v. majori* share the same forest in the south of Madagascar. It is possible, however, that *P. v. majori* may prove to be a melanistic phase of *P. v. verreauxi*: Petter remarks on the "strong tendency towards melanism among the *Propithecus* in the south and south-east where radioactivity is strongest from the thorianite deposits."

Unlike certain other lemurs, sifakas do not occupy permanent natural shelters. They neither construct nests nor do they occupy holes in trees—possibly on account of their size. The night is spent on a branch of a tree, chest and head covered by the arms, and tails either hanging down or curled up between the legs. In cold spells sifakas huddle together for mutual warmth. They are active throughout the day, especially in the morning; during the heat of the day they prefer to rest in a secluded part of the forest. They particularly appreciate the first rays of the rising sun; in the early morning they enjoy squatting with tail curled up between the hind legs, and hands either on their knees or held away from the body in an attitude of sun worship.

The sifaka makes two distinct calls: Petter describes them as "a characteristic click-grunt, which is the origin of the Malagasy name, pronounced by the natives 'sifak', and a series of barks that are emitted in unison by the group". When alarmed or disturbed, as for example at the approach of a hawk or an eagle, one sifaka sounds the alarm, which is immediately taken up by the remainder of the troop. In a moment the cries are synchronized, and the chorus carries a considerable distance.

The sifaka's sense of smell also plays an important part in communication between individual members of the troop. Males have a gland on the throat which they use to mark trees by rubbing their necks against the trunk. This is done throughout the year, but more frequently during the mating season, and may be linked to territoriality.

Mating occurs from January to March; a single young is born between May and August after about five months' gestation. The newborn sifaka's eyes are open, and its body is covered with down. It clings to the fur on its mother's stomach, but after the first month moves to her back, where it remains for about six months. At the age of two months it starts to eat green food; it is weaned after the third or fourth month. At about two years of age, when approaching sexual maturity, the young sifaka is abandoned by its parents: immature males are often chased from the group by the dominant male.

Sifakas live in small family groups of about half a dozen animals. A troop is usually led by the female while the male guards the rear. They are of gentle disposition, and only during the period of rut is there a tendency for the males to become quarrelsome.

The sifaka's temperament is apparent from Paulian's statement that "in areas where they are not hunted, they will approach to within a few meters of man; often in such a way that they present their backs to the visitor, turning their heads to size him up. Each prolonged inspection is accompanied by brief grunting which soon changes to a concert of hoarse barking if they become frightened."

There are now very few places in Madagascar where sifakas are as tame as this. One such undisturbed locality is the private estate along the Mandrary River in the extreme south of Madagascar, where Alison Jolly did her valuable field study of the species. She mentions a troop of five sifakas which "converged to a half circle less than 15 feet away. . . . Soon all five were mobbing me as birds mob a cat, and less than one spring away. At this point, say the local Malagasy, the sifaka fall on you and eat you, a wild misjudgement of these placid vegetarians. In fact, when the group chorus of snores and growls did not dislodge me, after half an hour of trying, the *Propithecus* turned to go."

Movement is normally very leisurely; individual animals remain reasonably close together, generally only a few feet apart, and move unhurriedly through the trees eating at random as they go. Their diet is strictly vegetarian, consisting mainly of leaves, bark, flowers, buds, shoots, and fruits. The food is not plucked by hand but taken by mouth, the hands being used only to draw a branch or fruit closer.

Sifakas are essentially arboreal animals and seldom leave the trees. But occasionally they descend to the ground; they then walk erect on their hind legs or move in a series of ungainly hops, balancing by raising and slightly flexing their arms and by keeping their hands away from the body and level with the head.

The extent to which each group maintains its own territory is not known with certainty. Observations on this aspect of sifaka behaviour are too few to enable definite conclusions to be drawn; but Petter has shown that there are invisible boundaries beyond which a group will not normally go: an animal which is being pursued will suddenly stop as if it had come up against a physical barrier, and, despite the possibility of danger from behind, will change course or even turn back. The invisible boundary may be nothing more than the gap between two trees which could be cleared at a single leap. Occasionally, separate troops of sifakas have been seen lined up on either side of such an invisible barrier, as if to defend their line against an attempt at intrusion. Any individual animal attempting to cross this boundary is normally repulsed not by violence but by menacing stares, intimidating postures and perhaps growls.

SIFAKA DE VERREAUX   *Propithecus verreauxi*   VERREAUX'S SIFAKA

Within each troop the importance of contact, grooming and play seems, in Jolly's words, "fundamental, as the social cement of the group. Monkeys groom by picking through the fur with their fingers or lips, while lemurs scrape each other with their lower canines and incisors, the so-called toothcomb. For years the toothcomb puzzled scientists: was there, perhaps, some frightful ectoparasite which could only be removed by sacrificing all the lower front teeth to make such a scraper? At last it became clear that there must be considerable selective advantage to a 'well-grooming' lemur in the social group, for lemurs, like monkeys, groom each other in greeting, pacification, mother-infant relations, sexual advances, when waking up and when going to sleep".

The sifaka's method of locomotion is unusual. The normal posture is in the crouched position, but whether the animal is either resting or poised to move, the body remains almost unvaryingly upright, with the tail curling up between the thighs. Even when seemingly relaxed, sifakas are prepared to leap on the instant, propelled by a powerful thrust from their hind legs.

Sifakas are incomparable acrobats, and few sights are more spectacular than a troop launching themselves into the air in quick succession as they leap from one tree to another, landing without apparent effort and taking off again immediately. They can clear a distance of more than 30 feet from a standing start. Their agility is such that they can launch themselves horizontally backwards into space, twisting in mid-leap to land feet first. The weak tail remains relaxed, and is used neither for balance nor for any other purpose.

An excellent description of a leaping sifaka is given by Jolly: "The first day after deciding to settle by the Mandrary, I walked into the woods. I suddenly saw staring lemon eyes, a black, heart-shaped face, and a square white-furred head. The sifaka clung vertically to a vertical trunk, its slim tail curled up like a watchspring below. Then, without warning, it leaped. The animal seemed to double in size. Its great hind legs, longer than head and body, propelled it backward into space. The white body gleamed against blue sky, soaring . . . in a curve taut as ballet. . . . The *Propithecus* turned in mid-air, to land with both feet first, like a jumping man. The legs folded, and again it clung vertically to a trunk, still watching me."

Until recently the Malagasy people in the more remote parts of the country respected the ancient taboos applicable to the sifaka: the animal was not hunted, and a sifaka found dead in the forest was accorded the same burial rites as a man. Unfortunately, however, this traditional attitude is increasingly ignored, and the modern Malagasy has little compunction in killing any lemur. Sifakas are defenceless against modern methods of hunting. The noise of gun-fire does not cause them to flee, even when one of their number is wounded. There are not many Europeans who having once killed a sifaka would wish to do so again, as the experience of Raymond Decary, a French administrator, bears out: "Early in my service in Madagascar, I happened to kill a female. . . . One [of a troop] of these animals squatted motionless on a branch gazing at me. I fired my pistol at it. Pierced through by the bullet, the animal briefly clutched the branch with one hand, before falling at my feet with a soft moan. It was a mother with her tiny offspring. The bullet that killed her had hit the thighs of the juvenile which she carried on her back and, being scarcely bigger than a clenched fist, I had not seen. The young . . . emitted cries of lamentation. It left the body of its mother and came to me, and despite its bleeding wound tried to climb my leg, before returning to cling to its mother's fur as if in search of one last haven of protection. . . . Since that moment I have never again fired at a sifaka."

Not many protein-deficient Malagasy tribesmen are likely to be deterred by such considerations, however, especially in the southern part of the country. In numerous villages it is usual to see lemurs of various species tied to trees by cords around their waists, being fattened for some future meal. Jolly was discouraged from studying the fauna of the western forests because "too many lemurs ended in a Malagasy stew for me to stay—it would have been ill-advised for them to trust humans too far".

Lemurs have been legally protected in Madagascar since 1927; and the hunting, collection, possession, and sale of all species are in theory prohibited, except under special licence. Although it is comparatively simple to enforce adequate controls over the export of lemurs for foreign zoological and museum collections, it is much more difficult to control their capture for local consumption.

Unregulated hunting has undoubtedly contributed to the decline of the sifaka. But the principal factor is the widespread destruction and spoliation by axe and fire of Madagascar's indigenous forests, on which the sifakas—like all Madagascar's wild fauna—are entirely dependent for existence.

While it is true that a dozen theoretically inviolable sanctuaries have existed for almost half a century, and that sifakas are represented in about half of them, the protection afforded by these reserves is inadequate, and, unless it can be strengthened, the future of several races of sifaka must remain uncertain.

Jolly: "The lemurs hold many more surprises for us, surely, more to learn and more to enjoy. But they, like so much of the world's wildlife, are threatened. One cannot blame the hunter who eats his rice with occasional lemur stew. But habitat destruction in Madagascar is irrevocable. The Malagasy forests, once burned, never grow back. The soil leaches away, and though alien teak or eucalyptus can take root, year by year the native flora retreats. Already, most of Madagascar is bare plateau, clothed in bunch grass, bleeding red earth through its eroding gullies into the sea. The lemurs survive in forests round the periphery, with the remaining Malagasy carnivores, insectivores, birds, butterflies. Many species seem in little danger now— Ringtails, for instance, will swagger on for many years. But all become rarer, and, with present trends will reach a point one by one past saving. Madagascar is uniquely rich, a record of the dawn of the age of mammals, but it is difficult to hope that the lemurs, so full of clues to our own past, have themselves much future."

AYE-AYE

Daubentonia madagascariensis

Madagascar has the distinction of possessing a greater variety of primitive primates than any other country in the world. The prosimians were once much more widely distributed. During the Paleocene and Eocene the ancestral lemurs inhabited both Europe and North America, but eventually disappeared in the face of competition from more advanced forms. They survived in Madagascar, however, by virtue of the island's separation from the continental land mass, some fifty million years ago. The absence of higher forms of primates and the existence of only a very limited number of endemic carnivores resulted in both competition and predation being minimal.

The aye-aye was originally discovered by Sonnerat in 1780 during his extended visit to Madagascar. His descriptions of the island's strange native fauna aroused both the scepti-

cism and the curiosity of the West. He brought the first pair of living aye-ayes to Europe, but neither survived more than a few weeks.

Initially, the aye-aye was regarded as a member of the squirrel family and was therefore classified among the rodents. The true taxonomic position remained a matter for zoological controversy until 1866 when Sir Richard Owen's monograph established it as an aberrant type of lemur.

The aye-aye is the most primitive of all living primates, and the sole representative of a once much larger ancestral family. In general appearance it bears a somewhat superficial resemblance to a cat-sized squirrel. Its predominant colour is black, with prominent, curved, rodent-like incisors, large eyes, and bushy tail. All the digits have claw-like nails, except for the big toe, which has a flat nail.

The most striking anatomical features are the hands, particularly the long thin third finger which is a highly specialized adaptation to the animal's diet. This elongated and astonishingly pliant finger is used partly to detect the larvae which constitute the animal's principal natural food, and partly as a probe. When searching for food the aye-aye moves slowly along a branch, gently scratching the bark with the tip of its finger, at the same time using its nose and ears to detect scent or sound. Having located a larva, it tears away the wood with its incisors to expose the cavity, and employs the hook-like tip of the finger to scoop out the larva.

The aye-aye has the further distinction of being the only large lemur to construct a complicated nest, a feat which is usually considered the prerogative of the great apes. The nest of twigs is built in the fork of a tree, the framework entwined among the branches. It is roughly spherical in shape, and big enough to accommodate a single adult, with the entrance at the side and the floor carpeted with leaves. Almost nothing is known of the breeding biology, but a single young is believed to be the rule. The low breeding potential is probably a significant factor in the decline of the species.

Distribution is limited to the eastern seaboard of Madagascar, with an extension reaching across to the Ampasindava Peninsula on the north-west coast, where a relict population was discovered in 1967. Within this range the species is restricted to indigenous rain forest near to the coast from sea level up to an altitude of about 2,000 feet. However, destruction of forest has taken place on such a large scale to accommodate the spiralling human population and the ever-increasing herds of domestic livestock that very few virgin stands remain.

The aye-aye is protected by law, but no amount of legal protection can compensate for deprivation of habitat, especially to so highly specialized an animal. Although two national parks, twelve integral natural reserves, and twenty-five forest reserves have been established in Madagascar, the aye-aye is not represented in any of them. Furthermore, even the existing reserves are vulnerable to the specious argument of powerful vested interests that the country's economic development is incompatible with the "protection of butterflies".

Deforestation is the essential cause of decline, but a subsidiary reason arises from the increasingly sophisticated attitude of the Malagasy people. In the past the aye-aye was venerated by most of the tribes. By some it was held to be an ancestral reincarnation possessed of supernatural powers, and none dared molest it. If one was accidentally trapped it was at once released, and if found dead it was ceremonially buried with the respect normally reserved for a great chief.

This traditional attitude has changed and the animal is now regarded as a beast of ill-omen and a harbinger of death. Its presence in or near a village is believed to portend the impending death of a villager. Concerted efforts are therefore made to drive any aye-ayes away from the villages, and in the process many are injured or killed. In some parts of Madagascar the animal is ritually slaughtered, but the precise nature and significance of these strange ceremonies are not known.

By the end of the Second World War the aye-aye was generally assumed to be extinct. No reports had been received for many years; though it is true that little attempt had been made to look for it. In 1957 Dr. J.-J. Petter undertook a systematic search and succeeded in finding a relict population in a small area of forest near Tamatave which, almost miraculously, had escaped destruction.

Subsequent investigation showed that a few other small scattered groups had survived. The aye-aye's status was known to be precarious, but the catastrophic extent of the decline was not fully appreciated until 1965 when André Peyrieras began a comprehensive survey which revealed that the population had been reduced to a few dozen individual animals, and that extinction was imminent.

The narrow environmental and climatic conditions necessary for the aye-aye's existence are found only in Madagascar. The animal's inability to adapt itself to change means that there is little likelihood of establishing viable breeding colonies elsewhere.

On the other hand, the unimpeded diminution of indigenous forests indicates all too clearly that the aye-aye's prospects of survival on the mainland of Madagascar are negligible. In an attempt to overcome this dilemma, Dr. Petter and Mr. Vadon proposed that the small island of Nossi Mangabe (1,285 acres) situated in the Bay of Antongil, a few miles off Maraontsetra, should be set aside as a Special Reserve. The Government assented, and in December 1965 the reserve was formally established.

Peyrieras then embarked on a programme to capture every available aye-aye on the mainland of Madagascar, estimated to number no more than about 50, and to transfer them to the island. Over a period of many months, he followed up every report of the occurrence of aye-ayes, and succeeded in capturing five females and four males, all of which were duly taken to Nossi Mangabe and released.

This little island has remained inviolate by virtue of its religious significance to the Malagasy people. For this reason the forest with which it is entirely covered has escaped destruction, and it is one of the few remaining unspoiled coastal rain forests in Madagascar.

On the assumption that the small colony of aye-ayes thrives and breeds, it is hoped that stocks will eventually be sufficient for introduction or re-introduction elsewhere. Such a possibility is naturally dependent upon suitable habitat being available; but, to judge from the present frenzied rate of destruction of Madagascar's forests, this appears to be a forlorn hope.

The critical status of the aye-aye and growing concern about the overall faunal situation led the I.U.C.N. Survival Service Commission in 1967 to send a mission (Petter/Simon) to Madagascar. This resulted in the drafting of a preliminary conservation programme, which was fully supported by the Malagasy Government, and was at once adopted by the World Wildlife Fund. The highest priority was given to proposals for the rehabilitation of the aye-aye.

The successful implementation of this programme is primarily attributable to Andre Peyrieras who since its inception has undertaken the difficult and time-consuming work of capture and translocation.

Not the least of the problems with which he had to contend lay in devising and perfecting a technique for capturing aye-ayes in the wild state, a procedure which frequently involved operating among the branches of trees 30 to 50 feet or more above the ground.

Over a period of more than two years he not only gave liberally of his own time and services in an entirely honorary capacity but in addition he paid out of his own pocket the wages of several men to patrol and guard the island of Nossi Mangabe. Funds contributed by W.W.F. have relieved him of this burden and enabled him to continue the work to which he has devoted himself with such conspicuous success.

During the course of this work, Peyrieras installed a pair of young aye-ayes under semi-captive conditions in a large cage built around a large copal tree close to his house. This project is designed to study the reproduction of the species, about which almost nothing is known, under near-natural conditions, as an important facet of the rehabilitation programme.

The project also includes an extensive survey of the remaining eastern rain forests, during the course of which Andre Peyrieras recently discovered a specimen of the hairy-eared dwarf lemur, *Allocebus trichotis*, previously known from only three specimens and thought to be extinct.

In summary, the aye-aye is one of the rarest and most remarkable animals in the world, the sole surviving representative not only of a species or even a genus but of an entire zoological family. Its status has deteriorated to the level at which its continued existence on the mainland of Madagascar is problematical. The one place where there is any reasonable prospect of the animal's long-term survival is on the island of Nossi Mangabe. The future of *Daubentonia madagascariensis* is thus wholly dependent on retention of this tiny island as the world's only aye-aye sanctuary.

AYE-AYE   *Daubentonia madagascariensis*   AYE-AYE

INDRIS

The indris, or *babakato*, to use one of its vernacular names, is the largest of the living lemurs. Its hind legs are long relative to its arms, and when standing erect it is more than 3 feet tall. Its hands and feet are unusually elongated; and the arrangement of the great toe, which is widely separated from the other four toes, allows the foot a powerful grasp, which assists in clasping the trunks and branches of trees. Its head is disproportionately small, and its tail little more than a stump.

Normally its colour is predominantly black and white. Its face, ears, shoulders, upper part of the back, hands, feet, and outer side of the legs are usually black, with white on the hindquarters expanding into a triangular patch across the lower back. There is considerable individual variation in the colour and pattern, however, ranging from black through varying shades of brown and grey to white. These differences are apparently unrelated to geographical distribution or to ecological factors.

The indris is arboreal, living in dense forest, generally among the larger branches of trees. It is not exclusively arboreal, however, and when on the ground it walks erect on its hind legs, or moves with a series of short hops or leaps, its hands extended in front of its body. This characteristic stance, in association with the shortness of the tail, doubtless accounts for the belief held by some tribes that the indris is descended from men who took to the forest. Paulian states that "as recently as 1948 two indrises captured on the peak of Ivohibe were exhibited in the Thosy district as dwarfs".

Until recently the indris was revered by the Malagasy people, and many myths and legends are associated with it. Sonnerat and other early observers were impressed by the care taken by the inhabitants to avoid doing anything that might harm an indris. The animal is no longer regarded with awe, and there is little compunction about eating it.

The species has a very limited range in the rain forests of north-eastern Madagascar, where it is restricted to the eastern side of the plateau from Vohémar in the north to the Masora River in the south, which is approximately halfway along the east coast.

The climate in this part of Madagascar is permanently humid. Rand found the indris from sea level up to the edge of the central plateau, and up to a height of 6,000 feet, but very localized.

A century ago the indris was much more numerous than it is today. At that time a separate troop occupied almost every one of the numerous hills and ridges within its range. Vinson, a medical practitioner living on the island of Réunion, visited Madagascar in the 1850s, and passing through the forest of Alanamasoatrao was, in Harper's words, "deafened during two days by the incessant clamor of apparently numerous but invisible bands of these animals".

The indris is more often heard than seen; and many travellers have commented on its call. It is the most vocal of all the lemurs, and its vernacular name *amboanala*, meaning "dog of the forest", is said to be an allusion to its dog-like howls. This is an inadequate simile, however; the cry of the indris is like no other sound on earth, except perhaps the ululation of colobus monkeys. But the indris's bark is incomparably louder; so loud indeed that it seems to be deafeningly close even when the animals are at a distance. The call is usually given in company for several minutes at a time, and then, after a pause, repeated. Each animal when calling throws back its head, the volume being magnified by the action of an air-sac in the larynx. A troop will frequently call when on the move, the chorus rolling in great waves across the canopy of trees, flooding the forest with sound.

Indrises live in family groups, usually consisting of a male, a female, and one or two young. Each group appears to occupy its own particular ridge or hill, usually preferring the highest part of its territory near the crest.

Petter, whose field studies have provided much information on the behaviour and habits of the species, states that indrises occasionally come into close contact with each other for mutual grooming, or when marking, but only briefly. "Play, which is frequent in captivity, has never been observed in the course of many hours of field observation. The animals merely rest, move about, and eat. Nor has fighting over food been observed between animals of the same group when the same piece of food attracts a certain number of individuals. Often food is quietly divided, or the possessor of a piece of fruit moves a few meters away with it and no one follows him."

Indrises are difficult animals to study as it is almost impossible to approach them closely or maintain contact with them. On the other hand, they seem to be creatures of fixed habit; and when undisturbed they generally visit the same place at the same time each day. They move from one tree to another by making spectacular jumps from trunk to trunk, propelled by the powerful hind legs, travelling through the air in an upright position, their outstretched legs and arms taking the impact of landing against the tree trunk.

Like all members of this family, the indris gives birth to only a single young. The length of the gestation period is not known accurately, but has been estimated by Milne-Edwards and Grandidier at 4 to 5 months. Other biologists believe that it is shorter, but as no indris has ever been born in captivity it is impossible to be sure.

Petter's studies of the species in the wild state show that the young of the Indriidae, like those of *Lemur*, "are able to grasp the mother's fur from birth and are carried in this way during group movements. For some days after the birth of the young the mother exhibits a special behaviour. When she is resting she attempts to form a sort of cradle with her body, the trunk slightly inclined backward and the thighs folded. The young can rest there and can even lean over the edge to look below. Keeping the same position, the female is also able to eat.

"When she wishes to move, the mother gives a quick pat of her hand to help the infant take up a perpendicular position beneath her, clinging tightly to the fur of her belly. When the female moves with the others it is often difficult to see if she has a young one with her; only the top of the infant's head is visible in the fold of the mother's thigh.

"Shortly after the birth of the infant the mother, when the group rests, usually stays a few meters from the others, whom she prevents from approaching. Then little by little she lets herself be licked by the male, then by other individuals of the group, all much attracted by the newborn, which they also try to lick.

"When it is two weeks old the infant more and more holds on to the mother's back, a position that it maintains until it is much older. The infant grips the mother's fur and holds its body parallel to hers. We have even observed young that have attained two thirds of their adult size in this position on their mothers' backs."

The indris does not thrive in captivity even in its native country. It appears to have been seen alive outside Madagascar on only one occasion: according to Hill, "eight or ten specimens were received at the Paris Ménagerie in 1939, all of which died within one month". The reasons for its intolerance of captivity have not been clearly explained, but are probably related to factors of diet, environment, and temperament. As with other leaf-eating primates, the indris's specialized natural diet is essential to its well-being, and its delicately adjusted digestive system is unable to adapt itself to changed conditions; it also appears temperamentally unsuited to confinement. As with the aye-aye, it seems probable that the particular environmental and climatic conditions under which the indris lives—and which cannot easily be artificially duplicated—are indispensable requirements for its existence.

The decline of the indris has been brought about by widespread deforestation. In this respect the species is in the same position as almost all the indigenous fauna of Madagascar. The indris is especially vulnerable, however, because of its extremely restricted range.

The scale and intensity of habitat destruction are hard to describe. In much of Madagascar the destruction is almost total, to the ruin of the country and the loss of much irreplaceable natural wealth. Perrier de la Bathie, writing in 1931, remarked that from September to Novem-

INDRI   *Indri indri*   INDRIS

ber the country is completely enveloped in smoke. At night from any hilltop fires can be seen in every direction; "the most remarkable flora on earth reduced to ashes under one's eyes ... over the whole island fierce fires, extensive cultivation, and uncontrolled exploitation lead to the same result: the absolute destruction of all indigenous flora. At the same time, the island's specialized fauna, which is essentially arboreal, is naturally destroyed together with the forest which protects it ... Madagascar is today more heavily deforested than any densely populated country in Europe. Seventy per cent of its flora and fauna have already been destroyed."

A few far-sighted foresters and botanists appreciated the necessity to protect some of the few remaining pristine areas from destruction. Their efforts led in 1928 to the creation of ten *réserves naturelles intégrales*, and another the following year. Those responsible wanted above all to secure a reserve on the north-eastern seaboard, in the intermediate zone between 600 and 1,000 feet above sea level, which they regarded as the richest of Madagascar's forests. By then, however, no unspoiled tract of sufficient size remained, except for the Masoala massif, where a 52,000 acre reserve was established. A smaller area of untouched eastern forest was incorporated into the Betampona Reserve (4,000 acres); and a few other fragments of coastal forest were secured on the lower eastern slopes of some of the montane reserves. Unfortunately, however, the Forêt de Masoala Reserve was summarily abolished in 1964 for commercialized logging purposes.

One of the few relatively easily seen populations of indris inhabits the Périnet Forest, which is situated in the central part of the species' range, roughly midway between Tananarive and the port of Tamatave. Now that the Masoala Reserve has been deproclaimed, Périnet is one of the best areas of eastern rain forest that remains; it is therefore of exceptional importance. Botanically it is rich; it also contains a wide variety of lemurs and other fauna. Périnet is officially classified as *Reserve Forestière*, but this status affords no protection to the fauna and appears to convey little practical advantage to the flora, which has for many years been heavily exploited for commercial timber production.

Few other places in Madagascar of comparable scientific interest have the advantage of such easy accessibility. It seems likely that Périnet is the most suitable place in which to conduct a field study of the indris; it is also an appropriate area for establishing an indris sanctuary. It seems important to the survival of the indris that early steps should be taken to give protective status to a large area around the Périnet Forest Station, to safeguard what remains of the native forest and the varied wildlife which it contains. But Périnet alone is insufficient to protect the species, and it is essential that a comprehensive survey should be carried out to discover precisely where the indris still occurs, and to ascertain what practical measures should be taken to ensure the perpetuation of the species. Unless this is treated as a matter of great urgency the indris's prospects of survival are slender.

ZANZIBAR RED COLOBUS   *Colobus badius kirkii*

The generally recognized classification of the genus *Colobus* is based on three species: *C. polykomos*, the black and white colobus; *C. badius*, the red colobus; and *C. verus*, the green colobus.

Monkeys of this family—which also includes the langurs and the snub-nosed monkeys—have complicated stomachs which bear some resemblance to the complex systems of the ruminants, and are an adaptation necessitated by the large quantity of cellulose food contained in a leaf-eating diet. Colobus monkeys differ from other members of the family, however, in having no cheek pouches, which gives them the appearance of being sunken-cheeked. They are further distinguished by a vestigial thumb, a fact reflected in the derivation of the generic name from the Greek *kolobos*, meaning "mutilated".

The loud barking alarm call is unforgettably characteristic of the black and white colobus. It is frequently the first indication of the animal's presence and, being quickly taken up by the entire troop, reverberates through the forest canopy long after they have vanished from sight. The red colobus has an alto voice and, according to Booth, the sound made by the Zanzibar form resembles that of the typical race from West Africa.

The red colobus occurs in a wide variety of red and black colour combinations, from rich rufous, chestnut and orange to mahogany, brown, grey and black. This diversity is reflected in the large number of subspecies. Opinions differ over the classification, but systematists generally recognize 20 races, though some authors (cf. Verheyen, 1962; Napier and Napier, 1967) accord the Zanzibar form specific rank.

The taxonomy of the colobus monkeys has received considerable attention, but comparatively little is known about their ecology or their behaviour in the wild state. This is partly because their shy and retiring disposition effectively discourages field studies. They are, moreover, exceptionally difficult to maintain in captivity, and have never been known to breed in confinement.

The red colobus belongs essentially to the West African fauna, the main area of distribution being the tropical forests around the Congo Basin, as far west as Senegal, and extending into the western fringes of East Africa. East Africa is marginal to the range, however; in both Uganda and Tanzania the species is uncommon and largely restricted to the western forests bordering the Congo as, for example, at Kabale, the Ruwenzori Range and along the Semliki River.

Beyond these limits to the east are three outlying populations, each a discrete race isolated by many miles from the main distributional zone and from each other. They are: the Uhehe race, *C. b. gordonorum*, from parts of Iringa District, Tanzania; *C. b. rufomitratus*, which is confined to a narrow strip of gallery forest along the Tana River in Kenya; and the Zanzibar race, *C. b. kirkii*.

The species remains widely distributed in West Africa and is still relatively common in some of the remoter parts of its range; but, being intolerant of disturbance, it has in recent years been driven from the more accessible forests which are being increasingly exploited for commercialized timber extraction or opened to cultivation. The three East African races, however, are regarded as rare and endangered and listed accordingly in the *Red Data Book*.

Colobus are the most arboreal of the African monkeys, seldom coming to the ground, and when they do their awkward gait indicates that they are out of their element. But in the trees they are astonishingly active and agile, making spectacular leaps with effortless grace. Normally they inhabit the upper storey of the primary forest, sometimes descending to lower levels to feed. *C. b. kirkii* is the exception to this rule, however, as no primary forest remains in Zanzibar and the animal has therefore been compelled to adapt to less congenial environmental conditions.

The Zanzibar form is a vividly coloured animal, whitish-grey on the underparts and throat; black on the shoulders, outer sides of the

COLOBE ROUX DE ZANZIBAR   *Colobus badius kirkii*   ZANZIBAR RED COLOBUS

arms, hands and feet; russet-brown on the lower neck and crown of the head. The face is particularly striking—blue-black surrounded by a yellowish-white band across the forehead and down either side of the face to the chin, with long hairs protruding beyond the sides of the head.

The discovery of the Zanzibar red colobus is attributable to Sir John Kirk, the British Consul in Zanzibar, who sent the first specimen to Europe in 1868. There is some uncertainty as to the original distribution of the animal. In 1884, Kirk wrote that it occurred in many of the forested parts of the island, but even at that time was "so rare as not to be procurable".

Sir Harry Johnston, writing in 1886, confirmed that it had almost completely disappeared except for in one remote stretch of forest. His hunters duly visited this area, returning with a dozen dead specimens which they reported to represent the entire population, thus leading Sir Harry to assume that the animal had been wiped out.

If Kirk was right, it can be assumed that the red colobus originally inhabited the primary forest, destruction of which was well advanced even in his day. Deforestation deprived the animal of its natural habitat and forced it to retreat into the less hospitable, but more secure, bush and scrub country on a few parts of the east coast. The most recent report estimates that about two hundred have survived, principally in the Jozani Forest.

Miss Helen Faulkner saw them on several occasions in 1963 during the course of her botanical work. She noted that they usually occur "in small companies of 6 or 7 individual animals, often quite close to the road, leaping from tree to tree and chattering".

The Jozani Forest is in an area of open savannah (principally *Calophyllum inophyllum*) with outcrops of coral rag, so rough that walking is difficult and cultivation largely impossible. Except for a few fishing villages, this part of Zanzibar's east coast remains thinly inhabited to this day; and the danger from settlement or agricultural development is remote. The little grazing that exists is poor and capable of supporting only a few cattle in the less stony

places. When Professor Th. Monod visited the forest in April 1964 he found it difficult of access, at least at certain times, and in some places he was obliged to wade knee-deep in water.

The main threat to the black and white colobus has long been the demand for its pelt, which is of a fine silky texture and among the most decorative known. The trade is centuries old, the original market being Central Asia where colourful furs have always been highly prized. The traffic was largely controlled by the Arab and Indian merchants of Zanzibar and Mombasa, who shipped the pelts by dhow to India.

At the end of the last century these skins became popular in Europe and America. Traders employed teams of collectors who operated over a wide area; and the slaughter was very great, reaching its peak in 1892 when 188,646 monkey skins (mainly colobus) were exported from the Gold Coast.

These events took place over a period of little more than a decade, but during that short time an estimated two million colobus pelts were exported to furriers. Thereafter the demand diminished as the whim of fashion changed. Even today, however, the pelt is popular among tourists for rugs, karosses and other curios; and Game Department records show that in 1960, 26,529 colobus skins were imported into Kenya from Moyale alone.

The uninhibited destruction of the colobus monkey caused a public outcry, and was one of the factors that stimulated the responsible governments to introduce protective legislation to control the trade in wild animal products; and led to the first International Conference for the Protection of Fauna and Flora which was held in London in May, 1900.

The red colobus was not subject to the same demand as its fur lacks the flowing shoulder mantle, elongated flank fringes, and long tufted tail of its more distinguished relative.

Shortly before the 1964 *coup d'état*, however, the Zanzibar red colobus was for a period endangered by the demands of the booming tourist trade and captive specimens were often purchased out of curiosity or pity, but being deprived of their highly specialized diet they had no hope of survival. Many others were of course killed during the process of capture.

Even in expert hands the red colobus is difficult to keep alive in captivity, and unless the correct precautions are taken during the critical period immediately after capture the monkeys are likely to die before they reach the hands of experienced keepers. In 1963, for example, 12 were brought into Kenya for sale to zoos. Of these, ten died within a short time, partly because of dietary difficulties and partly because of their susceptibility to climatic change. The unaccustomed cold of the Kenya Highlands proved too much for them.

Six more were exported from Zanzibar in August 1966, but by the time they reached Nairobi Airport one was already dead and the other five in very poor condition, two of which died subsequently. One had a mark around its neck such as would be made by a noose. Others were injured in different ways: one with shot gun pellets in its head and body. A female in early pregnancy had aborted, as frequently happens to monkeys following the shock of capture.

It seems of great importance that any future consignments of animals as rare and delicate as the red colobus should be under the direct control of a person experienced in their care and handling, who should supervise the capture operation as well as look after them during the critical period immediately following capture and during the ensuing journey to their ultimate destination.

The 1966 consignment was the last permitted out of the country. The Ministry of Agriculture and Land Reform subsequently expressed its intention of refusing further permits for the capture and export of the animal.

The Zanzibar red colobus has few enemies other than man. Unlike some monkeys which are addicted to *shamba* raiding, it is not a menace to native crops. Being strictly arboreal, it is content to remain in the forest, and does not therefore conflict in any way with human interests.

Its future is almost entirely dependent upon the Jozani Forest, for which reason it is essential that this small forest—which has had the status of "Forest Reserve" since 1960—should remain unexploited and undisturbed. Any attempt to replace the indigenous forest by plantations of exotic trees, as at one time was apparently contemplated, would clearly be disastrous for this rare animal's prospects of survival.

MOUNTAIN GORILLA *Gorilla gorilla beringei*

For more than a hundred years after its discovery in West Africa in 1847 the gorilla remained something of an enigma. The remoteness of the dense forests inhabited by the animal—and its massive size and strength, which gave it a reputation for ferocity and aggressiveness now known to be unwarranted—discouraged more than brief and superficial observations.

In 1959-60, however, all this changed. For twenty months George Schaller and his wife lived among mountain gorillas, mainly in the Virunga Volcanoes. His first-hand observations resulted in what is surely the most thorough study of a wild primate ever made. His published monograph on the animal is a model of its kind; as a result the gorilla has changed from being one of the least-known to one of the best-documented primates. Nearly all the following notes are extracted, entirely unashamedly, from Schaller's classic work *The Mountain Gorilla: ecology and behavior*, published in 1963.

The full species occurs in the dense equatorial forests of western and west-central Africa. It has been subdivided into two widely separated races, the lowland gorilla, *G. g. gorilla* which is restricted to the Congo River basin, and the mountain gorilla, *G. g. beringei*, which is found in the mountainous regions in the eastern Congo extending very slightly into south-western Uganda and western Ruanda. The lowland race is not at present endangered; but the mountain gorilla is.

During his remarkable walk from the Cape to Cairo in 1898, Ewart Grogan came across the skeleton of a gigantic ape, bigger than any he had ever seen, in the neighbourhood of the Virunga Volcanoes. This appears to have been the first record of the mountain gorilla, and if Grogan had thought of sending the skeleton to England, he would undoubtedly have been credited with the animal's discovery. However, four more years were to pass before the sub-species was first made known to science from a specimen collected by Captain Oscar von Beringe on Mount Sabinio in October 1902.

Gorillas are the largest and by far the most powerful of all the living primates. Together with their relatives, the chimpanzee and the pygmy chimpanzee of Africa and the orang-utan of eastern Asia, they are known collectively as the great apes. It is a sobering thought that three of the world's four great apes have the doubtful distinction of a place in the Survival Service Commission's *Red Data Book*.

An adult male mountain gorilla may weigh 300 to 400 pounds or more, and stand 5 feet 6 inches tall when fully erect, with an arm-spread greatly exceeding its height: females are much smaller, weighing 150 to 250 pounds. Their bodies are thickset, their arms very powerful but their legs relatively weak. Their heads are massive and have a prominent crest, with a low forehead and heavy ridges over the eyes. Their eyes and ears are small, their nostrils large. Their hands are very large, with thumbs larger than fingers. Their hair is brownish-black to blue-black, males over the age of about ten years being distinguished by a prominent silvery-grey saddle. Individuals vary greatly in appearance.

The mountain gorilla differs from its lowland relative by having a somewhat narrower head with a prominent fleshy callosity on its crest, arms somewhat shorter, legs longer and fur denser. Gorillas often stand erect, but prolonged bipedal movement is rare; they normally walk on all fours with the knuckles on the ground.

Although their large canine teeth might give a contrary impression, gorillas have a diet believed to be wholly vegetarian. Captive gorillas eat meat, but there is no evidence that they do so in the wild. They consume the juicy stems of wild celery, bamboo shoots, the fronds of tree-ferns, the bark of certain shrubs, leaves, berries, wild fruits and a variety of other herbage. Occasionally they raid standing crops in native *shambas*. At no time did Schaller see them drink, and they probably obtain their liquid requirements from heavy morning dew and succulent vegetation.

They are able to climb trees but, being primarily terrestrial animals, spend most of the time on the ground, where their preferred food is more abundant.

Rough platforms are constructed for sleeping at night or for rest during the day, either in a tree or on the ground. Adult males usually prefer the ground. A gorilla rarely takes more than a few minutes to make a nest, either standing or sitting in a central position, and pulling in the surrounding vegetation, which it tucks under and around itself.

According to locality and circumstances, the nests are made in a crude and casual way or may be much more elaborately built, but they are not normally occupied more than once.

The mountain gorilla lives in groups of any number between two and thirty (according to the area) but probably averaging between six and seventeen. Factors determining the size of each group are little understood, but may be dependent to some extent on the availability and type of forage. Each group is dominated by a silver-backed male.

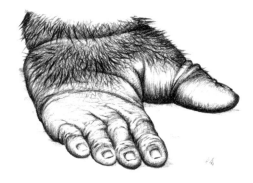

The mountain gorilla inhabits a region shaped like an inverted triangle, and extending about 300 miles south from the equator and about 220 miles from east to west at its widest point. The southern limit of the range is near Fizi, where the forest gives way to savannah and cultivation. The total range covers roughly 35,000 square miles; but within this region the area actually used by gorillas is much less since most groups are concentrated in sixty or so isolated areas varying in size from a few to 200 square miles and separated by anything up to 30 or more miles. Some groups undoubtedly come into contact with each other, but many live in isolation. The area actually occupied by gorillas is less than a quarter of the total range, or roughly 8,000 square miles, although stragglers—usually lone males but sometimes small groups—may wander into the large areas of forest surrounding the resident populations.

Within this range, the density of the gorilla populations varies from roughly three animals to the square mile in the Virunga Volcanoes, where there are about 400 or 500 in all, to about one and a half per square mile in the Kayonza Forest, and one or a fraction of one per square mile in the Utu region. The entire population has been estimated at between 5,000 and 15,000 animals.

The mountain gorilla is found in three types of environment: lowland rain-forest below 5,000 feet, mountain rain-forest from 5,000 to 11,500 feet, and bamboo forest from 8,000 to 10,000 feet. An estimated three-quarters of the population inhabits lowland rain-forest west of the Rift Valley; and most of the remainder lives in the mountain forests of the Rift escarpment. The bamboo zone is relatively unimportant to the subspecies, as it contains little suitable dry-season forage and it is in any event of limited distribution. The most favoured habitat consists of secondary forest; and the rotational felling of primary forest, and its subsequent regeneration, under the slash-and-burn system of shifting agriculture used in the past by primitive agriculturalists, undoubtedly created conditions favourable to the ape.

Females are believed not to reach sexual maturity until the age of six or seven, and males at about nine or ten years, when the hair starts changing to silver, a process that may take at least two to three years to complete. The gestation period of four captive specimens varies from 251 to 289 days. There is no evidence of a breeding season, but mature females normally produce a single young every three and a half to four and a half years, unless the young dies in infancy, in which event the interval is reduced. Mortality is high and probably between 40 and 50 per cent of the progeny die during the infant and juvenile periods.

The young remains with its mother for about three years, during which time she does not again conceive. On the assumption that a mature female reproduces about once every fourth year, her lifetime reproductive expectancy is probably about four or five young, assuming none dies in infancy.

Losses through predation by leopards or other carnivores are believed to be insignificant. By far the most important predator is man. Notwithstanding nominal legal protection, some tribesmen continue to hunt the gorilla, mainly for food and notably in the Utu and Mt. Tshiaberimu regions, by a variety of methods including nets, snares, and pitfalls. Schaller quotes a 1928 missionary report that tribesmen had killed and eaten eleven gorillas in a single day. He also mentions a mine official who admitted shooting nine for sport, and cites an instance of the shooting of females by collectors to obtain the young, including an occasion about 1948 when sixty were killed near Angumu to acquire eleven infants, only one of which ultimately survived.

Gorillas are subject to a wide variety of diseases and other ailments: virus diseases, bacterial infections, and various internal parasites may be responsible for the majority of gorilla deaths.

The numbers slaughtered every year for food are believed to be substantial, but do not so far appear to have had any serious effect on the total population. Losses from this cause can be substained just as long as killing rates do not rise much above their present level through the acquisition by the killers of more sophisticated weapons. A more immediate threat to the animal

GORILLE DE MONTAGNE *Gorilla gorilla beringei* MOUNTAIN GORILLA

occurs in areas such as the Virunga Volcanoes, the Kayonza Forest, and the Mount Tshiaberimu region, which are gradually being taken over by agriculturalists and pastoralists.

The latest threat to the gorilla, as well as to many other species of primates, is the increasing demands of medical research and the pharmaceutical industry.

Because only relatively small differences separate the mountain and lowland races, it is believed that their divergence must have been fairly recent. The distribution of the species was once probably continuous throughout the rain forest north of the Congo River; today a gap of about 650 miles separates the two races, but it does not result from any limitations of suitable habitat. Indeed, rain forest stretches unbroken throughout the region.

The dispersal of gorilla populations is restricted by the extent of humid forest that readily provides their favoured forage, such as vines and succulent herbs: they avoid grasslands and large areas of open woodlands. Moreover, although gorillas use fallen trees for crossing streams and small rivers, they are apparently unable to swim and seem to avoid even quite shallow streams. Deep, swift-flowing rivers, such as those of the Congo and Ubangi-Uele systems, would have presented impassable barriers.

With these limiting factors in mind, Schaller speculates that at one time the gorilla inhabited country to the north of the Uele River, and penetrated into its present habitat by way of the headwaters of that river. Although the region north of the Uele River is not now suitable for gorillas, there is evidence that during the late Pleistocene the rain forest extended farther to the north than it does today, thereby linking East and West Africa by way of the northern edge of the Congo Basin. This hypothesis is supported by evidence that several species of East African montane forest birds are not even subspecifically differentiated from their counterparts on Mount Cameroon in West Africa. Furthermore, Lake Chad during the late Pleistocene was almost five times the size of the present Lake Victoria, which means that it must then have received twenty times more

water than it does today. The resulting precipitation would have permitted the occurrence of suitable humid forest vegetation north of the Uele River.

Later a dry climatic period caused the forest to regress, leaving the two populations isolated from each other by the 650-miles gap. Additional evidence in support of the theory that the gorilla spread from north to south in the relatively recent past arises from the fact that colonization is more extensive in the northern than in the southern part of the range.

The colonization of the Virunga Volcanoes and the Kayonza Forest presumably occurred by way of forest bridges across the grasslands, which were afterwards severed by agriculture and burning, leaving the populations isolated. Failure to colonize the Ruwenzori Range, which contains much suitable habitat, is probably because the Semliki River formed an insurmountable barrier to penetration.

Schaller's work has shown conclusively that the mountain gorilla is not at present on the verge of extinction, as was thought when it was placed among the Class A mammals by the International London Convention of 1933. His study has revealed that both the range and the population are larger than previously supposed. The total area occupied by the subspecies is nevertheless small, and without doubt the animal is extremely vulnerable to direct destruction as well as to reduction or alteration of habitat. In some parts of the range, this form of indirect destruction constitutes a more serious and immediate threat than in others, particularly in areas such as the Virunga Volcanoes, where there is a dense and expanding human population that requires grazing for the constantly increasing herds of scrub cattle.

A notable step towards the protection of the mountain gorilla was the establishment in 1925, and the subsequent enlargement in 1929, of the Albert National Park, which was designed primarily for the long-term protection of the gorillas inhabiting the six dormant cones that constitute the Virunga Volcanoes. The park authorities have had a constant struggle to prevent violation of the park's boundaries, and in 1958 they were compelled to relinquish 37,500

acres of forest land. Wherever agriculturalists have been admitted, the forests have disappeared within a few years; the Congo National Park authorites deserve the highest commendation for their vigilance in safeguarding the park in the face of almost insuperable difficulties.

On the Uganda side of the Virunga Volcanoes, the northern slopes of Mounts Muhavura, Gahinga, and Sabinio were declared a gorilla sanctuary in 1930; but in 1950 the reserve was reduced from over 8,000 to less than 6,000 acres. The part cut out contained the most suitable gorilla habitat, much of which is now under cultivation, and the area is therefore subject to heavy disturbance.

The Kayonza Forest, otherwise known as the Impenetrable Forest, was declared a forest reserve in 1932 and became a wildlife sanctuary of nearly 74,000 acres in 1961. Selective exploitation of the forest, mainly by a limited number of licensed pit-sawyers, has been permitted since 1940, but it apparently causes little more than temporary disturbance in the areas actually being worked, and it may indeed benefit the gorillas by providing additional forage in the regenerating areas. Gorillas are seldom molested in the reserve, although occasionally a few may be unintentionally killed in traps set for wild pigs, and their status in the Kayonza Forest appears at present to be satisfactory.

The Mount Tshiaberimu massif is included within the boundaries of the Albert National Park, but is hemmed in by cultivation on three sides. Beyond the boundaries of the park the forest is being rapidly replaced by permanent agriculture. Furthermore, tribesmen in this region slaughter the gorilla for food. Failure to introduce and enforce more effective protection of the forests must sooner or later lead to the elimination of the ape from this region.

The situation is much more satisfactory in the extensive montane forests of the Rift and the huge areas of lowland forests lying to the west of Lake Tanganyika. Except around the towns, of which there are few, the human population is thin; and shifting cultivation will probably continue as in the past, a method of agriculture that in fact benefits the gorilla. True, African tribesmen undertake communal attacks on gorillas, and many animals are slaughtered, but the rate of kill is limited by the weapons and techniques employed, and the gorilla population should be capable of withstanding those losses so long as modern firearms are not made available.

Schaller concludes that it is essential for the mountain gorilla to remain on the list of fully protected animals, which involves doing everything possible, such as banning modern firearms, to prevent large-scale killing orgies by local tribesmen. A strict limit should be introduced, and enforced, on the numbers collected for zoos, museums, medical institutions, and so forth; and the technique of killing the female to obtain the young should be outlawed.

Strong measures should also be taken to prevent intrusion by agriculturalists and pastoralists into the existing gorilla sanctuaries, which should be extended to embrace more of the animal's natural range, notably in those areas where permanent agriculture is feasible. At the same time consideration should be given to the establishment of spacious reserves in the great, and at present almost uninhabited, areas of lowland rain forest while the opportunity still exists—as a precaution against the day when the expanding human population exchanges the present pattern of shifting cultivation for a more stable system of husbandry.

ADDAX

The addax is a somewhat ungainly looking animal, with thick-set body and relatively short legs. Males are larger than females, an adult bull standing approximately 42 inches at the shoulder. Both sexes carry horns, those of the male being heavier and normally having up to three spirals, whereas those of the female have a maximum of two. The record horns, from Darfur, attain a length of 43 inches along the curves. The hooves, a special adaptation to desert conditions, are broad and flat, to assist the animal in moving over sand. The shoulder skin of an adult male is three-quarters of an inch thick, and is used by the Tuareg and others for making shields.

In summer coat the upper part of the body is greyish white in colour, sometimes tinged with russet. The lower parts, including the hindquarters, legs and belly, are white. The neck and shoulders have long chestnut coloured hair, and there is a curious bushy tuft of dark hair on the forehead. A prominent butterfly-shaped white facial mark extends from above each eye down either side of the face and meets across the bridge of the nose. The lips are white also. In winter coat the hair, particularly the mane, becomes longer and the general colour darker. Young calves are a uniform sandy colour, becoming progressively whiter as they mature.

Addax live in small groups, normally half a dozen to twenty or so animals, headed by a mature bull; but Brocklehurst saw them in substantially larger formations. In areas where they were seldom disturbed he "encountered several large herds, which were easy to approach, and would wander along grazing and seldom looking up. Provided the wind was right, it was easily possible to walk openly up to them within a hundred yards before being observed. Even then they would only gallop away a short distance before stopping to look back, huddled together exactly like a flock of sheep."

The addax is most active during the early morning and evening. During the heat of the day it rests in whatever shade the desert can provide. Like the oryx, it sometimes excavates a shallow depression in the sand, in which it spends the night, thus obtaining a degree of protection from the cold.

The addax is capable of going for long periods without water: possibly it never drinks at all but obtains its liquid requirements from the succulents and other vegetation on which it feeds. Its highly developed senses enable it to detect distant showers of rain, which cause the desert vegetation to spring up overnight and to remain green for a surprisingly long period. The herd movements are governed by the occurrence of rain and by the constant search for grazing.

The addax is an inhabitant of the desert regions of northern Africa, the range being a long narrow strip across the southern Sahara from Mauritania in the west, through Mali, Niger and Tchad into the Sudan. The original range was much larger, and included the northern part of the Sahara from Algeria to Egypt.

Some authors aver that the historical range included the Arabian Peninsula, but the general consensus is that these assertions are untenable. An isolated population occurred east of the Nile, however, in Kassala Province, between the Nile and the Red Sea. This so-called eastern race was said by Mackenzie to be "very scarce" in the early 1950s, since when few people have visited the area. It is not known, therefore, whether any have survived.

The species no longer exists in Egypt, Tunisia or Rio de Oro. Valverde considers it unlikely that the Rio de Oro population was ever significant. Morales showed that in the early 1940s only a few small groups of addax remained, and were probably present only seasonally, in an area of sand dune country at Rabt Sebeta, about 44 miles from the coast. The last record of addax in Rio de Oro was of a solitary female seen in 1963 accompanying a herd of oryx.

It has virtually gone from Algeria and Libya also. The only recent reports of addax in these countries invariably refer to seasonal migrants moving across the southern frontiers from neighbouring countries.

Dupuy mentions three groups of addax on Algerian territory comprising: a small herd of four or five animals south of the In-Zize region; a few small groups, totalling barely 20 animals, in the In-Azoua region, close to the Niger frontier; and a slightly larger herd of about 30 animals south of the Admer Erg in the so-called Ténéré zone of Tafassesset.

Although Dupuy shows that the species still occurs in Algeria, he emphasizes that these small groups without exception are situated close to the southern frontier, and are thus almost certainly seasonal vagrants from Mali and Niger. It is evident that Algeria no longer possesses a resident addax population.

In the Sudan, too, the animal's status is precarious. The little information available indicates that numbers have declined drastically and that only a few small herds now remain.

One of the most recent reports on the status of the addax in the Sudan is by Lord Macpherson of Drumochter who visited Darfur Province in October 1968. He located a small herd of twelve adults and three calves in the Wadi Howar area. "I searched the territory north and west of Malha Wells very extensively up to and north of Wadi Howar. From my findings, there has been no addax for many years in the immediate vicinity of Malha Wells or on the Teiga Plateau. Undoubtedly since the time of . . . Captain Brocklehurst, of the 1920's, the addax has been pushed further north and I doubt whether today they ever move south of 16° latitude."

The nomads, together with their camels and other livestock, move into the desert at the commencement of the rains, about August, to take advantage of the flush of new grazing, returning three or four months later. "During this time the addax migrate further north and move south again when the tribesmen recede." The herdsmen are mounted and well armed with modern weapons which they use indiscriminately on any wild animals they can find.

Brocklehurst describes the technique: "Carrying enough water for six or seven days, a small party of these Arabs mounted on camels and accompanied by their dogs will push into the desert until they strike the fresh spoor or actually sight a herd of addax, which, owing to the almost dazzling whiteness of their coats during the winter, are visible at a very great distance, and by following the undulations of the ground, the party is able to get within a few hundred yards of their quarry without being observed. The addax being short-legged and heavy, is incapable of any great speed, and the cows and calves are soon brought to bay, and even some of the old bulls are run down and speared."

This method of hunting has gone on for centuries, but the technique employed and the relatively unsophisticated weapons available to the desert tribesmen imposed limitations on the kill. There were, moreover, wide expanses of desert which afforded the addax true sanctuary.

The remoteness and inaccessibility of parts of its habitat have been factors of paramount importance in providing the addax with effective natural protection. Since the end of the Second World War, however, these regions, hitherto regarded as almost impenetrable, have been opened up by oil prospectors and others, and no part of the Sahara however remote or forbidding is now beyond the reach of motorized man. Oil company employees living deep in the desert have little entertainment other than shooting. At the same time, modern firearms have become increasingly available to the nomads.

Monod draws attention to commercialized hunting parties operating from Adrar and Tagant which hunt addax systematically. Regular expeditions set out during the winter—the main calving season—when the herds, including gravid females and those with calves at foot, are remorselessly hunted down.

The addax is intolerant of disturbance, and the appearance of man and his domestic livestock suffices to cause the animal to quit an area. The animal's one defect, in Gillet's words, is its inability to "maintain a rapid flight for long. Hence it is most vulnerable. Closely pursued by a car travelling at 45 kilometres per hour it is completely blown at the end of eight minutes. Followed at a distance, at 20 kilometres per hour it is breathless at the end of 18 kilometres, and in under an hour it is exhausted and allows a point blank approach, without having the

ADDAX   *Addax nasomaculatus*   ADDAX

strength even to attempt a defensive gesture with its horns. An addax hunted on horseback is irretrievably lost. It suffices that the hunter is able to maintain a gentle trot for an hour and automatically he will catch the addax, the panic stricken antelope knowing that it is being pursued will flee desperately until it can go no farther."

The two most important zones for addax in the eastern sector of the range are the Ténéré region in Niger (to the east of the Aïr Massif), and the northern part of Tchad. Gillet defines the latter as comprising three areas "centred around Burka, Aska and Gassar to the north and west of Wadi Achim; around the northern part of the dunes of Djourab; and to the east and south-east of Largeau in the Mourdi Depression."

The last great addax reservoir in the western Sahara is the vast desert region, incorrectly named "El Djouf" on the maps, situated between the Mauritanian Adrar, the Tagant, the Dhar Tichit-Walata, the Azaouad and the Hank. This area, more than 200,000 square miles in extent, is uninhabited and totally devoid of water. Monod, who give this information, states that when crossing it a few years ago he had to travel about 560 miles between two wells. He noted that addax are abundant but are actively hunted by three groups of nomads—from the Adrar (especially Kedadra and Amgarij), from Tichit-Walata in the south, and from the Azaouad.

In summary, there are three principal areas in which efforts to conserve the addax should be concentrated: northern Tchad; the Ténéré region in Niger; and the area straddling the Mali-Mauritania frontier. Monod has repeatedly drawn attention to the particular obligations of the governments of Mauritania and Mali which share both the "privilege and the responsibility of possessing on their common border the last remaining large refuge for addax in the western Sahara. These two countries therefore have a very particular responsibility to the world for effectively safeguarding the species."

Proposals have been made to establish a huge game reserve of several million acres in northern Tchad, primarily for the protection of

the scimitar-horned oryx and the addax, but until there is more detailed information on the distribution and migratory movements of the herds it is difficult to know where to locate the boundaries. Despite its size, the proposed reserve would contain these species during only part of the year and it is therefore questionable whether a conventional game reserve, however large, would be adequate for the purpose. A further difficulty arises from the almost insuperable problem of law enforcement among nomadic tribes in remote parts of the Sahara, where for all practical purposes they are beyond reach of the law.

Many wild animal species have been reduced or eradicated because they are considered inimical to human progress. But this accusation cannot be levelled at the addax, an animal perfectly adapted and attuned to an ecological niche that is valueless in the conventional agricultural and pastoral sense. On the contrary, the addax is so highly specialized that it thrives under extreme environmental conditions which no domestic livestock could tolerate. It is one of the few animals capable as it were of converting desert into high quality protein, thus being of incomparable economic importance to the desert nomad, as well as fulfilling an important cultural role. Indeed, the traditional pattern of Saharan transhumance is almost symbiotically linked with the addax. The desert tribes themselves would be the main beneficiaries of any measures that would ensure the continuance of an animal which is virtually irreplaceable.

BONTEBOK

The genus *Damaliscus* includes four species: *D. lunatus*, the Sassaby; *D. korrigum*, the topi; *D. hunteri*, Hunter's hartebeest; and *D. dorcas*, which is divided into two subspecies, *D. d. dorcas*, the bontebok, and *D. d. phillipsi*, the blesbok.

The bontebok and the blesbok look very alike, and are often mistaken for one another. This has given rise to much confusion, which has persisted since the earliest records of the two animals.

The most obvious differences are that the pure-white rump patch of the bontebok is much more conspicuous than the pale rump patch of the blesbok; and the prominent white blaze on the bontebok's face differs from that of the blesbok by not being divided between the eyes. The bontebok is a rich dark brown colour, with the flanks and upper parts a glossy plum colour, the blesbok being a somewhat redder brown, lacking any purple gloss and with other less conspicuous differences. The bontebok's limbs are white below the knee, except for a brown stripe on the front part of its hind legs immediately above its hoofs. Its horns incline towards the lyre shape and are up to about 16 inches long.

Fossil evidence shows that the bontebok has existed in the same general region since Pleistocene times. When the first Europeans arrived at the Cape of Good Hope in the seventeenth century, it was restricted to a narrow strip of land in the south-western part of Cape Province between Swellendam and Caledon, between the mountain ranges in the north and the coastal belt in the south. But although the range was small, the animal was from all accounts abundant within this area.

Its relative the blesbok lived farther inland, in the highlands of the Karroo and the Transvaal. When the Cape colonists trekked to the Orange River and beyond, they assumed that the blesbok which inhabited this region was the same animal as the bontebok. An area of open plains to the south of the Orange River is known to this day as "bontebok flats". Selous described the blesbok as "once undoubtedly the most numerous of all African antelopes", but it was hunted so persistently that by the end of the nineteenth century it had ceased to exist in the wild state. Stringent protection has done much to restore numbers, however, and it is now a relatively common animal on many South African farms.

The blaauwbok (or blue antelope), *Hippotragus leucophaeus*, inhabited more or less the same area as the bontebok. This species was said to be restricted to the valley of the Soete-Melk in Swellendam district, and to the mountains between Swellendam and Algoa Bay. It was the first species of large African mammal to be exterminated after the start of European settlement at the Cape. The last specimen was shot in 1799 or 1800. In Renshaw's words: "So quickly· indeed was it exterminated . . . that it was hardly known before it had gone forever, and was for many years regarded, even by naturalists of the highest standing, as little more than a zoological myth. . . ."

The region inhabited by the bontebok was quickly taken over by settlement. With its very restricted range, the animal was particularly vulnerable to hunting, and before long had been severely reduced in numbers. Unrestricted hunting and pressure on the land forced the remnant into the sour lands of the coastal belt, where the poor grazing, deficiency of trace elements, and heavy parasitic infestations formed a combination of circumstances under which it was impossible for them to thrive. Bigalke shows that by 1835 the bontebok had been reduced to "a few herds inhabiting a small tract of country between the mountains and the sea-coast and bounded by the Breede and the Duivenhoek River".

In an attempt to preserve the few remaining animals, the Government imposed a penalty of 500 Rix dollars for unauthorized killing of a bontebok; but this measure did little to deter the local farmers from hunting. If it had not been for the initiative of a few interested landowners —principally the van der Byl and van Breda

DAMALISQUE BONTEBOK   *Damaliscus dorcas dorcas*   BONTEBOK

families—the species would certainly have been extinguished along with the blaauwbok and the quagga.

There are several different versions of the sequence of events which secured the bontebok from extinction. According to Selous, the credit belongs to Alexander van der Byl, who in 1864 while fencing his farm, Nachtwacht, near Bredasdorp, "conceived the idea of driving all the bontebok on the neighbouring plain within the enclosure. Circumstances favoured him, and he was able by a piece of good fortune, to drive the greater number of all the bonteboks still left alive into his own ground, within the enclosure. He puts the number that were thus secured at something like 300 *, and his nephews believe that there has been but little increase or decrease in their number since that time. I may not have seen all the bonteboks at Nachtwacht, but it certainly did not appear to me that there were anything like 300 of these animals on the enclosed ground at the date of my visit in 1895, and again in 1896. Mr. van der Byl's good example was followed by one of his neighbours, Dr. Albertyn, who also has now a small herd of bonteboks on his enclosed farm. Besides these carefully protected herds, there are a few still surviving on the plain, outside the enclosed farms, both in the neighbourhood of Bredasdorp, and near the village of Swellendam. Altogether, I doubt very much whether more than 300 of these animals are still in existence."

Despite stringent legal protection, numbers continued to decline. Bigalke quotes a report that in 1927 the total population stood at 121 bontebok on three farms in the Bredasdorp District and four farms near Swellendam. "It was clear, therefore, that if the animal was to survive in South Africa, it would have to be preserved on a national basis."

In 1930, in an attempt to meet the situation, the Government acquired 1,784 acres of land between Bredasdorp and Cape Agulhas for the specific purpose of preserving the bontebok.

* Another account states that this event took place in 1837, and Alexander van der Byl secured only 37 animals.

The following year this became the Bontebok National Park. At the time of its establishment the park contained 22 bontebok. By 1940 numbers had increased to the extent that the National Parks Board of Trustees adopted a policy of distributing surplus animals to local landowners and to suitable nature reserves in the southern part of Cape Province, within the original range of the species.

This system did not work out as had been hoped. Small herds on adjacent farms attempted to link up with each other, and many were killed or injured on the fences in the process. Moreover, there was a tendency for the males in these small enclosed groups to kill not only each other, but also calves. This policy had therefore to be abandoned.

In the Bontebok National Park all went well for a few more years: by the end of 1953 numbers had increased to about 120. Unfortunately the park was not well sited. During the winter much of it was inundated. Parasitic infestations spread in the land. The situation deteriorated so seriously that at the end of 1960 the authorites decided to transfer 61 bontebok to a newly-established national park near Swellendam. A smaller herd (of 11 animals) was also established on the Provincial Wildlife Farm de Hoop. Both these reserves are more favourably situated, and the animals thrived. By 1968 numbers at Swellendam had increased to 260; and the de Hoop herd reached a total of 70 in the same period, not counting about 20 animals which were distributed to other reserves and farms.

Other herds have been established in the Swellendam and Bredasdorp districts and elsewhere. Mr. F. W. M. Bowker, a landowner in the Grahamstown district, has been particularly successful at raising bontebok. Over a period of thirty years he succeeded by 1966 in building up a herd from a few animals to 200. Many bontebok from his herd have been distributed to other farms in the Eastern Cape. The success of this policy is shown by the satisfactory increase in overall numbers. Brand's 1961 census recorded 525 bontebok: since then numbers have increased to about 900.

As a result of these measures, the future of this subspecies appears to be assured.

WALIA IBEX

Capra walie

Ethiopia possesses two species of ibex: the walia, *Capra walie*, found only in the Simien Moutains; and the Nubian form, *Capra nubiana*, which ranges from Israel in the north through parts of the Arabian Peninsula into the Sudan, and reaches its southernmost limit in Eritrea.

The walia is larger and more powerfully built that the Nubian ibex. It stands about 38 inches at the shoulder, and has much more massive horns than the Nubian ibex—up to 45 inches long. Its general colour is a deep chestnut, with whitish under parts, and black and white markings on the front side of the legs. Adult females are paler and a good deal smaller than full-grown males. Males have a beard which becomes longer with age.

Some biologists give both the walia and the Nubian ibex the rank of full species: others classify them as races of a single wide-ranging species. The two animals differ not only in size and general appearance, but their ecological circumstances differ also. As Brown points out, the Nubian ibex is "an inhabitant of arid hills in Arabia, completely waterless for most of the time, whereas the walia lives in a relatively lush environment between 8,000 and 12,000 feet in a [50] inch rainfall, with abundant pasture and browse and water whenever required. The ecology of the habitats frequented by the two species is so different that it is difficult to believe that the one would thrive and breed in the habitat of the other."

The breeding habits are not well known. Females start breeding when about four years old; and in a good year most mature females have kids at foot. Single young appear to be the rule; and births are said to take place in inaccessible caves. Within an hour of birth the kids are able to accompany their mothers to the grazing grounds. After weaning, the immature animals of both sexes form loose yearling groups, usually in association with adult females. Mature males live either alone or in small groups, usually in secluded parts of the range.

Natural predation appears to be minimal. Brown observes that "apart from possible, but unconfirmed, predation by large birds of prey such as the Lammergeier *Gypaetus barbatus* and Verreaux's Eagle *Aquila verreauxi*, it seems unlikely that the walia has any natural enemies. Leopards are rare and could, in any event, hardly attack the walia in most of their precipitous haunt." Nevertheless, Nievergelt considers the leopard and possibly the serval to be the walia's main natural predators.

The walia ibex is confined to a narrow belt of precipitous crags and narrow ledges on the almost sheer cliff face, between the 8,000 and 11,000 foot levels, on the north-western escarpment of the Simien Mountains, in the Province of Begemder, Ethiopia, about 60 miles north-east of Gondar. When Maydon and Blaine visited the area in 1923, the walia occupied a larger range and was much more abundant than it is today.

The Simien Mountains, in Blower's words, are "one of the largest and certainly the most spectacular mountain massifs in Africa. They consist of a high undulating plateau deeply intersected by a number of rocky valleys, the average altitude of the plateau being 11,000–13,000 feet, but rising to 15,158 feet at its highest point [Ras Dedjen]. To the north and east the plateau drops away in immense vertical precipices 2,000–5,000 feet in height, which extend in an unbroken wall for some 40 kilometers or more, and are guarded by outlying pinnacles rising like immense Gothic cathedrals from the broken country beneath the cliffs almost to the

BOUQUETIN D'ÉTHIOPIE   *Capra walie*   WALIA IBEX

height of the plateau itself. This indescribably spectacular landscape is generally agreed by those who have seen both to exceed even the Grand Canyon in its breathtaking grandeur and beauty."

Brown considers the scenery to be "the most spectacular of its kind that I have seen anywhere, and certainly some of the most astonishing in the world. Maydon found that words failed him, and had to say, like me, that the Simien were like no other mountains to be seen anywhere."

But Simien is being rapidly devastated. The number of people living in the region has risen since the Second World War, with a corresponding increase in the herds of domestic livestock. Overgrazing and deforestation are widespread throughout the highlands. The forest is felled and burned primarily to increase the amount of land under cultivation; and where the land is too steep even for ox-drawn ploughs, the soil is tilled by hand. Even the most elementary rules of soil conservation are ignored. Steeply sloping land is frequently cultivated, often to the very edge of the cliffs, with the inevitable result that the soil, together with the natural vegetation which alone keeps it in place, is washed away. The area under cultivation must then be extended to compensate for the land which has been lost. At the upper levels the giant heath, twenty feet high, and other natural vegetation are cut for fuel, and cattle dung (which should be used to manure the soil) is collected for the same purpose. The idea of planting quick-growing trees for fuel does not seem to have been seriously considered.

Brown writes: "The extent of cultivation and grazing in the Simien highlands is alarming and it can be said that the cultivators, both at the lower levels and on the plateaux at 10,000 feet and above, are destroying or seriously damaging their own habitat with an energy and industry which would be highly commendable if it were not certain, in due course, to lead to large scale human tragedy. Cultivation extends in many areas to 12,000 feet, and slopes are being cultivated which cannot be cultivated by any method known to man without causing erosion. The mere act of ploughing throws clods and stones

downhill. As the soils are often not deep, a situation must inevitably arise in which rock is exposed on the steeper slopes and the large areas now under cultivation will have to be abandoned except for a few pockets where the soil is deeper or the slope more gentle."

The walia was originally distributed throughout the Simien Mountains. Nievergelt shows that the only part of the range where there is now any prospect of the species' survival is in an area of approximately 60 square miles along the escarpment from Sankaber, Geech, Emyet Gogo, and Amba Ras, as far as Chenek. A second small and isolated population lives at the foot of Silki Mountain, where Nievergelt saw 12 walia; but he concluded that "there is little hope for their future. Even worse is the facet of the whole range of escarpment around Ras Dedjen. I neither saw a walia nor could I find any sign of its existence."

The evidence of all who have been to Simien supports the view that the walia population has been heavily reduced since the 1920s. Brown conjectures that numbers are probably not a tenth of what they were at the time of Maydon's visit.

The decline of the walia is entirely due to indiscriminate killing. Hunting is not a new phenomenon; the local tribesmen have always hunted the animal for its meat, hide, and horns (which are valued as drinking vessels). But the rugged nature of the habitat made hunting exceptionally difficult, and this fact alone saved the walia from extermination. The introduction of sophisticated firearms during and after the

Second World War has, however, resulted in the situation becoming less favourable to the walia. Brown shows that pressure of hunting has made the upper and lower reaches of the escarpment untenable for the walia. Most of them now "frequent the middle levels of the precipice. . . . It is no light undertaking to ascend or descend the cliff into the main haunt of the walia. This is no doubt the reason why any survive at all."

The local people maintain that the species underwent a catastrophic decline during the Italian occupation of the country. At that time the Simien Range became a hide-out for guerilla fighters, many of whom spent a long period in the mountains, living to a large extent off the country. After the Second World War the species gained a short respite when the guerillas emerged from hiding and returned to their former mode of life. But this was not for long: once normal conditions had been re-established, the local people, armed with more efficient weapons than before, began hunting the ibex for food.

Brown explains that "it is convenient to blame the Italians for almost anything bad that has happened in Ethiopia, either directly or indirectly. The facts appear to be that legal protection by the Government means very little, that walia are hunted indiscriminately by local people, and that the main reason for their survival is that some of them, at least, live in places beyond the wit of man to reach without a great deal of trouble."

In theory the walia is protected by law, but in practical terms protection is merely nominal. Brown was "assured by the District Governor at Davarik [Debarek] that there were guards charged with the duty of protecting the animals. However, none of these guards contacted us, through we enquired about them." He concludes that "if protective edicts had gone out they had either not reached Geech or were largely ignored, and that the only thing that would cause any local hunter to spare a walia was difficulty in recovering the body. Our guide appeared to regard as absurd the idea that female walia with kids should be spared to breed some more. 'Someone else would shoot them before they could breed,' was his verdict."

For almost twenty years after the Second World War, reliable information on the walia ibex and other Ethiopian fauna was sparse. The walia was believed to be rare and endangered for which reason it was listed in the *Red Data Book*; but there was no positive information on which to gauge its status or to assess the measures needed for its effective protection. This uncertainty continued until October 1963, when Leslie Brown spent three weeks in Simien on an expedition which was partly financed by a grant from the World Wildlife Fund.

At about the same time, a UNESCO mission to Ethiopia, headed by Sir Julian Huxley, recommended the establishment of a conservation board with wide authority over wildlife, forests, and historic monuments. This was followed by the appointment of two consultants to advise the Government of Ethiopia on future policy. Ian Grimwood, former Chief Game Warden of Kenya, and Leslie Brown, former Chief Agriculturalist of Kenya, spent from late 1964 to early 1965 in Ethiopia. After undertaking a broad preliminary survey of the country's wildlife, they submitted detailed recommendations on the introduction of new legislation and the establishment of a system of national parks, including one in the Simien Mountains.

The primary purpose of the Simien Mountains National Park is to ensure the perpetuation of three mammals found only in Ethiopia: the walia ibex; the Simien fox, *Simenia simensis*; and the gelada baboon, *Theropithecus gelada*. An important additional function is to protect a variety of Afro-alpine flora in a setting of unsurpassed scenic splendour.

The proposed national park will cover the 60 square miles of precipitous terrain which forms the main walia habitat. An adjoining area of forest reserve will serve as a buffer zone. The Government of Ethiopia has approved this proposal in principle; but several years have elapsed without adequate practical steps being taken towards its implementation. This prolonged indecision reflects the lack of concern shown by responsible officials. Forestry officers appear indifferent to the eradication of the native forests; agricultural officers seem unmindful of the need to introduce improved methods of cultivation to reduce erosion; officials of the Ethiopian Wildlife Conservation Department disdain even to visit the area, which is potentially one of the great national parks of Africa.

An essential feature of the proposals submitted to the Ethiopian Government was the recommendation for a detailed ecological survey of the walia and its habitat, to form the framework of a management plan for the national park. Dr. Bernhard Nievergelt, an acknowledged authority on the Alpine ibex, was invited to undertake this work. The costs of the survey were met jointly by the World Wildlife Fund, the Swiss Foundation for Alpine Research, and the Swiss National Fund for the Promotion of Scientific Research. Nievergelt and his wife spent a year in Simien, from February 1968 to February 1969, working from a base they established at a height of over 11,000 feet on a plateau in the centre of the proposed national park, and close to the main walia habitat.

Nievergelt's work has provided much valuable material on the walia and its ecology, and has dispelled any remaining uncertainties about the measures that require to be taken for its effective protection. He has shown that the walia population is now no more than 150 individual animals. Despite the heavy depletion that has taken place over the last forty years, however, sufficient stocks remain for the survival of the species. Given adequate protection from hunting the walia should soon recover their numbers, and gradually reoccupy parts of their original range. But unless prompt and vigorous action is taken to give practical effect to the measures which the Ethiopian Government itself has already approved, the species will continue moving towards early extinction.

LONG-TAILED GROUND ROLLER *Uratelornis chimaera*

If the large island of Madagascar is of special interest to zoologists with its primitive mammals, especially its lemurs, ornithologists are no less attracted by its avifauna. While the Indonesian archipelagoes doubtless possess a greater wealth of bird life, out of 184 breeding species, 122 to 125, or more than two-thirds, are original and endemic to Madagascar. Amongst these are the ground rollers of which the five species constitute a family of the Coraciiforme order. Whereas four of them live in the rain forests, the fifth is confined to a small and very dry region in the south-west and is one of the island's rarest birds.

The *bokitsé* or *teroboky*, as the Malagasy call it, is found only on a strip of flat country some 125 miles long and barely 30 miles wide between the Fiherenana and Mangoky rivers, bordered on one side by the sea and by the savanna and mountains on the other. Due to its scattered distribution in this restricted area, the long-tailed ground roller population is small. Its habitat, dry because of the climate and sandy soil, resembles a forest or, more exactly, fairly thick scrub vegetation, 10 to 20 feet high, partially spiny and leafless in the dry season. The succulents, trees and bushes are plentiful and a characteristic element is the strange *Didierea madagascariensis*. The firm sand and dead leaves which partly cover the ground seem to be essential components of the biotope; an almost complete lack of herbaceous vegetation allows the long-tailed ground roller freedom of action when it moves around in the lower branchless zone under the thickets.

More than half this little bird's length is comprised by its tail which measures approximately eight inches. Its russet upper plumage,

bedecked with a complicated pattern of grey and black, gives it excellent camouflage. Otto Appert noted that it is almost invisible when it remains still under a bush against a background of dead leaves. In the play of light and shade of the forest, its white under-parts and pectoral collar hardly show. The characteristic blue of the rollers is most noticeable when the bird opens its wings for flight. Head erect, tail raised or lowered, this bird suggests a thrush rather than a roller. Like a blackbird, it searches for food by probing amongst the dead leaves with its beak; insects probably supply the major portion of its food and its activities are partly nocturnal.

Uratelornis has a stolid disposition. From the shadows it watches intruders, generally in silence, for a long time. It seldom flies, and then generally only to perch on lower branches, preferring to move around by running on its long legs. The species sometimes reveals its

presence by a series of "coucoucoucou" cries, rather like a native cuckoo, the toloho *(Centropus toulou)*. It is difficult to approach amongst the spiny trees, in the dense branches and lianas. Reproduction, about which little is known, begins just before the rainy season in October. According to Appert, from whom we have obtained most of our information, the couple dig a burrow more than three feet long in the sand; Lavauden says that the female lays three or four white eggs. We have no further details.

This species does not, in fact, appear to be threatened at present. Considered a rare species because of its limited distribution, it is evidently bound to a very special habitat. If this were destroyed, it would be impossible for the bird to adapt itself to different ecological conditions. There is, of course, the possibility of deforestation, the calamity of Madagascar, but, luckily, the dry south-west regions of the island, where the sandy soil is not favourable for cattle raising or agriculture, have been spared. Moreover, as the botanist Perrier de la Bathie pointed out, the dryness prevents both grasses from developing there and fires from ravaging the almost fire-proof woods. Father Otto Appert also confirmed that during the seven years he spent between the Mangoky and Fiherenana rivers, he noticed no change in the extent of the *Didierea* forests where the long-tailed ground roller lives. He did not see fires destroy them or plantations replace them, except in small areas of no interest. Finally, if the villagers in this sparsely inhabited country occasionally killed birds for food, this did not seem to be of great significance to the future of the species.

Contrary to observations made in other forest areas on the large island, and which are to be deplored, the primitive vegetation is better conserved here than elsewhere and the status of the *Uratelornis* has remained unchanged for a long time.

In spite of this encouraging stability, great care should be taken of a natural habitat, still intact and highly original. Where its fauna and flora are concerned, the saying "prevention is better than cure", is still valid in this apparently desolate region peculiar to Madagascar.

Uratelornis chimaera

ROLLIER TERRESTRE
LONG-TAILED GROUND ROLLER

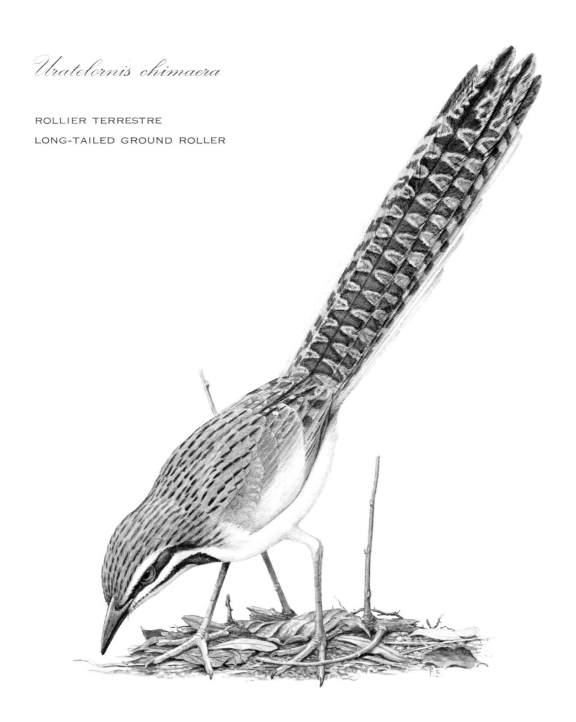

OCEANIA

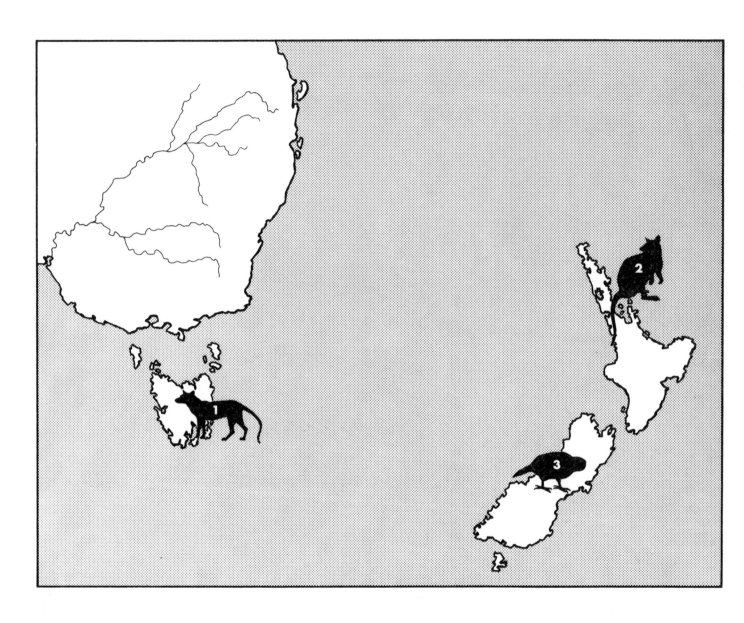

1, Thylacine — 2, White-throated wallaby — 3, Kakapo

THYLACINE

Thylacinus cynocephalus

Tasmania has the distinction 'of possessing the largest of the living carnivorous marsupials, the thylacine, known by a variety of vernacular names, such as "tiger", "wolf" and "hyaena", all of which are derived from the combination of two notable characteristics: the animal's predatory habits and its distinctive dorsal stripes.

It is certainly a remarkable creature, superficially resembling the wolf but in no way related to it, and an outstanding example of parallel development; that is to say the occurrence of unrelated animals in widely separated parts of the world which fill similar ecological niches and, in the course of evolutionary development, have come to bear a marked resemblance to each other, both in physical appearance and in habits.

The very apt scientific name means "pouched dog with wolf head". The animal is a little smaller than a wolf (though early accounts mention specimens sometimes measuring six feet from snout to tail), tawny grey in colour, with up to eighteen conspicuous dark brown transverse bands commencing at the root of the tail, extending across the rump and flanks, and becoming progressively narrower as they reach the shoulder. The massive head is remarkably wolf-like, the jaws having an unusually wide gape, almost to the ears. The tail resembles that of a kangaroo, being unusually broad at the base and so inflexible that it is incapable of being wagged. Its rigidity is such that if grasped by the tail the animal is unable to turn on its captor. The hind-quarters also have kangaroo-like characteristics, and early reports state that when hard pressed the thylacine would rise on its hind legs and bound along in the manner of a kangaroo.

Almost nothing is known of the thylacine's life history and reproductive biology, as at the time the animal was common and could so easily have been studied, little thought seems to have been given other than how best to accomplish its destruction. The pouch, enclosing four mammae, is situated forward of the hind limbs, with the opening to the rear. Three or four young constitute the normal litter, which, after leaving the pouch, are deposited by the mother in a secure hiding place.

Before Tasmania became separated from Australia, the thylacine had a wide distribution. The fossil record shows that during the Pleistocene, and possibly earlier, it occurred on the Australian mainland. The ancestral range has recently been further extended by the discovery in 1960 of the left half of a mandible of *Thylacinus* in the Eastern Highlands District of New Guinea.

The extinction of the mainland thylacine has been attributed to the introduced dingo, reputedly a more successful predator with which it could not compete. It continued to thrive in Tasmania, however, and was still abundant at the commencement of European settlement.

Under natural conditions the thylacine favoured the open savanna woodlands, where kangaroo and wallaby, which formed its chief prey species, were most abundant. Such open country was of course the land most in demand for stock raising.

The early settlers' practice of burning off the bush and scrub by way of clearing the land for pastoralism not only radically altered the complexion of the countryside but, in the process, eradicated much indigenous wildlife, with the inevitable result that in the settled areas the thylacine was obliged to seek alternative prey. It developed a taste for fresh-killed sheep, which it found easier prey than the native animals, and which at once brought the thylacine into sharp conflict with the sheep farmer. It was reputed to kill not merely to satisfy its immediate requirements but for the sheer pleasure of killing, and one thylacine could slaughter a considerable number of sheep in a single night. This was a sufficient reason for the "tiger" to be systematically hunted down, and either destroyed or driven from the open savannas which comprised its natural environment into the western forests where prey was scarce and conditions were substantially less suitable for existence.

The thylacine's partiality for mutton was not the only reason for its downfall. It was also unpopular because of its habit of pilfering trap lines, a practice that could hardly be expected to endear it to the trappers. In Sharland's words, "a trapper would seldom begin the business of snaring without first laying poison baits in the hope of clearing his territory of these unwelcome predators. Over the years, when trapping was lucrative for the professional bushman, hundreds of tigers must have been destroyed in this way." It was also customary for extra powerful snares to be set at regular intervals along the length of the trap line. Thylacines caught in this way were usually too severely injured to be of much use to zoological gardens, even if the trapper could have bothered to transport them.

As settlement expanded, demands for the thylacine's extermination became more insistent, and it was destroyed at every opportunity and by any means. An indication of the scale of the slaughter can be gathered from one man's claim to have killed twenty-four in a day. It was sometimes hunted with packs of dogs, but few dogs would willingly risk an encounter with a mature "tiger". However, it seems to have been easily snared.

Destruction was encouraged by the provision of a bounty. Guiler states that this system was first introduced by the Van Diemen's Land Company in 1840, payment being on a graduated scale of "six shillings per scalp for less than 10 scalps, eight shillings each for 10 to 20, and ten shillings each for more than 20 scalps". In 1888 a government bounty was brought in, the rate being £1 for an adult and 10s. for an immature thylacine. This proved a lucrative side-line for shepherds, who would go the rounds of the district exhibiting the severed head to various landowners, obtaining a reward from each before finally claiming the bounty. Official statistics show that between 1888 and 1909 (the year the bounty was withdrawn), up to 1914, 2268 thylacines were killed (including 84 for which bounty was paid by the Van Diemen's Land Company). The true figure was certainly substantially higher.

Although hunting was widespread and continuous it was not, however, the principal cause of near-extinction. The thylacine appeared to maintain itself at a satisfactory level until about 1910. The population then underwent a drastic decline, so sudden and so widespread that it could only have been attributable to disease, possibly distemper. Guiler alludes to a grazier's statement that all the Dasyures were similarly affected at the same time.

The last living "tiger" was obtained in 1933 in a trapper's snare in the Florentine Valley, a few miles to the west of Mt. Field National Park. By then the species was widely assumed to have been exterminated; but a small remnant which had been driven from the pastoral lands managed to cling to existence in the more inaccessible and inhospitable parts of the country.

During the last thirty years occasional reports of sightings or footprints have been received chiefly from the north and north-west of the country, and from the south-west. On investigation many have proved false, but some are unquestionably authentic.

The south-west of Tasmania is a high rainfall region, most of it comprising rain forest and swampy button grass plains, a description that is applicable to much of the west coast. This explains why it was not taken up for settlement. The reasons that make it unattractive for settlement render it equally unsuitable for the thylacine, and the few that have managed to survive must be having a desperate struggle for existence, because of severe climatic and environmental conditions and dearth of natural prey.

LOUP MARSUPIAL   *Thylacinus cynocephalus*   THYLACINE

The Tasmanian authorities have long been aware of the need to do everything possible to safeguard the surviving remnant. The thylacine has been legally protected since 1936, with heavy penalties imposed for any infringement of the law. In 1937, and again in 1938, expeditions were dispatched into the huge natural amphitheatre, up to 40 miles long and 25 miles wide, bounded by the Raglan, Frenchman's Cap, Prince of Wales and King William Ranges, and including the Cardigan and Jane Rivers, to search for evidence of the animal's existence, but found nothing more substantial than footprints. This part of the country is exceptionally harsh. Parts of it have never been visited, even by trappers and prospectors. It is rugged and broken, covered with dense, almost impenetrable, bush which makes movement exceptionally difficult and in places impossible. In 1945-46 a third expedition traversed the same general area with equally disappointing results.

The accidental killing of a young male thylacine at Sandy Cape on the west coast in 1961 encouraged the Tasmanian Government to support the Animals and Birds Protection Board in organizing further expeditions, designed to obtain positive evidence either by capturing or photographing a specimen. In October 1963 an expedition led by Dr. Eric R. Guiler, concentrated on the Sandy Cape area, later moving to a private property on the north-west coast where

since 1956 there have been several reports of sightings, footprints and droppings.

In spite of working for an extended period under intensely difficult conditions, the expedition failed to obtain the evidence it sought, but the Board intends to undertake further investigations. In Dr. Guiler's words: "At the moment we know of two positive lairs which are used intermittently by thylacines, and we know of many areas in the country where animals have been seen or tracked. We hope that our luck will change."

For many years the Animals and Birds Protection Board has been actively urging that large areas to the east of Macquarie Harbour should be reserved for the thylacine. The Board's persistence was finally rewarded in 1966 when an area of 1,600,000 acres in the South-West District was proclaimed a sanctuary. The reserve includes the areas traversed by the three expeditions already mentioned, and a large part of the region in which the thylacine is considered to have the greatest prospect of survival.

This is an extremely important development, not only for the survival of the thylacine, but also for the protection of other indigenous fauna, including the echidna, or spiny anteater, *Tachyglossus setosus*, and the duck-billed platypus *Ornithorhynchus anatinus*, as well as the rare Tasmanian ground parrot *Pezoporus wallicus leachi*, all of which live in this region.

WHITE-THROATED WALLABY   *Macropus parma*

When first discovered by Gould the white-throated, or Parma, wallaby occurred in two separate zones in New South Wales: the Illawarra District, extending southward to Nowra and Sassafaras; and the Dorrigo area in the north-eastern part of the state. These two localities are isolated from each other by approximately 300 miles of country in which the animal has never been recorded.

This is a small wallaby weighing up to about 10 pounds, very distinctive, the shoulders and

back being uniformly rich brown in colour, with a fairly well-defined dark stripe on the nape of the neck, commencing between the ears and extending to the shoulders. The throat up to the chin is white: there is also a white stripe on the cheeks, and the tail has a whitish tip.

Since the time of its discovery the species seems always to have been uncommon and local in distribution. In the first half of the present century only two specimens were collected, both taken in 1932 in the Dorrigo area, though this information was not recorded for a further sixteen years when Tate published his account in 1948. By that time the species was assumed to be extinct.

The disappearance of the animal is almost certainly attributable to loss of habitat. The Illawarra District was originally covered with rain forest, but this was virtually eradicated in the course of agricultural development.

In 1958, Dr. W. D. L. Ride, Director of the Western Australian Museum, formed the opinion that certain wallaby skins emanating from Kawau Island, New Zealand, and labelled *Macropus dorsalis* had been wrongly identified and in all probability were *Macropus parma*, a much smaller animal; but as the skulls were missing he could not be certain. Ride suggested that Dr. D. A. Wodzicki should visit Kawau to search for the animal, which he did in 1961 and again in 1965. It was not until his third trip in May 1966, however, that he succeeded in procuring five specimens, which were at once sent to Australia for positive identification. After careful comparison with existing museum specimens and skeletal material, it was definitely established that the Kawau wallaby was the supposedly extinct *M. parma*.

Kawau Island, situated about 30 miles north of Auckland in the Hauraki Gulf, is about five miles long by three miles wide and covers approximately 5,120 acres. It was purchased from the Maoris in 1837, largely for its mineral rights, and for a time was mined for copper. Later, in 1862, the island became the property of Sir George Grey, who introduced a number of exotic animals and plants, including five species of Australian marsupials, among them a small wallaby of unknown origin. Early accounts of these introductions were imprecise regarding both the source and the identity of some of the species released.

The wallabies thrived to the extent that Sir George Grey's successors regarded them as pests. The new owners encouraged shooting parties and even employed contractors to exterminate the animals, but, although there was heavy slaughter, some wallabies survived and the population remained in being despite the most determined efforts to destroy it.

After 1910, Kawau was subdivided into several smaller estates. More recently, as sheep farming became less profitable, much of the island was planted to exotic pines. Measures to reduce damage to the young plantations and newly established pastures necessitated constant attempts to destroy the wallaby and other wild fauna by a variety of methods.

Between 1965 and 1968 an intensive eradication campaign was undertaken on Kawau, mainly by poisoning but also involving night shooting, in the course of which 13,000 wallabies were killed. This figure does not include the large number shot by sportsmen and private persons, both from land and from boats along the coast, for which records were not kept: nor does it include wallabies that were live-trapped for export to zoos, estimated to amount to several hundred.

An interesting feature of this situation is that for a number of years certain New Zealand animal dealers had been offering white-throated wallabies for sale, and several zoos had purchased them. Conservationists were so certain that the species was extinct, however, that the dealers' assertion was attributed to mistaken identity and was not therefore taken seriously.

WALLABY À GORGE BLANCHE   *Macropus parma*   WHITE-THROATED WALLABY

The position today is that *M. parma* is the second most abundant species on Kawau after *M. eugenii*. The island also contains a population of the brush-tailed rock wallaby, *Petrogale penicillata*, another marsupial which has been greatly reduced in its homeland. The gradual modification of the natural cover in the course of land clearance and agricultural development has destroyed the best wallaby habitat, however, and rendered the island less favourable to *M. parma*.

Many of the exotic species in New Zealand including all wallabies, have been classified as noxious pests, and every encouragement is given to their destruction. The large-scale ravages caused by introduced animals fully justify this policy. As soon as the identity of the Kawau Island wallaby had been positively established, however, the New Zealand Forest Service took prompt action to ensure that it was not destroyed. Since January 1969 it has been officially protected on the island, though, as Wodzicki points out, only experienced shooters are likely to be able to distinguish the white-throated from the dama wallaby.

The New Zealand Forest Service has declared that this prohibition will remain in force until sufficient animals have been sent to Australia to re-establish a breeding colony, or, alternatively, until the Australian authorities indicate that they have secured adequate stocks from other sources. This latter provision arises from the possibility that the Parma wallaby may conceivably have survived in New South Wales. There have been several unconfirmed reports of small wallabies resembling *parma* in densely wooded country not far from places in which it was known to occur a century ago.

Not all the coastal forest of New South Wales has been destroyed. Several sizeable tracts remain which are almost unexplored in the zoological sense. Because of the possibility that *M. parma* may have survived in secluded parts of this coastal region, measures are being taken to carry out a detailed study throughout the historical range of the species with the purpose of ascertaining whether a wild population exists, and of selecting suitable areas as potential nature reserves. Any decision on the question of re-introductions into Australia will be dependent on the outcome of this survey. The Australian authorities are understandably reluctant to introduce specimens of unknown origin from New Zealand so long as there is a possibility that the original wild stock is extant in New South Wales.

KAKAPO   *Strigops habroptilus*

The islands of New Zealand, cut off from other land masses perhaps about 70 million years ago, possessed a unique terrestrial fauna before the arrival of man. Indeed, the only mammals living there were two species of bats. In the absence of carnivora, birds incapable of flying were able to develop; for example, the famous moas or dinornis, runners deprived of fore-limbs, of which the largest species attained a height of 12 feet.

This giant seems to have disappeared before men (probably of Polynesian origin) arrived in the tenth century. But even in the stone age, invaders hunted the moas to the extent of exterminating them in three centuries. The Maoris, their successors, were not without responsibility either for the decline of other vulnerable species, and particularly the parrot, to which they gave the name of kakapo.

From the end of the eighteenth century, the arrival of the first Europeans brought about a zoological upheaval of another kind. In 1774, Captain Cook landed on these islands with domestic animals such as pigs, sheep and goats. Before long, in addition to dogs and rats introduced earlier by the Maoris, there were also cats and ferrets, terrible predators, which, in taking to the wild, reproduced to the point of constituting an extreme danger for all the terrestrial birds poorly equipped to escape from them. Throughout the nineteenth century, also, the British colonists contrived to "enrich" New Zealand by introducing mammals and birds imported from several continents.

Today, the New Zealand fauna comprises at least 65 flourishing foreign species out of more than 175 on which acclimatization was attempted. From the Alpine chamois to the Australian opossum, from the European yellow bunting to the Canadian goose, it is a zoological miscellany. But the endemic fauna has greatly suffered from predation and competition from alien animals and birds, as well as from the upsetting of the natural balance in the habitats because of these intruders. At least 11 species of birds have disappeared from New Zealand since the beginning of the nineteenth century.

Such is the destiny of the kakapo. With a maximum length of about two feet, this ground parrot has radiating wreaths of feathers around the eyes, black hairy feathers on each side of the beak and a soft plumage which gives it a somewhat owl-like look. The kakapos are mainly nocturnal. Their back and wings are a rich moss-green flecked with brown and black, providing excellent camouflage when they hide during the day between the roots of trees or in mossy gaps. Their stumpy wings do not allow them to fly, although they help for balancing when climbing with their feet and beak and they can be used for slowing up a fall when they regain the ground from the trees. They can also travel quickly downhill by alternately running and gliding. When Julius van Haast described these birds' habits in 1863, he was amazed to find they forgot they had wings. He saw his first kakapo perched ten feet from the ground in a native fuchsia tree eating berries: when it saw him, the bird threw itself off the tree like a stone without even opening its wings and disappeared under some large rocks. Another bird released in an open space escaped by running like a chicken towards the nearest thicket.

If these parrots are practically unable to fly, they can move around by walking and climbing. At night they cover considerable distances in search of berries, seeds, leaves, flowers and moss, which are their main food; however, they occasionally eat lizards and other small creatures. At dusk, the kakapos emerge from their daytime hiding-places in clefts or fissures in rocks and holes under the trees. In single file they make their way through the forest to the sub-alpine levels, making a strange procession accompanied by incessant croakings and gruntings. Their regular comings and goings cut well-defined tracks along which they peck at small obstructions as they pass. Reischek, who observed them in the high mountains of South Island in 1884, saw them pass in the moonlight, in single file, like greenish ghosts, across steep slopes and snow masses. When daylight overtakes them before they reach their usual shelter, they dig a hole if, full of berries, they are not content to slumber among the shrubby trees. In winter, they hole up cosily under thick bushes covered with snow.

The species was formerly widespread on the islands, in all the beech-tree *Nothofaqus* forests that cover the flanks of the mountains. Heavy rainfall (as much as 150 inches a year) keep these dense woods extremely humid and mosses and ferns conceal a rocky and uneven surface. Higher up, the forests give way to sub-alpine shrubs and alpine grasses beyond which are snowy peaks up to 10,000 feet or more. Although the kakapos' habitat extends as low as sea-level in the Fiordland, it is mainly mountainous, often impossible for man to cross, and with a harsh climate. For these reasons, it is difficult to observe this nocturnal bird or even to know whether it still exists.

These strange parrots, living apart from man, are not at all shy. Several naturalists have related how they were able to take them in their hands, even to stroke them with no reaction other than pecks and raucous cries. Nevertheless, we have very little information on reproduction. Henry's claim that breeding takes place in alternate years has not yet been confirmed.

At the end of November—during the southern summer—the males move up to the higher slopes, to the undergrowth of shrubby trees; from there, they call to the females hidden in the forests below. Their deep, slow muffled cries repeated five or six times are said to be audible

KAKAPO   *Strigops habroptilus*   KAKAPO

up to a distance of six miles. In December or January, the female lays two to four white eggs, either in a burrow up to six feet deep which it has dug, or in crevices amongst tree roots or in a hollow tree. The period of incubation is unknown and there is a high mortality rate among young birds before they learn to forage for themselves. These factors seem to prove a low reproduction rate, a biological element which has led to the tragic diminution of this species.

Originally, the kakapo lived in the two larger islands as well as in Stewart Island and perhaps Chatham Island. The Maoris had probably already reduced the numbers of these parrots by hunting them for their flesh and feathers, the latter being used for making coats for the Maori chiefs; the dogs and rats they brought may also have caused a great reduction. From the middle of the nineteenth century, the decline has accelerated. The subsequent introduction of carnivora, especially ferrets, weasels and martens, was disastrous for the defenceless kakapos. Another factor was deforestation which considerably reduced their habitat. At the beginning of colonization, the forest surface was estimated at 100,000 square miles; in 1922, only 29,000 square miles remained, that is, less than 30 per cent. The competition for food with the deer and other herbivorous animals introduced has perhaps exercised a negative influence, while the wild pig destroyed the kakapos' nests. Finally, the species has also suffered from wanton hunting, either for specimens to sell to museums abroad, or for their excellent flesh, or merely for the pleasure of killing unusual game.

The disappearance of the kakapo was not immediately evident, due to their wary habits. They were still abundant in certain parts towards the end of the nineteenth century, but the last sighting in North Island was in 1927 and William confirms its extinction there in 1930. Although some evening "boomings" were reported in 1961, the chances of survival on this island are almost non-existent. There are perhaps still some birds on Stewart Island where cries were last heard in 1959. South Island, the largest and most mountainous, seems to be the ultimate refuge; eight localities were known in 1950, most of which were in the high

mountains of the Fiordland covered with thick forests. In 1960, the population was estimated at less than 200 parrots, in 1961 at less than 100, of which 30 lived in the Cleddau Valley. These estimates are very approximate as these regions are rarely visited and research on such a bird is difficult. However, it can be seen that the kakapo is in danger of complete extinction.

Unlimited protection has been given to these parrots by law, but it is almost impossible to suppress their enemies, in particular the too numerous carnivora to which they so frequently fall victim. Breeding in captivity has been attempted several times, but without success. The Wild Life Branch of the New Zealand Internal Affairs Department captured five kakapos in 1961, but all were males and four quickly died. At the beginning of the century, other attempts at reintroduction also failed. From 1894 to 1908, no less than 370 parrots were captured to be released at Dusky Sound, from where Gray described the species in 1845. All these birds disappeared, obviously eliminated by the predation of weasels which swarm in these parts. Another unsuccessful attempt of this kind was made in North Island.

In view of the reduced numbers of surviving kakapos, these disappointing experiments were abandoned in order to concentrate on research efforts in the Fiordland. It is in its natural habitat that the species has the greatest chance of survival, but for how much longer?

OCEANS

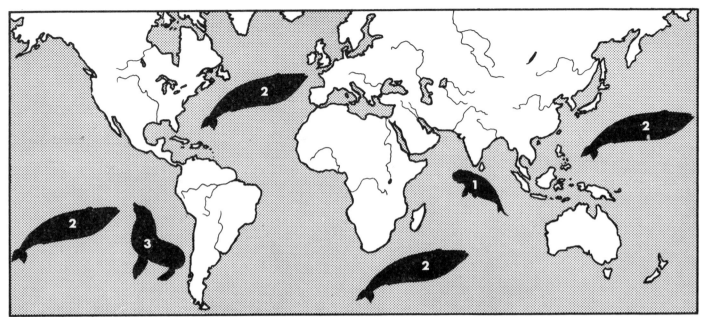

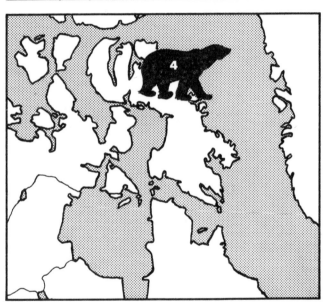

1, Dugong — 2, Blue whale — 3, Juan Fernandez fur seal — 4, Polar bear — 5, Mediterranean monk seal

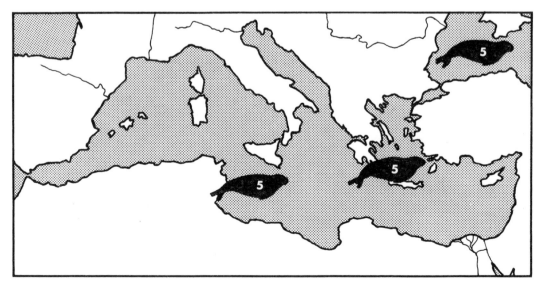

POLAR BEAR

Thalarctos maritimus

The polar bear is one of the largest living carnivorous land mammals, and is rivalled in size only by the huge brown bears of Alaska. Adult males are substantially larger than females, and usually weigh 1,000 pounds, although much heavier weights have been recorded. Mature animals stand about 5 feet at the shoulder and are 7 to 8 feet or more in length; but some are bigger. The fur is uniformly white tinged with yellow, the neck and body long and slender, the head relatively small, the limbs powerful, and the feet broad with fur-covered soles.

The species exists only in and around the Arctic Ocean, well beyond the limits of international territorial boundaries. Individual animals have been seen as far as 88° North, but such reports are exceptional. Polar bears live for much of the year in the pack ice, and are more at home in the sea than on land. They are exceptionally powerful swimmers and are frequently seen many miles from the nearest land, as well as being capable of swimming submerged for long distances. The cubs take to the water at an early age, and when tired climb on their mothers' backs to rest.

The polar bear is the most carnivorous of all the bears. It subsists very largely on several species of seal, particularly the ringed seal, *Phoca hispida*. It therefore favours stretches of open water frequented by seals, and where pack ice is present to facilitate hunting. From autumn through winter to spring seals form by far the most important item of diet; but when the ice breaks up during the summer the bears are compelled to leave the ocean and move to land, where suitable food is limited. During this lean period they eat berries, roots, grass, lichen and other vegetation, or almost anything else that happens to come their way, including carrion. There are numerous accounts of bears congregating in large numbers around dead whales, walruses, or other animals. Loughrey mentions one occasion when 42 polar bears were seen gathered around the carcass of a whale stranded on the shore of Southampton Island.

Distribution of the polar bear is largely regulated by the occurrence of seals; but during part of each year it is also governed by the animal's need for land, particularly when seals are scarce and alternative sources of food have to be found, as well as during the denning season. But the polar bear's ecological requirements mean that it uses only a relatively small portion of the total land area available in the Arctic.

In Canada mating takes place in the spring when the young seals, or "whitecoats", are plentiful on the pack ice. According to Harington, "the gestation period averages about eight months, and although there is no scientific proof of delayed implantation in polar bears, there is good reason to believe that it exists and that embryonic development begins about late September or early October".

Denning may start in October, the young being born mainly in December. Pedersen believes that twin births are normal, single young being less frequent, and triplets unusual. Uspensky shows that on Wrangel Island almost half the females bear only a single cub. The new-born cubs—like those of all members of the bear family—are tiny. At birth they are about 10 inches long and weigh about 1 ½ pounds. They are blind and deaf for the first month of their lives, but develop rapidly on the rich milk provided by their mothers, which, in Harington's words, "has the appearance and consistency of cow's cream, smells somewhat like seal, and tastes like cod-liver oil". By the time the cubs leave the den, at the age of 2 or 3 months, they are about 2 feet in length, weigh from 20 to 30 pounds, and are so swift that a man has some difficulty in catching them.

The family leaves its den in March or April, and moves towards the sea to hunt for seals. The cubs remain with their mothers, and hunt as family units, until the following season. Harington states that they "are usually abandoned in the late summer or autumn when they are approaching two years of age. At this stage they are extremely vulnerable, for if they do not starve during the winter, they may be killed by older bears or human hunters."

With the onset of winter, pregnant females move inland to seek out denning sites, usually remaining fairly close to the coast but sometimes going many miles from the sea. During the whole of the denning period they subsist entirely on the thick layers of fat which have accumulated in their own bodies during the previous summer.

Opinions differ on the frequency of reproduction. Some biologists state that it takes place in alternate years; but both Uspensky and Harington believe that an adult female does not normally breed more often than every third year, unless she loses her cubs. "This accounts for the rather slow rate at which depleted populations may revive."

Opinions also differ on the question of whether both sexes or only the pregnant females go through a dormant period in winter. Uspensky's observations have shown that dens on Wrangel Island are used exclusively by cubbing females. A different situation prevails in more northerly latitudes, however, where severe cold or blizzards can cause both males and dry females to take temporary shelter in snow drifts; but they emerge as soon as conditions improve in order to continue the constant search for food.

The largest polar bear population is found in the Canadian Arctic, where Harington estimates the total at about 6,000. The most productive polar bear area by his definition is contained within a quadrangle extending from 63° North to 75° North, and from 60° West to 95° West. "Denning seems to be commonest on northern Baffin Island, Southampton Island, Simpson Peninsula, and the smaller islands near Cornwallis Island."

Protective measures taken by the Canadian Government include the prohibition of bear hunting for sport in Manitoba, Ontario, Quebec and the Northwest Territories. The only people permitted to hunt the animal in Canada are Eskimos, Indians, and the very small number of holders of general hunting licences.

The economic and cultural values of the polar bear to Canada's coastal Eskimos are emphasized by Loughrey: "It occupies the place in their legends that the wolf does in the legends of the North American Indians. Primitive hunting of the polar bear was a hazardous occupation, and to kill one of these animals was a mark of distinction for the hunter. In the winter an Eskimo might hunt bears by chasing them with his dogteam. When the team commenced to overtake the bear he would cut one or several of his dogs free of the sled so that they might run ahead and hold the bear at bay. When the bear was at last brought to bay the hunter approached and attempted to kill it with his long-handled lance while the dogs kept it preoccupied. There are even stories of famous hunters, armed only with a long-bladed snow knife, who were able to kill a bear by ducking under the raking claws of the upright bear to stab and fatally wound it. In the summer they killed swimming bears from their kayaks. At present some of the northern Eskimos still hunt bears in the winter with their dogteams, but they now use a high powered rifle rather than a lance to deliver the *coup de grace*."

Loughrey also enumerates some of the items formerly made by the Eskimos from the skin, including clothing, bedding and sledge covers. "At present less use is made of the bear skin as an article of clothing because it is heavy and difficult to sew, but these fine robes still find their use in the Eskimo economy. By far the most important value of the bear to the Eskimo is for the meat which is consumed by both humans and dogs." The same author stresses that any plan to manage the polar bear for the benefit of the Eskimos must not lose sight of the fact that "the meat of the polar bear is of more importance to them than the money that they might derive from the sale of skins".

So long as the few Eskimos and Indians inhabiting the Arctic lived in harmony with their harsh environment, their predation on the bear and on the other wild animals with which they shared their habitat did no harm. During the last few years, however, there has been a strong tendency for the indigenous people to turn from the traditional subsistence economy to a more sophisticated mode of life; a trend which has been greatly stimulated by the search for minerals, culminating in the discovery of vast

OURS BLANC   *Thalarctos maritimus*   POLAR BEAR

oil deposits in northern Alaska. Increasing sophistication includes greater mobility made possible by vehicles such as the "snowmobile", which have opened previously impenetrable parts of the Arctic to exploitation.

The polar bear can tolerate subsistence hunting; but it is practically defenceless against hunting with precision weapons from powered boats (which have become increasingly popular in some parts of the Arctic) or from aircraft. In Alaska, subsistence hunting by Eskimos is now a relatively minor part of the total kill. The emphasis has shifted to hunting by affluent non-resident sportsmen, many of whom hunt from aircraft and kill the bears on the offshore pack ice. This method of hunting is no longer permitted over the mainland and territorial waters, but there is nothing to prevent it from being used in international waters beyond the three-mile limit. The Government of Alaska has introduced increasingly restrictive regulations, including the total prohibition on shooting of cubs and females, and a close season during the summer. No trophy hunter may shoot more than one polar bear every four years, and no guide may escort more than six hunters each year. The total number of professional guides is also rigorously controlled.

The economic importance of the polar bear is stressed by Flyger who states that "their hides, depending on size and condition, have a retail value of between $300 and $800 apiece*. Hunters pursuing polar bears for sport in Alaska or Norway may bring up to $1,500 or $2,000 into either of these countries for each bear shot, in the form of revenue from licences, food and lodging, guide fees, and other expenditures, Hunters travelling to Alaska and harvesting 300 or more bears bring into the state something like $500,000 every year. Because polar bears are one of the more easily exploited resources of the Arctic, serious consideration must be given to the economic aspect in any management plan concerning this species."

The average overall annual kill of polar bears has been estimated by Harington at about

1,300, of which 600 are from Canada, 200 from Alaska, 300 from the Norwegian Arctic, and 150 from Greenland. These figures need to be seen against the total world population, which both Uspensky and Harington agree is probably about 10,000, of which more than half are in Canada.

Uspensky believes that the range of the polar bear is slowly decreasing. Climatic conditions in the Far North have become progressively milder during the last century. Water temperatures around the fringes of the Arctic have risen sufficiently to cause the pack ice to recede, and the arctic cod (which favours very cold waters) to move farther north. This fish is the principal food of the ringed seal, which therefore follows; and the polar bear is obliged to conform. The disappearance of the arctic cod from the coastal waters of Greenland has coincided with the marked decline of the polar bear which Spärck shows to have taken place in Greenland since the 1930s. This has been particularly pronounced along the west coast and the southern part of the east coast, where he estimates the average annual kill to have dropped by almost 90 per cent. Other factors have contributed to the general decline, in particular the increase in the numbers of humans and domestic livestock in the Arctic, which has resulted in a higher incidence of disease, notably trichinosis.

Concern at the deteriorating status of the polar bear led the 1955 I.U.C.N. General Assembly to adopt a resolution recommending the Arctic countries to take effective measures to safeguard the species. The following year the Russian Parliament adopted a special decree imposing a ban on the shooting of polar bears throughout the Soviet Arctic. At the same time the catching of cubs was prohibited except under special licence. As a result of these protective measures, the bear population in the Soviet Union has remained stable since 1960, and may have increased slightly.

Other constructive measures taken by the Soviet Union include the establishment in 1960 of a nature reserve on Wrangel Island, one of the most important denning grounds in the Soviet Union—others are on Franz Josef Land, Novaya Zemlya, Severnaya Zemlya, and the

---

* Pelts appear to have a lower value in Canada, where "prices vary from $70 to $200" (Harington).

New Siberian Islands. Approximately two hundred dens have recently been identified on Wrangel and the neighbouring island of Herald. Uspensky estimates that approximately 10 per cent of the pregnant females occurring in the Soviet Arctic use Wrangel Island for denning, a fact which underlines the importance of this reserve to the species. Everything possible is done to maintain the most favourable conditions for the polar bear, including such measures as the banning of motor vehicles and dog-drawn sledges from known denning areas.

In the Norwegian Arctic, Kong Karl's Land has been a designated polar bear reserve since 1939, and certain limitations have been imposed on the capture of cubs—until the 1960s many sealing vessels made a useful supplementary income from the capture and sale of cubs. Otherwise, polar bears may be hunted throughout the year, the only restriction being a bag limit of one bear for each foreign sportsman. The Norwegian authorities have, however, announced their intention of introducing new regulations to control both the numbers killed and the methods of hunting.

In Greenland, policy is governed by the paramount need to maintain the polar bear primarily for aboriginal use. The Danish authorities have therefore prohibited the killing of polar bears except by residents, most of whom are Eskimos. In keeping with this principal, hunting from powered boats is not permitted in certain areas; and females and cubs are protected in the most important denning areas.

Some biologists (cf. Pedersen, 1945) maintain that all polar bears belong to a single population which is distributed throughout the Arctic and moves around the Pole. Others believe that there are a number of separate populations living in isolation. It is clearly impossible to think in terms of the proper management of the species until this basic issue has been resolved.

Prevailing ignorance is at least partly attributable to the difficulty of studying the animal in the remote and inhospitable Arctic no-man's-land in which the life cycle of the polar bear takes place. Furthermore, much of the animal's habitat lies far beyond territorial boundaries; for which reason international co-operation and agreement are necessary if effective action is to be taken both to acquire the necessary data and to use that knowledge advantageously.

This line of thought led to the First International Conference on Polar Bears, held at the University of Alaska, Fairbanks, in September 1965; and was followed early in 1968 by a working meeting convened by I.U.C.N. and attended by leading polar bear scientists from each of the five circumpolar nations—the Soviet Union, United States, Canada, Norway and Denmark.

This meeting allowed a frank exchange of views on the research work being conducted by each country up to that time; and resulted in agreement being reached on co-ordination of future work and the development of a Pan-Arctic research programme. Among the subjects covered by this agreement are: the definition of certain critical areas of research to which priority would be given; the assignment of specific research work to particular scientists, thereby avoiding unnecessary duplication; the standardization of research methods to enable comparable data to be obtained; and arrangements for the exchange of research results and other information.

Continuity is assured through the establishment of a permanent committee of international scientists engaged on polar bear research. This "Polar Bear Group", working under the auspices of I.U.C.N.'s Survival Service Commission, provides a forum for the exchange of information and the advancement of the programme. It plans to meet in alternate years to review progress, and to ensure that the programme's momentum is maintained.

The scientists are unanimous in stressing the importance of obtaining much more informa-

tion on polar bear numbers, distribution, migratory movements, and ecology. Such basic studies are necessarily long-term, and involve the capture and marking of large numbers of bears. This ambitious programme would have been impossible but for the invention of the syringe-gun and the development of special drugs which, in conjunction with spotter aircraft and vessels designed to operate in pack ice, have permitted new methods to be used for immobilizing wild animals under field conditions.

Satisfactory results have already been obtained by the Norwegian Polar Bear Programme in operations off Spitsbergen (Svalbard). As it is impossible to reach bears on the thick ice, capture operations are confined to animals in the water. The bears are followed in the pack ice by a sealing vessel which shepherds it in the required direction, thus allowing time to estimate its weight on which to assess the correct dosage rate. The vessel is then manoeuvred

close enough to use the syringe gun, the bear being immobilized as it climbs from the water on to an ice floe. After being tagged and examined the bear is released. The Norsk Polarinstitutt offers a reward for each recovery.

Similar operations are being conducted by the other nations engaged in this programme, the aim being to increase knowledge of the polar bear and to gain a better understanding of the extent to which the management of the species is an international problem.

Apart from its immediate importance to the conservation of the polar bear, this programme has succeeded in establishing a degree of collaboration among international scientists which could be of obvious value both in connection with broader questions bearing on the Arctic fauna and environment as a whole, and with ecological situations elsewhere in the world that can be satisfactorily resolved only at the international level.

DUGONG   *Dugong dugon*

The dugong and the manatee are the only surviving representatives of a once much larger order. Together with the cetaceans, they have achieved a more extreme form of adaptation to an aquatic environment than any other mammals. Although the entire life cycle of both orders is completely aquatic and both have lost their hind limbs, the two groups are unrelated. Whereas the cetaceans (whales and dolphins) have evolved from carnivorous stock, the anatomical evidence shows that the sirenians are descended from terrestrial herbivores, and were therefore probably allied to the ancestral elephants.

The largest of the recent sirenians was Steller's sea-cow *Hydrodamalis stelleri*, which attained a length of 24 feet. This animal was exterminated about 1768, within less than thirty years of its discovery. The sirenian order is now represented by the dugong, fringing the Indian Ocean and extending into the western Pacific;

and by the three species of manatee found in equatorial latitudes on both sides of the Atlantic. The manatee is primarily a fresh water animal, whereas the dugong is wholly marine.

The sirenians are named after the sirens of mythology, whose sweet singing was supposed to lure mariners to their destruction. This fable undoubtedly derives from the female's habit of raising the upper part of her body vertically above the water and clasping her offspring to her bosom. Being a shy and largely nocturnal animal, the dugong would not normally be seen except at a considerable distance or at night, so it is not difficult to understand how the lively imagination of mariners long deprived of feminine company transformed these unprepossessing creatures into the alluring sirens of classical mythology or how, centuries later the early Portuguese and Dutch explorers claimed to have verified their existence during the course of their epic journeys to the East.

The dugong is not only a slow breeder, producing only a single calf (twins have been known but are rare) after a prolonged period of gestation, but the mortality rate among calves is believed to be high during the first few months of their lives. The young are suckled for at least a year, during which time the mother is very solicitous for her offspring.

Most accounts state that the male attains a greater size than the female, but Norris's statistics, though a small sample, include one gravid female which had attained a length of 12 feet and a weight of 740 pounds, whereas his largest male was 9 feet long and weighed 420 pounds. Mani gives particulars of a female caught by a fisherman in 1959 which was 13 feet 4 inches long and weighed a ton.

The dugong's vision is poor, but its sense of hearing is highly developed, which makes the animal difficult to hunt by primitive means. Troughton tells us that the Australian Aborigines would look for the trail of floating weed left by the animal while feeding, "watching silently and striking as the browsing dugong rises to breathe".

Annandale, writing in 1905, stated that before his time "flocks of many hundreds" were said to occur in the Gulf of Mannar, in south-eastern India. The absence of such concentrations in this region is attributable to the constant harassment to which the remnant population has long been subjected. Under undisturbed conditions the dugong is a naturally gregarious animal, but in Indian waters it is nowadays usually found singly, rarely in pairs, and never in large formations. Such gatherings now take place only off the Australian coast (though perhaps not as large as the one seen in Moreton Bay, near Brisbane, in July 1893, which, according to Troughton, was estimated to be three miles long and three hundred yards wide); and in Manda Bay, Kenya, where herds of over eighty are still occasionally to be seen, moving in extended line abreast with almost military precision, the entire formation rising simultaneously to the surface to breathe as if at a word of command. The significance of these spectacular seasonal aggregations of dugong is not understood.

This dull-witted, inoffensive animal is widely distributed in tropical seas, ranging from the eastern seaboard of Africa to India and Australia, but its specialized ecological requirements restrict it to a very small part of this immense region, limiting it to areas of shallow, coastal waters, devoid of strong currents, large waves and oceanic swells. Moreover, the dugong is seldom found in waters deeper than six fathoms, because the submarine pastures, which are its only source of food, do not occur at a greater depth. These conditions have the advantage of being generally unsuitable for most predators, as they are too shallow for large sharks and killer whales, and too saline for most crocodiles.

Perhaps the only serious disadvantage of these environmental limitations is that shallow inshore waters render the animal particularly vulnerable to human predation. And as the meat is not only tender and of an excellent flavour but reputedly possesses remarkable aphrodisiacal properties, the reasons why the animal is assiduously hunted wherever it is found can be readily appreciated. The meat, which is said to resemble a cross between beef and pork, is not the animal's only attribute: almost every part is used.

Allen shows that at one time the Chinese used certain "stones" found in the head of the dugong, probably the tympanic bones, because of their reputed "property of clearing the kidneys of every kind of sand and gravel and of removing obstructions from the lower parts afflicted by them". According to Sowerby, however, there is no evidence that the dugong ever occurred on the coast of mainland China, and it seems likely that Imperial China derived its dugong products from outlying regions of the Empire. Support for this assertion can be deduced from the fact that in the Ryukyu Islands the animal was at one time subject to an annual hunt undertaken by feudal lords for tribute.

A viscous substance, the so-called "dugong's tears", is copiously excreted from the eyes when the animal is removed from the water. The Malays believe these "tears" to be a powerful aphrodisiac, a belief that does not extend to India, where it is the flesh that is credited with possessing rejuvenating powers.

BALEINE BLEUE   *Balaenoptera musculus*   BLUE WHALE

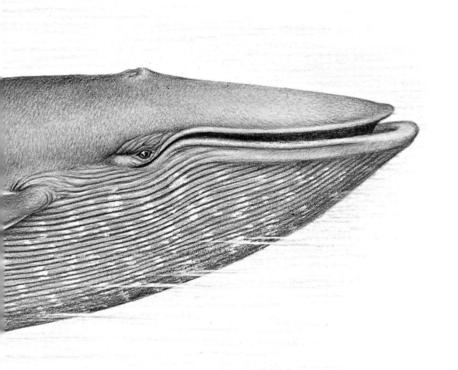

Dugong dugon

DUGONG

DUGONG

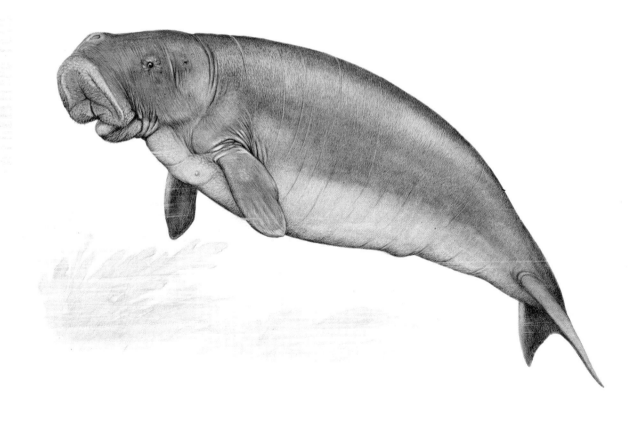

For this reason the demand for dugong meat is enormous. This may seem strange in a country where among some sections of the community there is such strong religious antipathy to taking life, and among others equally strong objections to consuming an animal which because of its vernacular name of "sea-pig" might be considered unclean. However, Muslim susceptibilities have been overcome through the expedient of declaring the dugong a fish.

The tusks, which occur only in the male and measure up to nine inches, are used in Australia for such articles as knife handles; while in Madagascar they are ground into powder as an antidote against contaminated food. They are also highly prized by Arab fishermen. The bones, which are remarkable for their density, are used for the high-grade charcoal in demand for sugar refining. The hide, almost an inch thick, can either be processed into glue or used for making into exceptionally durable leather.

A valuable oil is produced from the blubber, five or six gallons being obtained from a female in prime condition. Gohar notes that old Red Sea fishermen consider the oil good for cooking purposes, as it has a pleasant taste and smell, and possesses the quality of keeping "exceptionally well without special treatment and may hold for some few years without getting rancid". According to Troughton, this oil was at one time highly esteemed for medicinal purposes, notably as a supposed cure for tuberculosis. This discovery heralded a period of heavy commercialized slaughter, starting about 1860 and extending over a period of approximately thirty years.

Enough has been said to indicate that the dugong has long been in demand by man. In the past, when the human population was relatively small and hunting techniques were unsophisticated, losses were quickly made good through natural increment; but, more recently, pressure on the animal has been steadily increasing, partly because of the massive rise in human numbers and partly because of the enhanced efficiency of modern fishing gear.

Methods of hunting vary from place to place, and range from spearing and harpooning to the deplorable practice of dynamiting still used along parts of the coasts of India and Ceylon.

Dugong can remain submerged for between five and ten minutes, possibly longer, but they are obliged to surface to breathe. Many are caught in nets set for turtle, shark, or fish. These nets may be anything up to a mile long and three or four fathoms deep, and are set at night in shallow inshore waters, weighted to keep them in position. The dugong is primarily a nocturnal feeder and therefore most active at night, but in murky water the nets are difficult to detect in the dark except by touch, from which it is only a short step to becoming enmeshed. The animal might have struggled clear from the old-fashioned coir or cotton net, but the recent introduction of more efficient nylon nets has substantially lessened its chances of escape.

There are at present no restrictions or controls on the catching of dugong in Ceylonese waters. According to Jones, "the demand is so great and the price so high that fishermen scour the area and catch any that they find, especially along the Jaffna coast". The principal market on the Indian side is at Kilakarai. Jonklaas explains that the Ceylon fishermen "either harpoon it or take it alive, plug its nostrils with wooden plugs and let it die a slow death of suffocation. Or it is taken alive in the hot sun, its skin blistering and eyes tearing in agony, till someone offers to buy it, whereupon it is butchered without the slightest thought for its suffering. Humane butchery is not exactly a virtue of our fishermen, much less the turtle-catchers of the North; and the dugong, by far the most harmless and sensitive mammal of the sea, comes in for less consideration than a lobster."

The combination of low reproductive rate and over-exploitation has severely reduced the dugong throughout the greater part of its range. It has already disappeared from many areas as, for example, the Red Sea where it was almost eliminated by over-exploitation and excessive disturbance, to the extent that during a continuous search for specimens commencing in 1942 and extending over a period of 13 years, Gohar succeeded in procuring only 15 specimens.

There are a few places, however, in which it still occurs in reasonable numbers and in which conservation efforts should be concentrated.

Of these, the Australian situation is by far the most healthy. Although numbers are less than a century ago, a study undertaken by the Bertrams in 1965 with support from the World Wildlife Fund, revealed that the species' major stronghold is in Australian waters, ranging the length of the Queensland coast inside the Great Barrier Reef, through Torres Strait to southern New Guinea, and extending to Western Australia as far south as Perth. Hunting is now prohibited except by Aborigines for their own subsistence, as a result of which the species is maintaining itself very satisfactorily and in some areas may have recovered from the over-exploitation of the last century.

Outside Australia, one of the few flourishing dugong populations remaining anywhere in the world is in the Lamu inland sea, on the coast of Kenya. Although the species has either diminished or disappeared from most other parts of the East African coast, the Lamu population is still plentiful and shows every sign of maintaining itself satisfactorily.

In the Indian region the dugong's strength is in the Gulf of Mannar and adjoining Palk Bay, where environmental conditions are almost ideal. Long-standing and unconstrained exploitation has, however, reduced the population to a remnant. The situation was further worsened by the December 1954 cyclone which was accompanied by such torrential rain that the salinity of the water in Palk Bay was sufficiently reduced to kill all the sea-grass and cause heavy mortality among the dugong. If the species is to survive in Indian waters, part of this area should be set aside as an effective marine sanctuary.

The sirenians fill an important ecological niche in that they are the only mammals to convert submarine vegetation into protein, each mature animal yielding several hundred pounds of high quality meat, as well as other products. Given proper management, the dugong could form the basis of an important industry in regions where protein is generally in short supply. Unfortunately, however, its unusual potentialities as a source of nutritious meat in tropical regions have not yet been sufficiently appreciated. The species is secure in the Australian region: elsewhere, however, with the exception of the relatively small population at Lamu, the animal's status is precarious, and unless rational controls are introduced and enforced, it is only a matter of time before the dugong, like Steller's sea-cow, becomes as legendary a creature as the mermaid.

BLUE WHALE

Balaenoptera musculus

The larger whales reach a greater size than would be possible with any terrestrial animal, such bulk being attainable only in an aquatic environment where the body can be supported by water. Of all the whales, the blue is the biggest; indeed, it is the largest animal ever known, dwarfing any other creature in the whole of creation, including the gigantic dinosaurs that dominated the earth over 150 million years ago.

Slijper estimates the average adult blue whale to be about 85 feet long and to weigh 106 tons. He cites a female taken in 1948 that weighed 136.4 tons, remarking that because she was only 90 feet long "it seems likely that others are heavier still". Another taken in 1950 weighed 134.25 tons.

The disappearance of the dinosaurs remains an unresolved mystery, but it is not necessary to speculate about the reasons for the decline of the blue whale. Man's rapaciousness is solely responsible. One would have thought that the oceans, which cover 70 per cent of the earth's surface, would provide a sanctuary sufficiently large to ensure the blue whale's survival, but man's technological ability means nowhere is beyond the reach of his unconstrained greed.

The range of the blue whale is immense, embracing the oceans of the world from the

Arctic and Antarctic feeding grounds to the temperate breeding grounds; but the principal populations are found in the Southern Hemisphere, summer distribution being governed by the availability of food supplies. While the summer feeding grounds are in the cold waters among the pack ice, the blue whale's autumn migration to temperate or sub-tropical waters is motivated by the animal's reproductive needs. It is essential for births to take place in warmer waters as the new-born calf has only a very thin layer of blubber.

Although much remains to be learned of these migratory movements they are known to be extensive and may cover thousands of miles. Slijper mentions one marked blue whale which is known to have travelled 1,900 miles in 47 days. Because these breeding migrations take the whale away from its feeding grounds, it has been estimated that for at least four months of the year the adult blue whale eats little or nothing. During that period it lives on reserves accumulated during the feeding season.

Mature females normally give birth to a single calf at intervals of at least two years, after a gestation period of a little under 11 months. At birth the calf is of gargantuan size, being about 23 feet long and weighing two tons or more: this weight is doubled within the first week of life. The calf is suckled for about five to seven months, by which time it will have doubled its birth length to about 50 feet.

The blue whale normally occurs either singly or in pairs, but small "packs" or "schools" have sometimes been recorded. Slijper describes a school of 30 to 50 blue whales spread over an area of ten miles which was seen in the Indian Ocean in 1953.

Apart from man, the blue whale has little to fear from any animal, with the exception of the killer whale. These voracious predators usually attack only the immature whales, but it is known that packs of them will sometimes attack adults.

Living whales are divided into two main groups, the baleen whales (the sub-order Mysticeti) which have baleen plates in their mouths, and the toothed whales (the sub-order Odontoceti) which are equipped with teeth and are carnivorous.

The baleen, or "whale-bone", consists of a series of several hundred horny plates suspended from either side of the roof of the mouth. Each is covered with bristle-like fibres which act in the form of a sieve. This system equips the baleen whales for consuming the "krill" which in the antarctic forms almost their exclusive source of food.

Up to a hundred parallel ventral grooves or throat pleats, each about 2 inches deep, extend from the lower jaw along the throat to the belly. These folds allow the throat to expand, thus accommodating the huge tongue when it is depressed and the mouth opened to its full gape, and thereby allowing a large quantity of krill to be taken at a single gulp. The action of closing the mouth raises the tongue and forces the water through the baleen, expelling it through the sides of the mouth, and trapping the krill on the mat formed by the plates, before being swept into the throat.

The "krill" are small, shrimp-like crustaceans *(Euphausia superba)* found in the cold waters of Antarctica in immense concentrations. Arctic and Antarctic seas are much richer in plankton than the tropics, and the krill multiplies astonishingly rapidly. In some areas the density is so great that the sea has the appearance of reddish brown porridge. This colour derives from carotene contained in the microscopic plant plankton on which the krill feeds. Concentrations of krill are patchily distributed and difficult to locate, and it is not known how the whale detects them.

Man has hunted the whales for at least a thousand years, and probably much longer, but until about a century ago whaling was conducted from open boats and only the smaller whales could therefore be taken. Because of the blue whale's great speed and powers of endurance—it can cruise at 10 to 12 knots for long periods, and is capable of bursts of almost double that speed—it was virtually immune from primitive hunters. It was not until Svend Foyn's invention of the harpoon gun in 1864 that a weapon capable of killing these huge rorquals was produced. The harpoon gun was introduced at a time when both sperm and right whales were becoming more difficult to obtain, and therefore boosted a flagging industry. This invention marked the genesis of the modern whaling industry, but it also carried the seeds of the industry's own destruction.

Until the end of the last century whaling was restricted almost entirely to the Northern Hemisphere, but after 1864 the efficiency of hunting techniques improved so rapidly, including the development of ocean-going catchers as vehicles for the new harpoon gun, that whale stocks in northern waters were soon nearly exhausted. By the turn of the century the increasing scarcity of whales encouraged the whaling industry to turn its eyes to the untouched seas of the Southern Hemisphere. The first land station was established in South Georgia in 1904, and by 1910 had expanded to six shore stations and fourteen factory ships, operating from the Falkland Island Dependencies, with others in Chile, South Africa and elsewhere.

Pelagic whaling in the Antarctic required ships to operate under severe conditions and huge distances from their home bases, thus presenting a challenge to the industry that was met by the development of new techniques. A major innovation, which greatly extended the radius of operations, was the development of the factory ship.

At first these vessels remained at anchor in sheltered bays, but in the early 1920s a start was made on operating ocean-going factories, each with its covey of catchers forming a self-contained task force. This became the accepted method of conducting whaling operations. Such fleets were capable of remaining at sea for long periods, freely quartering the southern oceans, and transferring the accumulated oil in bulk to attendant tankers for conveyance to the home port. The modern whaling fleet is supported by added refinements such as helicopters for spotting purposes and sonar devices.

Flensing originally took place alongside the ship, but in 1925 the procedure was revolutionized by the introduction of the slipway built into the stern of the factory ship up which the whales could be hauled for flensing on deck.

This facilitated the work to the extent that a fully grown whale could be disposed of in an hour or so.

Every part is utilized and the animal provides a variety of valuable products. Besides yielding about twice as much oil as the fin whale, the blue whale supplies large quantities of meat (both for human and animal consumption), meat meal, bone meal, and pharmaceuticals, to mention only some of the products.

Because the blue whale was the largest and most valuable commercial species it at once became the whalers' principal quarry. The search for it was the dominant activity of the pelagic whaling fleets during the first half of the twentieth century, which thus became a lucrative period for the whaling industry as well as a time of unprecedented exploitation.

Each year saw an increase both in the catch and in the number of vessels participating. The heaviest catches were attained in the 1930s when the pelagic fleets had reached their greatest strength.

The Norwegians led the field but were soon followed by Britain, Japan, Germany, South Africa, the U.S.A. and Chile. After the Second World War, the U.S.S.R. and Holland joined in at a time when the demand for oils of all kinds was unprecedentedly high.

Ruud estimates that during the sixty years since the commencement of antarctic whaling approximately 340,000 blue whales were killed. The peak years were from 1927 to 1936, when the total annual catch only once dropped below 12,000, and reached its apogee in the 1930-31 season when 29,410 blue whales were taken. Many of these were immature animals which had had no chance to breed. At that time 80 per cent of the total Antarctic catch consisted of blue whales. By then it was apparent that several species, particularly the blue whale and the humpback, were being heavily overexploited and could no longer withstand the rate of attrition.

It was clear that some form of restriction was necessary if Antarctic whaling was not to go the way of the northern fishery. Shortly before the the Second World War, the British, German and Norwegian governments agreed to certain limitations being placed on Antarctic whaling. After the war, in 1946, the International Whaling Convention was signed and the International Whaling Commission established, with the declared purpose of regulating the whale catch and thus to ensure the effective conservation of the world's whale stocks.

In 1960, the Commission appointed a special group to undertake a study "on the condition of the Antarctic whale stocks, on the level of sustainable yield that can be supported by these stocks and on any conservation measures that would increase this sustainable yield".

The "Committee of Three Scientists" who carried out this study issued a strongly worded report that confirmed, "the drastic need for action", and concluded that the blue whale was in imminent danger of extermination. Evidence provided by the scientists indicated that by 1963 the stock of blue whales "will be reduced ... probably to between 650 and 1950 whales—which is a level at which there must be a distinct risk of complete extinction. ..."

In 1964 the International Whaling Commission agreed to impose a ban on the hunting of blue whale in the Antarctic except in one sector between latitudes 40° and 50° South and longitudes 0° to 80° East, inhabited by the pygmy blue whale, which occurs principally in the vicinity of Kerguelen Island, and was estimated to number about two to three thousand in 1963. The smaller North Atlantic stock is also virtually protected and, since 1966, the prohibition has applied to the North Pacific. At its nineteenth meeting in June 1967, the International Whaling Commission extended this ban to all waters south of the Equator.

The species is therefore now totally protected by international agreement, but the prohibition is applicable only to those governments represented on the International Whaling Commission. In practice, therefore, the agreement is restricted to pelagic whaling, because land stations have thus far remained outside the convention. Some countries, such as Canada and South Africa, have voluntarily extended the ban to their shore stations, but others have continued to take as many blue whales as they could. The Peruvian whaling station at Paita, for example, included 80 blue whales among its 1965 catch, which is a high proportion of the overall stock.

It is therefore gratifying to record that in 1966, on behalf of I.U.C.N., Charles A. Lindbergh and Ian Grimwood undertook a personal investigation of the situation in Peru. Following their representations, the Cia Ballenera del Norte, owners of the Peruvian whaling fleet, issued instructions to suspend all further catching of blue whales for a minimum period of two years, and to co-operate in any additional measures that might prove necessary to further the conservation of endangered whale species.

The decline of the blue whale is seen in better perspective when viewed against Mackintosh's estimate that the southern stock may originally have been in excess of 150,000. By the mid-1930s it had fallen to about 40,000; by the early 1950s to 10,000 or less; and by 1963 to fewer than 2,000. Since the start of Antarctic pelagic whaling in 1904, the blue whale population has been reduced by 99 per cent. Thus, during a period of little more than half a century the mightiest animal in creation, and one of great value in the service of man, has been reduced from abundance to near-extinction.

It is a sardonic fact that belated protection was granted only when the species had been so drastically reduced that for all practical purposes it had ceased to be of any commercial significance. Having exploited it to the brink of extinction, the whaling industry could afford to tolerate its protection.

MEDITERRANEAN MONK SEAL   *Monachus monachus*

The genus *Monachus* comprises three living species, all of which are confined to subtropical waters in the Northern Hemisphere. The three species are widely separated from each other: *M. monachus* inhabits the Mediterranean region; *M. tropicalis* the Caribbean; and *M. schauinslandi* the Hawaiian Islands. The monk seals are the only pinnipeds (with the exception of the California sea lion) to live in subtropical regions. All three species are rare—especially the Caribbean monk seal, which is almost extinct—and are listed in the *Red Data Book*.

An adult male Mediterranean monk seal may be 8 to 9 feet long with upper parts ranging in colour from brownish-grey to greyish-yellow, and with contrasting white or yellowish-white under parts. Its fur often has a white ventral patch, which is entirely absent on the other two species. Its fore flippers have well-developed claws but those on the hind flippers are small.

Its breeding habits are not well known. Mature females are believed to breed only in alternate years; Troitzky states that the single young is born on land in September or October, after an eleven-month gestation. The female mates again about seven or eight weeks after giving birth. The pups are suckled for six or seven weeks, after which they moult their black juvenile coats and enter the water for the first time. The pups remain with their mothers for three years. They do not breed until the age of four years.

The distribution of *M. monachus* centres on the Mediterranean, with extensions eastwards into the Black Sea, and westwards to Madeira, the Canary Islands, and the north-west coast of Africa as far south as Cape Blanc. The monk seal was once numerous and well-distributed throughout this region.

Little was known of its current status, however, until in 1961 Wijngaarden began assembling data and collating sighting reports from every part of the animal's range. The results of his work are contained in a series of reports which reveal that the species is now uncommon throughout its range. It is mostly found in a series of about twenty to thirty very small colonies, each consisting of fewer than twenty individual animals. Only one bigger colony is known. Some interchange of populations may take place between the different colonies, but this is not certain.

The species once inhabited many parts of the Black Sea, including the southern and south-western coasts of the Crimea. The last monk seal on Russian territory was killed shortly after the Second World War. It survives in Romania, however, in the Danube delta; and Bulgaria possesses two small colonies, one near Cape Caliakra and the other at Cape Maslenos.

The southern shore of the Black Sea once supported a large population of monk seals. Mursaloglu cites a number of records from Turkey, ranging from the Black Sea coast through the Sea of Marmara, the Gallipoli Peninsula, and along the Turkish Mediterranean coast almost to the Syrian frontier. He comments: "Luckily for seals on the Turkish coasts, there is a widespread superstition among Turkish fishermen that it is fatal to capture seals." More recently, Israeli naturalists have discovered several monk seal colonies inhabiting caves on Turkey's south coast, which they urge should be designated nature reserves.

Seven or eight small colonies are reported from the coast of Cyprus. Numbers have much declined, but the suggestion has been made that this decrease is not directly attributable to human interference: the increasing scarcity of fish in Cyprus waters may be responsible.

Kumerloeve shows that the species still exists on parts of the Lebanese coast, including caves in the "Grotto des Pigeons", near Beirut; but numbers are very small.

The seal is now rarely seen on the coast of Israel; but there is a sighting report from near Dor in 1958, and another the following year from Rosh-Hanikrah.

Early in the nineteenth century the species was abundant along the coast between Alexandria and Benghazi, but since then has been

PHOQUE MOINE   *Monachus monachus*   MEDITERRANEAN MONK SEAL

almost exterminated. The last authentic report was of a seal seen off El Arish about 1940; but it is possible that solitary animals may from time to time still come ashore on some of the remoter parts of the North African coast. Algeria is known to have had a resident population until 1943, but there does not appear to be any more recent record from that country. There is, however, a small colony on the tiny island of Galata off the coast of Tunisia. A small but static population exists along parts of the mainland coast of Greece, as well as on several of the Greek islands. There are recent records from Crete, Rhodes, the Cyclades, the Sporades, and the Ionian Islands.

At one time the monk seal was well distributed around the shores of the Adriatic, particularly on the numerous islands off the coast of Yugoslavia, but by the 1920s the population had already been heavily depleted. Occasional reports are still received of solitary animals seen on some of the Dalmatian Islands; and a small colony is resident in the Illyrian Islands.

Monk seals are no longer found on the French Mediterranean coast where they were once common. The only recent records from French territory are of a small colony living in a cave near Calvi on the north-west coast of Corsica. Breeding is said to occur regularly, but attempts to rear the young are less successful as the local people make determined efforts to destroy them. Seals are occasionally reported from some small islands off the coasts of Sardinia and Tuscany.

The species was once dispersed along the mainland coast of Spain between the Gulf of Alicante and Almeria. Solitary animals are still sometimes seen on the smaller offshore islands. Monk seals were particularly common around the Balearic Islands, and were regularly seen until the 1940s, but are now rare. The most recent report from these islands is of one killed in 1960 near Tuent on the north coast of Majorca.

Beyond the Mediterranean, there is believed to be a small colony in the Desertas Islands (south-east of Madeira), but it is menaced by local fishermen who regard it as a threat to their livelihood. Monk seals were once common in the Canary Islands also, but the present position is uncertain.

One of the most important breeding colonies remaining today lives in caves near Villa Sanjurjo (Al Hoceima), in the Bay of Alhucemas, Morocco. Valverde draws attention to the exceptional significance of this colony, which he believes may be the principal reservoir in the western Mediterranean for replenishing stocks of monk seals. The survival of the species would be greatly helped by giving these caves the status of a nature reserve and effectively protecting them from disturbance. Elsewhere in Morocco, the seal may still exist on the Chafarinas Islands off the Mediterranean coast of Spanish Morocco, where several are known to have been killed between 1945 and 1950.

Only one relatively large colony still exists. This is in the extreme south-west of Rio de Oro, on the western side of Cape Blanc, and about 12 miles north of La Güera. The most recent account is given by Wijngaarden, who in 1968 spent a fortnight there. He describes the cliffs along this part of the coast as about 50 feet high and deeply underscored by the sea. "The prevailing north-easterly swell is regular, and hurls 2- to 3-meter high breakers against the cliffs and into the caves. The compressed air escaping here and there through rock fissures produces a whistling sound and causes the whole cliff to tremble."

Wave-action has created many caves locally called *las Cuevecillas*, or *Cueva de las Lobos*—some up to 150 feet deep, and with steep sandy beaches at the interior end; but only one cave is at present occupied by seals. "The reason for this preference was not at first clear, but later it became apparent that this cave was the only one with the entrance lying at a certain angle to the direction of the breakers, thereby permitting a relatively gradual closure of the entrance, for which reason air compression in the cave was presumably lower than elsewhere."

Wijngaarden saw only eight seals, but he obtained information indicating that the population probably totals about sixty, and has remained more or less stable in recent years. "Seals have been observed over a wide area, fishing on the high seas, sometimes at a considerable distance from land. Some are frequently seen lying on the beach, even to the south of La Güera. The British crews of two helicopters of the Araco Oil Company flying almost daily between Port Etienne and Timiriz and Cape Timothé, told us that no seals were ever seen on the low shores of the Golf du Lévrier, the Banc d'Arguin, and the island of Tidra, As other observations are also lacking from this area, Cape Blanc must be the presumed southern limit of their occurrence."

The La Güera seal colony is efficiently protected by the Spanish authorities, and apparently tolerated by the local fishermen. Despite the constructive measures taken by the Spanish Government, however, numbers remain surprisingly static, and the species has failed to re-occupy parts of its original range. Seals which are presumed to have originated from La Güera have been seen moving along the coast of Rio de Oro. This suggests that the natural increase is being slaughtered elsewhere, possibly in the Banc d'Arguin, in Mauritania, where the monk seal was at one time commercially exploited, and where a solitary immature seal was recently seen on a beach. There is a self-evident need for a thorough ecological study of the La Güera colony as the basis for a positive monk seal conservation programme.

Wijngaarden estimates that the entire Mediterranean monk seal population numbers no more than 500 animals. The precarious status of the species is better appreciated when it is realized that almost all the known colonies seem to have adapted themselves to living in caves, often with submarine entrances: in the past the seals commonly occupied open beaches. The only logical explanation is that they have resorted to this practice to escape incessant persecution by man. A contributory factor is disturbance in and around the breeding colonies by skin-divers.

The monk seal is legally protected in several countries, but the law is extremely difficult to enforce. The perpetuation of the species is largely dependent on adequate protection being given to the few remaining colonies, particularly those at La Güera in Rio de Oro, and at Villa Sanjurjo (Al Hoceima) in Morocco.

JUAN FERNANDEZ FUR SEAL *Arctocephalus philippii philippii*

The genus *Arctocephalus* comprises seven species of fur seals which are almost entirely confined to the Southern Hemisphere. They range accross the southern oceans from Australia, New Zealand, South Africa, and various subantarctic islands to South America. The only representative of the genus to occur in the Northern Hemisphere is the Guadalupe fur seal, *Arctocephalus philippii townsendi*, which lives about 30° north of the Equator.

Two species of fur seals inhabit South American waters: the South American fur seal, *A. australis*, which is distributed along both the east and the west coasts of mainland South America, and nearby islands; and Philippi's fur seal, *A. philippii*, known only from the Juan Fernandez archipelago 500 miles west of Chile, and from the island of Guadalupe off the coast of Baja California. The physical differences between seals from these two islands are of a minor character, but sufficient to warrant separation into distinct subspecies (though some authors believe that both qualify as full species).

These two discrete populations are segregated from one another by more than 4,000 miles; but the fur seals of the Galapagos Islands (which are situated roughly midway between Guadalupe and Juan Fernandez) are not, as might be expected, of the same species.

There is some uncertainty as to the original range of the Juan Fernandez race. According to J. A. Allen, this fur seal ranged from the Straits of Magellan northward along the west coast of South America. He alludes to "numerous records at many points on the coast of Chili, at the Chincha Islands, and in the Bay of Callao on the coast of Peru. . . . The chief congregating places for breeding, however, seem to have been the small islands of Masafuera and Juan Fernandez off the coast of central Chile; [and] the little group comprising St. Felix, St. Ambrose, and St. Mary's Islands, about 9° of latitude farther north and on the same meridian of 80°. . . ."

Other biologists question this statement, however, and consider that the fur seal living along the coasts of Chile and Peru was more probably *A. australis*. The present consensus is that *A. p. philippii* is endemic to the Juan Fernandez archipelago. The available evidence shows moreover that this subspecies is known from only two islands within the archipelago: Isla Más a Tierra and Isla Más Afuera. King considers it unlikely that *A. philippii* once inhabited the Galapagos and was subsequently replaced by *A. australis*, or, alternatively, that both species lived together on the same group of islands.

At the time of its discovery in 1563, the island of Más Afuera "swarmed with seals". Allen's account shows that for two centuries nothing was done to exploit them. In 1792, however, "the ship *Eliza* of New York secured a cargo of 38,000 skins which were taken to Canton and sold for $16,000. In 1798 Captain Edmund Fanning, of the ship *Betsey*, also of New York, visited the island and secured the better part of 100,000 sealskins there. These also were disposed of at Canton. In leaving the island he estimated that there were still left in this rookery between 500,000 and 700,000 seals. Captain A. Delano tells that about this time there were, on one of his visits, people from 14 ships killing seals on the island. He estimated that in a period of seven

years more than 3,000,000 skins had been taken thence to Canton, and he makes the statement that when first discovered the total seal population was two or three million. This great slaughter very soon depleted the stock so that by 1807, according to Captain Morrell, 'the business was scarcely worth following', and in 1824 there were practically none left."

Events followed a similar course on Juan Fernandez. When Dampier, the famous buccaneer, visited the island in 1683, seals were so numerous that he wrote: "There is not a Bay or Rock that one can get ashore on that is not full of them. . . . Here are always thousands, I might say possibly millions of them. . . . Large ships might here load themselves with Seal Skins and Trayne Oyl, for they are extraordinary fat."

Allen notes that Juan Fernandez was settled before Más Afuera: by 1800 there were already 3,000 people living on the island, "so that according to Delano there were not then any seals left on any part of it". A few seals appear nevertheless to have survived until the 1890s, but in such small numbers that no profit was to be had in exploiting them.

This situation is confirmed by King, who writes: "On Masafuera about 1,797 sealers from fourteen ships were all on the island at the same time, all killing seals, and in seven years three million skins were taken. It is not surprising then, that by the end of the 19th century sealing had ceased to be a commercial proposition along this coast."

It was not until 1866, by which time the animal had already been nearly exterminated, that Peters published his description of a new species of seal from the Juan Fernandez archipelago, based on a skull obtained two years previously by Philippi.

The last record of the commercial exploitation of the Juan Fernandez fur seal appears to be the report quoted by Scheffer, which states that "fifty skins were taken on Isle Más a Tierra in 1898 and sold in London for from 13 to 32 shillings each". By the turn of the century the species was believed to be extinct.

Seventy years later, during a visit to the Juan Fernandez archipelago in November 1968,

Kenneth S. Norris and William N. McFarland discovered a few seals on the island of Más a Tierra, living either in caves or on the rocky shore. They estimated the total at about thirty animals of all ages. Local fishermen informed them that other seals were to be found on the neighbouring island of Más Afuera.

The Chilean Government has taken prompt action to give the re-discovered seal legal protection; but local officials and others are probably not sufficiently aware of the animal's great rarity and scientific interest, or of the need to discourage fishermen from killing it for use as lobster bait.

It seems important that an early appraisal should be made of the entire population to gain an indication of its size and to ascertain if other groups exist elsewhere, particularly on the little islands of St. Ambrose, St. Felix, and St. Mary, where seals were once common.

Practically nothing is known about the biology and behaviour of the Juan Fernandez fur seal. It would therefore be useful if the suggested survey could be combined with a study of the animal's reproductive potential, and especially valuable if it could include recommendations for ensuring the rehabilitation of this rare subspecies.

Arctocephalus philippii

OTARIE DE JUAN-FERNANDEZ

JUAN FERNANDEZ FUR SEAL

BIBLIOGRAPHY

GENERAL

SCOTT, PETER (1965). *The Launching of a New Ark: First Report of the World Wildlife Fund.* Collins, London.

VOLLMAR, FRITZ (1968). *The Ark under Way: Second Report of the World Wildlife Fund 1965-1967,* Lausanne.

— (1969). *World Wildlife Fund Yearbook 1968,* Lausanne.

SIMON, NOEL (1966). *Red Data Book,* vol. 1: Mammalia IUCN, Morges.

VINCENT, JACK (1966). *Red Data Book,* vol. 2: Aves, IUCN, Morges.

FISHER, JAMES, SIMON, NOEL ET VINCENT, JACK (1969), *The Red Book: Wildlife in Danger.* Collins, London.

AMERICA

HAITIAN SOLENODON

ALLEN, GLOVER M. (1942). *Extinct and Vanishing Mammals of the Western Hemisphere with the Marine Species of all the Oceans.* American Committee for International Wild Life Protection, Special Publication No. 11.

BRIDGES, WILLIAM (1958). Two Rare Insectivores. *Animal Kingdom* 61(3): 90-91.

TIJSKENS, J. (1967). *Solenodon paradoxus Brandt. Zoo d'Anvers* 32(3): 142-144.

MOHR, E. (1937). Schlitzrüssler. *Mitt. zool. Gart. Halle* 32(4): 1-5.

VOLCANO RABBIT

LEOPOLD, A. STARKER (1959). *Wildlife of Mexico: the Game Birds and Mammals.* University of California Press. Berkeley.

MILLER, G.S. (1911). The Volcano Rabbit of Mount Iztaccihuatl. *Proc. Biol. Soc. Washington* XXIV: 228-229.

DURRELL, GERALD (1969). *Fifth Annual Report 1968 from the Headquarters of the Jersey Wildlife Preservation Trust at the Zoological Park, Jersey, Channel Islands.* The Jersey Wildlife Perservation Trust.

VILLA, R.B. (1953). Mamiferos Silvestres del Valle de Mexico. *Anal. Inst. Biol.* 23: 269-492.

PELHAM WRIGHT, N. (1965). Teporingo—the Vanishing Volcano Rabbit. *Animals* 8(4): 96-97.

SIMON, NOEL (1966). *Red Data Book,* vol. 1. Mammalia. IUCN, Morges.

FISHER, JAMES, SIMON, NOEL, & VINCENT, JACK (1969). *The Red Data Book: Wildlife in Danger.* Collins, London.

DURREL, G. & MALLINSON, J. (1970). The Volcano Rabbit, Romerolagus diazi, in the Wild at Jersey Zoo. *International Zoo Yearbook* 10: 118-122.

RED WOLF

PIMLOTT, D.H. and JOSLIN, P.W. (1968). The Status and Distribution of the Red Wolf. *Trans. N. Am. Wildl. Conf.* 33: 373-389.

OGILVIE, PHILIP W. (1970). Interim Report on the Red Wolf in the United States. *Int. Zoo Yearbook,* Vol. 10: 122-124.

GOLDMAN, E.A. (1937). The Wolves of North America. *J. Mamm.* 18: 37-45.

LAWRENCE, B. and BOSSERT, W.H. (1967). Multiple Character Analysis of *Canis lupus, latrans* and *familiaris* with a Discussion of the Relationship of *Canis niger. Am. Zoologist.* 7: 223-232.

MCCARLEY, H. (1962). The Taxonomic Status of Wild *Canis* (Canidae) in the South Central United States. *S. West. Nat.* 7(3-4): 227-235.

PARADISO, J.L. (1965). Recent Records of Red Wolves from the Gulf Coast of Texas. *S. West. Nat.* 10(4): 318-319.

— (1968). Canids Recently Collected in East Texas, with Comments on the Taxonomy of the Red Wolf. *Amer. Midl. Nat.* 80(2): 529-534.

NOWAK, RONALD M. (1967). The Red Wolf in Louisiana. *Def. Wildl. News* 42(1): 60-70.

GOLDMAN, E.A. (1937). The Wolves of North America. *J. Mammal.* 18(1): 37-45.

JOSLIN, PAUL W. and PIMLOTT, D.H. (1966). *Report to the Survival Service Commission of the IUCN on the Status of the Red Wolf, Canis niger, in the Southern United States. 21 pp.,* cyclostyled.

YOUNG, S.P. and GOLDMAN, E.A. (1944). *The Wolves of North America.* Amer. Wildl. Inst., Washington. 588 pp.

MCCARLEY, HOWARD (1962). The Taxonomic Status of Wild Canids *(Canidae)* in the South Central United States. *The Southwestern Naturalist.* 7(3-4): 227-235.

NORTHERN KIT FOX

ALEN, GLOVER M. (1942). *Extinct and Vanishing mammals of the Western Hemisphere.* Spec. Publ. Amer. Comm. Int. Wildlife Prot. No. 11.

BAILEY (1926). The Mammals and Life Zones of Oregon. *N. Amer. Fauna* 55: 1-r16.

GRANDALL LEE S. (1964). *The Management of Wild Mammals in Captivity.* Chicago.

MEXICAN GRIZZLY BEAR

KOFORD, CARL B. (1969). The Last of the Mexican Grizzly Bear. *IUCN bulletin N.S.* 2(12): 95.

LEOPOLD, A. STARKER (1959). *The Wildlife of Mexico.*

— (1967). Grizzlies of the Sierra del Nido. *Pacific Discovery* 20(5): 30 32.

GIANT OTTER

DAVIS, JOSEPH A. (1968). River Otters, Sea Otters, and Part-time Otters. *Animal Kingdom,* 71(5): 2-7; 71(6): 8-12.

HARRIS, C.J. (1968). *Otters: a Study of the Recent Lutrinae.* Weidenfeld and Nicolson, London.

GRIMWOOD, I.R. (1969). *Notes on the Distribution and Status of Some Peruvian Mammals.* Special Publication No. 21., American Committee for International Wild Life Protection and New York Zoological Society.

MOUNTAIN TAPIR

GRAY, J.E. (1872). Notes on a New Species of Tapir (*Tapirus leucogenys*) from the Snowy Regions of the Cordilleras of Ecuador, and on the Young Spotted Tapirs of Tropical America. *Proc. Zool. Soc. London,* pp. 483-492.

SCHAUENBERG, PAUL (1969). Contribution à l'étude du Tapir pinchaque *Tapirus pinchaque* Roulin 1829. *Revue Suisse de Zoologie* 76(8): 211-256.

SCHAUENBERG, PAUL (1969). A la recherche du Loup-garou. *Musée de Genève* 93:3-7.

HERSHKOVITZ, PHILIP (1954). Mammals of Northern Colombia, Preliminary Report No. 7: Tapirs (genus *Tapirus*), with a Systematic Review of American Species. *Proc. U.S. Nat. Mus.* (Smithsonian Inst.) 103(3329): 465-496.

POURNELLE, GEORGE H. (1965). Tapirs Resist the Change of Time. *Zoonooz* 38(7): 3-7.

CRANDALL, LEE S. (1951). The Mountain Tapir in the Bronx Zoo. *Animal Kingdom* 54(1): 3-8.

RICHTER, WOLFGANG von (1966). Untersuchungen über angeborene Verhaltensweisen des Schabrackentapirs *(Tapirus indicus)* und des Flachlandtapirs *(Tapirus terrestris)*. *Zoologische Beiträge. Aus dem Zoologischen Institut der Universität Erlangen-Nürnberg* 1(12): 67-159.

ANON (1968). Ecuador: *Plight of the Mountain Tapir. I.U.C.N. Bulletin N.S.* 2(9): 69.

SCHAUENBERG, PAUL (1970). The Equator National Reserve in Ecuador. *Biological Conservation* 2: 140-41.

VICUNA

KOFORD, CARL B. (1957). The Vicuna and the Puna. *Ecological Monographs* 27: 153-219.

FLOWERS, NANCY (1969). The Royal Fleece of the Andes. *Natural History* 78(5): 36-43.

YOAKUM, JIM (1969). Viva la Vicuna. *Our Public Lands* 19(3): 14-17.

DENNLER de la TOUR, G. (1954). The Vicuna. *Oryx* 2(6): 347-352.

BATES, MARSTON (1964). *The Land and Wildlife of South America.* Life Nature Library. New York.

GRIMWOOD, I.R. (1969). *Notes on the Distribution and Status of some Peruvian Mammals.* Special Publication No. 21. American Committee for International Wild Life Protection.

GARCILASO de la VEGA, (1964). *The Incas: the Royal Commentaries of the Inca.* Avon Books, New York.

THE GALAPAGOS PENGUIN

BEEBE, W. (1924). *Galapagos, World's End.* Putnam, New York.

BROSSET, A. (1963). La reproduction des oiseaux de mer aux Galapagos en 1962. *Alauda* 31: 81-109.

EIBL-EIBESFELDT, I. (1960). *Galapagos. Die Arche Noahs im Pazifik.* Piper, München.

HARRIS, M.P. (1969). Breeding Seasons of Sea-birds in the Galapagos Islands. *J. Zool. Lond.* 159: 145-165.

LEVEQUE, R. (1963). Le statut actuel des vertébrés rares et menacés de l'archipel des Galapagos. *La Terre et la Vie* 110: 397-430.

— (1964). Notes sur la reproduction des oiseaux aux îles Galapagos. *Alauda* 32: 5-44.

PERRY, R. (1969). *Conservation and Scientific Report from the Charles Darwin Research Station No. 17.*

CALIFORNIA CONDOR

KOFORD, C.B. (1953). *The California Condor.* Rep. No. 4 National Audubon Society, New York.

MACMILLAN, I. (1968). *Man and the California Condor.* E.P. Dutton & Co., New York.

MILLER, A.H. & I.I. & MACMILLAN, E. (1965). *The Current Status and Welfare of the California Condor.* Rep. No. 6 National Audubon Society, New York.

SMITH, D. & EASTON, R. (1964), *California Condor, Vanishing American.* McNally & Loften, Sta Barbara.

WHOOPING CRANE

ALLEN, R.P. (1952). *The Whooping Crane.* Rep. No. 3 National Audubon Society, New York.

— (1956). *A report on the Whooping Crane's Northern Breeding Ground.* National Audubon Society, New York.

MAC NULTY, F. (1966). *The Whooping Crane.* E.P. Dutton & Co, New York.

ATTWATER'S PRAIRIE CHICKEN

BENT, A.C. (1932). *Life-histories of North-American Gallinaceous Birds.* U.S. Nat. Mus. Bull. 162.

KIRTLAND'S WARBLER

MAYFIELD H. (1960). *The Kirtland's Warbler.* Cranbrook Institute of Science. Bull. 40, Sloomfield Hills.

PETERSON T. (1948). *Birds over America.* Dodd, Mead & Co., New York.

STRICKER V. (1965). Kirtland's Warbler: Feathers and Flame. *National Parks Magazine* 39 (No. 217): 16-19.

van TYNE J. (1963). In Bent: *Life Histories of North American Wood Warblers* (417-428). Smithsonian Inst. Washington.

EUROPE

SPANISH LYNX

MOUNTFORT, GUY (1958). *Portrait of a Wilderness: the Story of the Coto Doñana Expeditions.* Hutchinson, London.

BEAUFORT, F. DE (1966). Le Lynx. *Science et Nature,* 77: 21-26.

BEAUFORT, F. DE (1965). Lynx des Pyrénées, *Felis (L.) Lynx lynx* (L.). *Mammalia* 29(4): 598-601.

BEAUFORT, F. DE (1968). Survivance du Lynx dans le Parc national des Pyrénées occidentales. *Mammalia* 32(2): 207-210.

SCOTT, PETER (1965). The Launching of a New Ark: *First Report of the World Wildlife Fund.* Collins, London.

VOLLMAR, FRITZ (1969). *World Wildlife Fund: Yearbook 1968.* Lausanne.

VOLLMAR, FRITZ (1968). The Ark under Way: *Second Report of the World Wildlife Fund 1965-1967.* Lausanne.

VALVERDE, JOSÉ A. (1957). Notes écologiques sur le Lynx d'Espagne *Felis lynx pardina* Temminck. *La Terre et la Vie* 104(1): 51-67.

EUROPEAN BISON

KRYSIAK, K. and PUCEK, Z. (1967). The European Bison: Current State of Knowledge, and Need for Further Studies. *Proceedings of 2nd. Symposium of the Mammal Section of the Polish Zoological Society, held at Bialowieza on September 23-24, 1966.*

ZABINSKI, JAN (1957). The Progress of the European Bison. *Oryx* 4(3): 184-188.

ZABINSKI, JAN (1949). Conclusions obtained from twenty years of Bison breeding in Poland. *J. Soc. Fauna Pres. Emp.* N.S. 59: 11-28.

KRYSIAK, K. (1963). News of the European Bison in Poland. *Oryx* 7(2/3): 94-96.

LANDOWSKI, J. (1966). Die Wisente in Polen. *Freunde des Kölner Zoo* 9(4): 115-117.

AHRENS, T.G. (1921). The present status of the European Bison or Wisent. *J. Mammal.* 2(2): 58-62.

MOHR, ERNA (1949). Development of the European Bison during Recent Years and Present State. *J. Soc. Pres. Fauna Empire*, N.S. No. 59: 29-33.

THE IMPERIAL EAGLE (Western Subspecies)

LATHBURY, SIR G. (1970), A Review of the Birds of Gibraltar and Its Surrounding Waters. *The Ibis* 112: 25-43.

MAYAUD, N. & HEIM DE BALSAC, H. (1962). *Oiseaux du Nord-Ouest de l'Afrique.* Lechevalier, Paris.

VALVERDE, J.A. (1960). La population d'Aigles impériaux *Aquila heliaca* des marismas du Guadalquivir; son évolution depuis un siècle. *Alauda* 28: 20-26.

— (1960). Vertebrados de las Marismas del Guadalquivir· *Archivos del Instituto de Aclimatacion, Almeria. Vol. IX.*

— (1967). Estructura de una Comunidad de Vertebrados Terrestres. *Monogr. Est. Biol. Doñana,* No. 1.

GEROUDET, P. (1965). *Les Rapaces diurnes et nocturnes d'Europe.* Delachaux & Niestlé, Neuchâtel.

AUDOUIN'S GULL

BOURNONVILLE, D. de (1964). Observations sur une importante colonie de Goélands d'Audouin — *Larus audouinii* Payraudeau — au large de la Corse. *Le Gerfaut* 54: 439-453.

BROSSET, A. (1957). Etude de quelques associations en Afrique du Nord. *Alauda* 25: 122-132.

— (1957) Excursion aux îles Chaffarines. *Alauda* 25: 293-295.

— (1961) Ecologie des Oiseaux du Maroc oriental. *Trav. Inst. Sc. Chérifien. Zoologie* n° 22.

BROSSET, A. & OLIER, A. (1966). Les îles Chaffarines, lieu de reproduction d'une importante colonie de Goélands d'Audouin. *Alauda* 34: 187-190.

MAKATSCH, W. (1968). Beobachtungen an einem Brutplatz der Korallenmöwe. *Journal für Ornithologie* 109: 43-56

— (1969) Studies of Less Familiar Birds. 154 Audouin's Gull. *Brit. Birds* 52: 230-232.

REISER, O. (1905). *Materialien zu einer Ornis balcanica. III. Griechenland und die griechischen Inseln.* Vienne.

WALLACE, D.I.M. (1965). Observations on Audouin's Gulls in Majorca. *Brit. Birds* 62: 223-239.

ASIA

SNUB-NOSED MONKEY

NAPIER, J.R. and NAPIER, P.H. (1967). *A Handbook of Living Primates.* Academic Press.

HILL, W.C. OSMAN (1966). *Primates : Comparative Anatomy and Taxonomy.,* vol. 6. Catarrhini Cercopithecoidea. Edinburgh University Press.

TATE, G.H.H. (1947). *Mammals of Eastern Asia.* The Macmillan Co. New York.

BOURLIERE, FRANÇOIS (1964). *The Land and Wildlife of Eurasia.*

ELLERMAN, J.R. and MORRISON-SCOTT, T.C.S. (1951). *Checklist of Palaearctic and Indian Mammals 1758 to 1946.* ANON (1952) *Oryx.,* vol. 1. p. 215.

PFEFFER, PIERRE (1968), *Asia : a Natural History.* Random House, New York.

JARVIS, CAROLINE (1966). Zoos in China. *Animals* 8(17): 450-455 and 8(19): 522-527.

MERRIMAN, R.B. (1944). *Suleiman the Magnificent 1520-1566.* Harvard University Press. Mass.

SOWERBY, ARTHUR DE CARLE (1937). Mammals of China, Mongolia, Eastern Tibet and Manchuria Requiring Protection. *China Journal, vol. 27 : 248-258.*

MILNE-EDWARDS, A. 1872. Mémoire sur la faune mammalogique du Tibet oriental et principalement de la principauté de Moupin. pp. 231-386. In: *Rech. Hist, nat. Mamm.* G. Masson, Paris. Vol. 1: 394 pp. Vol. 2: 105 pls.

MILNE-EDWARDS, A. and POUSARGUES, E. de (1898). Le rhinopithèque de la vallée du haut Mékong. (*Rhinopithecus bieti* Milne-Edwards) *Nouv. Archs Mus. Hist. nat. Paris* (3) 10: 121-142.

ALLEN, GLOVES M. (1938-40). *The Mammals of China and Mongolia.*

OSGOOD, WILFRED H., (1932). Mammals of the Kelley-Roosevelts and Delacour Asiatic Expeditions. *Field Mus. Nat. Hist. Publ. 312 Zool.* Series 18(10): 191-339. (pp 206-208).

FURGUSSON, W.N., (1911). "Adventure Sport and Travel on the Tibetan Steppes". Charles Scribner's Sons, New York, pp 124.

GEE, E.P. (1952). Possible Occurrence of the Snub-nosed Monkey (Rhinopithecus roxellanae) in Assam. *J. Bombay Nat. Hist. Soc.,* vol. 51, 264-265.

GEE, E.P. (1964). *The Wild Life of India.* Collins, London.

ORANG-UTAN

CARPENTER, C.R. (1938). A Survey of Wild Life Conditions in Atjeh North Sumatra: with Special Reference to the Orang-Utan. *Netherlands Committee for International Nature Protection*, Amsterdam, *Communications* No. 12. 34 pp.

HARRISSON, BARBARA (1961). Orang-utan: What Chances of Survival? *Sarawak Mus. J.* N.S. 10 (17-18): 238-261.

HARRISSON, B. (1962). *Orang-utan.* Collins, London.

SCHALLER, GEORGE B. (1961). The Orang-utan in Sarawak. *Zoologica,* N.Y. 46(2): 73-82.

HARRISSON, BARBARA (1963). Education to Wild Living of Young Orang-utans at Bako National Park, Sarawak. *Sarawak Mus. J.* N.S. 11 (21): 221-258.

MILTON, OLIVER (1964). The Orang-utan and Rhinoceros in North Sumatra. *Oryx* 7(4): 177-184.

MEDWAY, LORD (1965). *Mammals of Borneo.* Field Keys and an Annotated Checklist. Malaysian Branch of the Royal Asiatic Society.

DAVIS, D. DWIGHT (1962). Mammals of the Lowland Rain-Forest of North Borneo. *Bull. natn. Mus. St. Singapore* No. 31.

STOTT, KEN, JR. & SELSOR, C. JACKSON (1961). The Orang-utan in Northern Borneo. *Oryx* 6(1): 39-42.

HILLABY, JOHN (1964). The Fate of the Orang-utan. *New Scientist* 22(388): 232-233.

GIANT PANDA

BROCKLEHURST, H.C. (1936). The Giant Panda. *J. Soc. Pres. Fauna Empire,* N.S. 28: 21-23.

HAAS, GERHARD (1958). Ein Bumbus-Bär im Frankfurter Zoo. *Kosmos,* 54(10): 405-410.

SAGE, DEAN (1935). In Quest of the Giant Panda. *Natural History,* 35(4): 309-320.

SHELDON, W.G. (1937). Notes on the Giant Panda. *J. Mammal.* 18(1): 13-19.

ROOSEVELT, KERMIT (1930). The Search for the Giant Panda. *Natural History*, 30(1): 3-16.

PFEFFER, PIERRE (1968). *Asia : a Natural History*. Random House, New York, 298 pp. "The Continents we live on".

ALLEN, GLOVER M. (1938). *The Mammals of China and Mongolia*. Natural History of Central Asia, vol. 11, Part 1. The American Museum of Natural History, New York.

DAVIS, D. DWIGHT (1964). The Giant Panda: A Morphological Study of Evolutionary Mechanisms. *Fieldiana : Zoology Memoirs*, vol. 3. Chicago Natural History Museum.

SOWERBY, ARTHUR DE CARLE (1937). Mammals of China, Mongolia, Eastern Tibet and Manchuria Requiring Protection. *China J.* 27(5): 248-258.

TIGER

ABRAMOV, V.K. (1969). Area and Abundance of the Amur tiger *(Panthera tigris amurensis)* in the Far East. Abstracts of Symposium Papers. Increasing of Productivity of Game Management. *International Congress of Game Biologists*, Moscow 1969, pp. 92-94.

ANON (1968), India: Status of the Bengal Tiger, *IUCN Bulletin* 2(6): 44.

BANNIKOV, A.G. and ZHIRNOV, L.V. (1968). *The Bactrian Wapiti, Cervus elaphus bactrianus, in the U.S.S.R.* Unpublished.

BANNIKOV, A.G. (1969). *The Status of the Siberian Tiger Panthera tigris altaica.* Unpublished.

BAUDY, ROBERT E. (1966). Report on the Siberian Tiger. *Int. Zoo News* 13(3): 67.

BURTON, R.G. (1933) *The Book of the Tiger.* Hutchinson & Co. Ltd., London.

BURTON, R.W. (1952). A History of Shikar in India. *J. Bombay Nat. Hist. Soc.* 50(4): 845-869.

CAUCHLEY, GRAEME (1969). Wildlife and Recreation in the Trisuli Watershed and Other Areas in Nepal. *F.A.O., UNDP, Project Report*, No. 6.

FIELD, JULIA and HENRY (1965). Game and Wildlife Preserves in the U.S.S.R. *Man and Nature Series*, No. 1.

HEMMER, HELMUT (1969). Zur Stellung des Tigers (Panthera tigris) der Insel Bali. *Z. Säugetierk.* 34(4): 216-223.

HEYNSIUS-VIRULY and VAN HEURN (1936). Nature Protection in the Netherlands Indies. *Spec. Publs. Amer. Comm. int. Wild Life Prot.* No. 8: 58-59.

KIRK, GUSTAV (1966), Lob-Nor-Tiger ausgerottet. *Das Tier* 6(2): 46.

KITCHENER, H.J. (1961). The Importance of Protecting the Malayan Tiger. Nature Conservation in Western Malaysia, 1961. *Malayan Nature Journal*, 21st Anniversary Special Issue, 202-206.

LYDEKKER, R. (1924). *The Game Animals of India, Burma, Malaya, and Tibet*. Rowland Ward, London.

MAZAK, VRATISLAV (1965). Der Tiger, *Panthera tigris* Linneaus, 1758. *Die Neue Brehm-Bücherei*, Heft 356.

— (1968). Nouvelle sous-espèce de Tigre provenant de l'Asie du Sud-Est. *Mammalia* 32(1): 104-112.

MILTON, OLIVER and ESTES, RICHARD D. (1963). Burma Wildlife Survey, 1959-60. *Spec. Publs. Amer. Comm. int Wild Life Prot.*, No. 15.

MILTON, OLIVER (1964). The Orang-utan and Rhinoceros in North Sumatra. *Oryx* 7(4): 177-184.

MISONNE, XAVIER (1959). Analyse zoogéographique des Mammifères de l'Iran. *Mém. Inst. roy. Sci. nat. Belg.* 2e série, fasc. 59.

MOUNTFORT, GUY and POORE, DUNCAN (1968). *Report on the 1967 World Wildlife Fund Expedition to Pakistan.*

PEACOCK, E.H. (1933). *A Game-book for Burma and Adjoining Territories.* Witherby, London.

PERRY, RICHARD (1964). *The World of the tiger.* Cassell, London.

ROOSEVELT, THEODORE and ROOSEVELT, KERMIT (1926). *East of the Sun and West of the Moon.* New York.

RUKOVSKY, N.N. (1968). Some Problems of the Amur Tiger *(Panthera tigris longipilis)* Related to the Protection of this Species. *Zoologichesky Zhurnal* 47(5): 786-788.

SCHALLER, GEORGE B. (1966), The Tiger and its prey. *Natural History* 75(8): 30-37.

— B. (1967). *The Deer and the Tiger : a Study of Wildlife in India.* University of Chicago Press.

SCHALLER, GEORGE B. and SIMON, NOEL (1969). *The Endangered Large Mammals of South Asia.* Paper prepared for the IUCN General Assembly, New Delhi.

SESHADRI, B. (1968). The Indian Tiger Fights for Survival. *Animals* 10(9): 414-419.

SODY, H.J.V. (1932). The Balinese Tiger, *Panthera tigris balica* (Schwarz). *J. Bombay Nat. Hist. Soc.* 36(1): 233-235

SONG GIL SON (1966). State of Korean Tiger and its Specific Feature. *Korean Nature.* No. 1: 6-8.

SOWERBY, ARTHUR de CARLE (1923), *The Naturalist in Manchuria*, vols. 1 and 2. Tientsin Press.

SPILLETT, JUAN (1967). Pesticide Poisoning of Tigers. *Oryx* 9(3): 183-184.

TRENSE, WERNER (1959). Note sur quelques mammifères menacés du Proche-Orient. *La Terre et la Vie* 106 (Suppl.): 81-85.

BAZE, WILLIAM (1957). *Tiger! Tiger!* Elek Books. London.

LOCKE, A. (1954). *The Tigers of Trengganu*, Museum Press, London.

BAIKOV, N. (1936). *Big Game Hunting in Manchuria.* Hutchinson & Co. London.

SESHADRI, BALAKRISHNA (1969). *The Twilight of India's Wild Life.* John Baker Publishers, London.

GEE, E.P. (1964). *The Wild Life of India.* Collins. London.

MAZAK, VRATISLAV (1967) Notes on Siberian Long-haired Tiger *Panthera tigris altaica* (Temmiack, 1844) *Mammalia* 31(4): 537-573.

SNOW LEOPARD

CALVIN, LARRY, O. (1969). A Brief Note on the Birth of Snow Leopards *Panthera uncia* at Dallas Zoo. *Int. Zoo. Yearbook.* vol. 9. p. 96.

DANG, HARI (1967). The Snow Leopard and its Prey. *Cheetal* 10(1): 72-84.

GEE, E.P. (1967). Occurrence of the Snow Leopard *Panthera uncia* (Schreber), in Bhutan. *J. Bombay Nat. Hist. Soc.* 64(3): 552-553.

GLADKOV, N.A. AND NASIMOVICH, A.A. (1958). *Rare and disppearing Animal Species and Their Preservation in the U.S.S.R.*

HIBBERT, R.A. (1967). Wildlife Protection in Mongolia. *Oryx* 9(3): 196-210.

KULLMANN (1967). Über Leoparden Afghanistans und ihre Parasiten. *Freunde des Kolner Zoos* 10(4): 126-135.

LYDEKKER, R. (1924). *The Game Animals of India, Burma, Malaya, and Tibet.* Rowland Ward, London.

MUKHERJEE, A.K. (1966). *Extinct and Vanishing Birds and Mammals of India.* Indian Museum, Calcutta.

PRATER, S.H. (1965). *The Book of Indian Mammals*. Bombay Natural History Society and Prince of Wales Museum of Western India. 2nd Edition.

SALOMON, HUGO (1957). Protection of India's Wildlife as Seen by a Foreign Observer. *Nature Protection throughout the World*. 43-50.

SESHADRI, BALAKRISHNA (1969). *The Twilight of India's Wild Life*. John Baker Publishers, London.

POCOCK, R.I. (1930). The Panthers and Ounces of Asia. *J. Bombay Nat. Hist. Soc.* 34(1): 64-82, (Part 1). 34(2): 307-336, (Part 2).

CEYLON ELEPHANT

KURT, FRED (1968). Elephant Survey in Ceylon. *Oryx* 9(5): 364-365.

— (1969). Some Observations on Ceylon Elephants. *Loris* 11(5): 238-243.

— (1969). Ceylonelefanten. *Freunde des Kölner Zoo* 12(2): 35-44.

NORRIS, C.E. (1959) *Preliminary Report on the Ceylon Elephant Field Survey*. Wild Life Protection Society of Ceylon.

NORRIS, C.E. (1965). Ceylon's Problem Elephants. *Animals* 7(14): 37-373.

de SILVA, IAN (1969). Man Versus Elephant in Ceylon. *Loris* 11(5): 250-254.

BAKER, SAMUEL W. (1855). *Eight Years in Ceylon*. Longmans, Green & Co., London.

POURNELLE, GEORGE H. (1968). Asian Elephants. *Zoonooz* 41(8): 16-18.

DERANIYAGALA, P.E.P. (1955). *Some Extinct Elephants, their Relatives and the Two Living Species*. Ceylon, Nat. Mus. Publ.

INDIAN WILD ASS

GROVES, C.P. and MAZAK, V. (1967). On Some Taxonomic Problems of Asiatic Wild Asses; with the Description of a New Subspecies (Perissodactyla; Equidae). *Z. Säugetierkunde* 32(6): 321-355.

GEE, E.P. (1963). The Indian Wild Ass: A Survey. February 1962. *J. Bombay Nat. Hist. Soc.* 60(3): 516-529.

GEE, E.P. (1963). The Indian Wild Ass. A Survey—February 1962. *Oryx* 7(1): 9-21.

SPILLETT, J.J. (1968). Wild Life in Gujarat State. *J. Bombay Nat. Hist. Soc.* 65(1): 15-46.

ALI, SALIM (1946). The Wild Ass of Kutch. *J. Bombay Nat. Hist. Soc.* 46(3): 472-477.

WYNTER-BLYTH, M.A. (1956). An Account of the Wild Ass and a Brief History of the Indian Lion. *Indian Forester* 82: 644-648.

SCHALLER, GEORGE and SIMON, NOEL (1969). *The Endangered Large Mammals of South Asia*.

JAVAN RHINOCEROS

GUGGISBERG, C.A.W. (1966). *S.O.S. Rhino*. André Deutsch, London.

HAZEWINKEL, J.C. (1933). *Rhinoceros sondaicus* in Zuid-Sumatra. *De Tropische Natuur* 22(6): 101-109.

HOOGERWERF, A. (1948). *Nature Protection in the Indonesian Archipelago* (Netherlands Indies). Cyclostyled.

HOOGERWERF, A. (1954). Nature Protection in Indonesia. *Oryx* 2(4): 221-227.

KIES, C.H.M.H. (1936). Nature Protection in the Netherlands Indies. *Special Publication of the American Committee for International Wild Life Protection* No. 8: 11-23.

MILTON, OLIVER (1964). The Orang-utan and Rhinoceros in North Sumatra. *Oryx* 7(4): 177-184.

NEUMANN, J.B. (1885-1887). Het Panek- en Bila-Stroomgebied op het eiland Sumatra. *Tijdschrift Koninklijk Nederlandsch Aardrijkskundig Genootschap*, 2. Serie II/IV.

SCHENKEL, R. and SCHENKEL-HULLIGER, L. (1969). The Javan Rhinoceros *(Rh. sondaicus Desm.)* in Udjung Kulon Nature Reserve. Its Ecology and Behaviour. Field Study 1967 and 1968. *Acta Tropica* 26(2): 97-135.

SODY, H.J.V. (1959). Das Javanische Nashorn, *Rhinoceros sondaicus*, historisch und biologisch *Z. Säugetierk*, 24: 109-240.

TALBOT, LEE M. (1960). A Look at Threatened Species. *Oryx* 5(4-5): 153-293.

THOM, W.S. (1936). Rhinoceros Shooting in Burma. *J. Bombay Nat. Hist. Soc.* 38(1): 137-150.

SCHENKEL, R. and LANG, E.M. (1969). Das Verhalten der Naschörner. *Handbuch der Zoologie*, 8(10): 1-56.

PERSIAN FALLOW DEER

AHARONI, J. (1930). Die Säugetiere Palästinas. *Z. Säugetierk.* 5: 327-343.

BOURLIÈRE, FRANÇOIS (1964). *The Land and Wildlife of Eurasia*. Life Nature Library.

HALTENORTH, TH. (1961). Lebensraum, Lebensweise und Vorkommen des Mesopotamischen Damhirsches, *Cervus mesopotamicus* Brooke, 1875 *Säugetierk. Mitt.* 9(1): 15-39.

HARRISON, D.L. (1968). *The Mammals of Arabia.*, vol. 2. Carnivora, Hyracoidea, Artiodactyla. Ernest Benn Ltd., London.

HATT, ROBERT T. (1959). The Mammals of Iraq. *Misc. Publs. Mus. Zool. Univ. Mich.* No. 106.

HEPTNER, V.G. and NAUMOV, NP (1966). *Die Säugetiere der Sowjetunion*. Band I. Paarhufer und Unpaarhufer. Gustav Fischer Verlag. Jena.

KRÄMER, WILHELM (1963). Auf der Suche nach dem Mesopotamischen Damhirsch. *Freunde des Kölner Zoo* 6(3): 81-82.

LAY, DOUGLAS M. (1967). A Study of the Mammals of Iran Resulting from the Street Expedition of 1962-63. *Fieldiana: Zoology.*, vol. 54.

PEPPER, HUBERT J. (1964). The Persian Fallow Deer. *Oryx* 7(6): 291-294.

POCOCK, R.I. (1946). The Persian Fallow Deer *(Dama mesopotamica) J. Soc. Pres. Fauna Emp.* N.S. 53: 53-55.

REED, CHARLES A. (1965). Imperial Sassanian Hunting of Pig and Fallow-deer, and Problems of Survival of these Animals Today in Iran. *Postilla (Peabody Mus. Nat. Hist, Yale Univ.)* No. 92.

TAMARAW

CARTER, HILL and TATE (1945). *Mammals of the Pacific World*

MORRIS, D. (1965). *The Mammals:* a Guide to the Living Species.

WALKER, (1964). *Mammals of the World*.

HARPER, FRANCIS (1945). *Extinct and Vanishing Mammals of the Old World*. New York. American Committee.

MANUEL, C.G. (1957). Status of Tamaraw, Anoa mindorensis (Heude) *Proc. 8th Pacific sci. congress* (Manila) 1953, vol. 3A (1957): 1463-1472.

HARRISSON, TOM (1969). The Tamaraw and Its Survival — *IUCN Bulletin* 2(11): 85-86.

TALBOT (1964). *Renewable Natural Resources in the Philippines*.

ARABIAN ORYX

LOYD, M. (1965). The Arabian Oryx in Muscat and Oman. *East African Wildlife Journal*, 3: 124-127.

STEWART, D.R.M. (1963). The Arabian Oryx (*Oryx leucoryx Pallas*) *East African Wildlife Journal*, 1: 1-16.

STEWART, D.R.M. (1964). The Arabian Oryx (*Oryx leucoryx* Pallas): 2. *East African Wildlife Journal*, 2: 168-169.

GRIMWOOD, I.R. (1962). "Operation Oryx". *Oryx* 6(6): 308-334.

GRIMWOOD, IAN (1964). "Operation Oryx": the Second Stage. *Oryx* 7(5): 223-225.

GRIMWOOD, IAN R. (1967). Operation Oryx: the Three Stages of Captive Breeding. *Oryx* 9(2): 110-118.

TALBOT, LEE MERRIAM (1960). *A Look at Threatened Species*.

HATT, ROBERT T. (1959). *The Mammals of Iraq*.

THORP, JACK L. (??). The Arabian Oryx 1963-64. *Arizona Zoological Society, Special Bulletin No. 1*.

HARRISON, DAVID L. (1968). *The Mammals of Arabia.*, vol. 2.

THESIGER, W. (1949). A Further Journey Across the Empty Quarter. *The Geographical Journal*, vol. CXIII.

THE BROWN-EARED PHEASANT

BEEBE, WILLIAM (1918), *A Monograph of the Pheasants*, vol. I. Witherby, London.

CHENG TSO-HSIN (1963). *China's economic Fauna : Birds*. Science publishing Society, Pékin (traduction U.S. Dept. of commerce, Washington).

DAVID, A. (1867). Jounal d'un voyage en Mongolie fait en 1866. *Nouvelles Archives du Muséum d'histoire naturelle de Paris*. 3. Bulletin, p. 37.

DELACOUR, JEAN (1951). *The Pheasants of the World*. Country Life, London.

VAURIE, CH. (1965). *The Birds of the Palearctic Fauna. Non Passeriformes*. Witherby, London.

JAPANESE CRESTED IBIS

CHENG, TSO-HSIN (1963). *China's Economic Fauna: Birds*. Science Publ. Soc. Pékin (traduction U.S. Dept of Commerce, Washington).

OUSTALET, M.E. (1872). Remarques sur l'*Ibis sinensis* de M. l'Abbé A. David. *Nouvelles archives du Muséum d'Histoire naturelle de Paris*, 8 (Bulletin p. 129-137).

VAURIE, CH. (1965). *The Birds of the Palearctic Fauna. Non Passeriformes*. Witherby, London.

WON PYONG-OH (1967). The Present Status of some Threatened and Rare Birds in Korea, 1962-66 *X. Bull. ICBP* p. 110.

YAMASHINA, Y. (1962). History and Present Status of Japanese Crested Ibis *Nipponia nippon* (Temminck) *VIII Bull. ICBP*, p. 77-78.

— (1967). The Status of Endangered Species in Japan. *X Bull. ICBP*, p. 100-103.

MONKEY-EATING EAGLE

BROWN, L. & AMADON, D. (1968). *Eagles, Hawks and Falcons of the World*. Country Life Books, Hamlin Publ., Feltham.

GONZALES, R.B. (1969). A Study of the Breeding Biology of the Monkey-eating Eagle. *Silliman Journal* XV (4): 461-496.

TALBOT, L.M. & TALBOT, M.H. (1964). *Renewable Nature Resources in the Philippines. IUCN*.

AFRICA

INDRIS and VERREAUX'S SIFAKA

PERRIER DE LA BATHIE, H. (1931). Les Réserves Naturelles de Madagascar. *La Terre et la Vie*. N.S. no 7.: 427-442

FORBES, HENRY O. (1894). *A Hand-book to the Primates*. London, W.H. Allen & Co. Ltd. 2 vols.

PETTER, JEAN-JACQUES (1965). The Lemurs of Madagascar.

In: DE VORE, I. Editor, *Primate behaviour*—Field studies of monkeys and apes. New York, Holt, Rinehart and Winston.

PAULIAN, R. (1955). *Les Animaux Protégés de Madagascar*. L'Institut de Recherche scientifique Tananarive — Tsimbazaza.

— (1960). Des Animaux précieux: les Lémuriens. *Revue de Madagascar* 2(9): 20-25.

PETTER, J.J. (1962). Remarques sur l'Ecologie et l'Ethologie comparées des Lémuriens Malgaches. *La Terre et la Vie* no 4: 394-416.

— (1962)a. *(See Red Data Book bibliography)*.

— (1962)b. *(See Red Data Book bibliography)*.

BOETTICHER, HANS VON (1958). *Die Halbaffen und Koboldmakis*. Die Neue Brehm-Bucherei.

JOLLY, ALISON (1967). Malagasy Lemurs—Clues to our Past. *Animal Kingdom* 70(3): 66-75.

JOLLY, ALISON (1966). *Lemur behavior : a Madagascar Field Study*. University of Chicago Press.

PETTER, J.J. (1962). Ecological and Behavioral Studies of Madagascar Lemurs in the Field. *Ann. N.Y. Acad. Sci.* 102(2): 267-281.

PETTER, J.J. and SIMON, N.M. (1967). *Summary Report of the 1967 IUCN Mission to Madagascar*. Cyclostyled.

PETTER, J.J. (1963). Madagascar Lemurs: Insularity Permitted Their Varied Development. *Natural History* 72(3): 22-26.

ATTENBOROUGH, DAVID (1961). *Zoo quest to Madagascar*. Lutterworth Press.

RAND, A.L. (1935). On the Habits of some Madagascar Mammals. *J. Mammalogy* 16(2): 89-104.

AYE-AYE

HILL, W.C. OSMAN (1953). *Primates : Comparative Anatomy and Taxonomy*, vol. I—Strepsirhini. Edinburgh University Press. 398 pp.

PETTER, J.J. (1962). Recherches sur l'écologie et l'éthologie des lémuriens Malgaches. *Mem. Mus. natn. Hist. nat. Paris*. 27(1): 1-146, 26 pls.

PETTER-ROUSSEAUX, A. et PETTER, J.J. (1967). Contribution à la systématique des Cheirogaleinae (lémuriens malgaches). *Allocebus*, gen. nov., pour *Cheirogaleus trichotis* Günther 1875. *Mammalia* 31(4): 574-582.

PETTER, J.J. (1967). Protection of the Aye-aye. *IUCN Bulletin* N.S. 2(4): 25-27.

PETTER, J.J. and SIMON, N.M. (1967). *Summary Report of the 1967 IUCN Mission to Madagascar*. Cyclostyled.

ZANZIBAR RED COLOBUS

SANDERSON, IVAN T. (1957). *The Monkey Kingdom*. Hamish Hamilton, London.

WEBB, CECIL S. (1964). Red Rarity. *Animals* 4(5): 128.

SCHWARZ, ERNST (1929). On the Local Races and Distribution of the Black and White Colobus Monkeys. *Proc. zool. Soc. Lond.* pp. 585.

BOOTH, C. (1963). *Memorandum on Colobus badius kirkii Gray 1868.* Tigoni Primate Research Centre. Unpublished.

NAPIER, J.R. and NAPIER H. (1967). *A Handbook of living Primates. Morphology, Ecology and Behaviour of Nonhuman Primates.* Academic Press, London, New York.

HARPER, FRANCIS (1945). Extinct and Vanishing Mammals of the Old World. *Spec. Publ. Amer. Comm. Int. Wildlife Protection* 12.

VERHEYEN, W.N. (1959). Summary of the Results of a Craniological Study of the African Primate genera *Colobus* Illiger, 1811 and *Cercopithecus Linnaeus,* 1758. *Revue Zoo. Bot. afr.* 60: 1-2.

VERHEYEN, W.H. (1962). Contribution à la craniologie comparée des primates. *Musée Roy. Afrique Centrale — Tervuren, Belgique.* Sér. 8. *Sci. Zool.* 105: 1-256.

SCHWARZ, E. (1928) Bemerkungen über den roten Stummelaffen. *Z. Säugetierk.* 3: 92-97.

BERE, R.M. (1962). *The Wild Mammals of Uganda and neighbouring Regions of East Africa.* Longmans, London.

SANDERSON, IVAN T. (1957). *The Monkey Kingdom : An Introduction to the Primates.* Hormish Hamitton, London.

MOUNTAIN GORILLA

EMLEN, JOHN T. and SCHALLER, GEORGE B. (1960). In the Home of the Mountain Gorilla. *Animal Kingdom,* 63(3): 98-108.

SCHALLER, GEORGE B. (1963). Mountain Gorilla Displays. *Natural History* 72(7): 10-17.

— (1963). *The Mountain Gorilla : Ecology and Behavior.* University of Chicago Press.

— (1965). The behavior of the Mountain Gorilla. In: *Primate behavior : field studies of monkeys and apes.* New York, Holt, Rinehart and Winston.

SCHÄFER, ERNST (1964). Gorillas im Kongo-Urwald. *Freunde des Kölner Zoo* 7(3): 83-86.

BLOWER, JOHN (1956). The Mountain Gorilla and Its Habitat in the Virunga Volcanoes. *Oryx* 3(6): 287-297.

HILLABY, JOHN (1968). Birth of a Gorilla. *New Scientist* 38(602): 627-628.

PITMAN, C.R. (1937). The Gorillas of the Kayonza Region, Western Kigezi, Southwest Uganda. *Smithsonian Report for 1936,* 253-275.

MILTON, OLIVER (1957). The Last Stronghold of the Mountain Gorilla in East Africa. *Animal Kingdom,* 60(2): 58-61.

ADDAX

BROCKLEHURST, H.C. (1931). *Game Animals of the Sudan : Their Habits and Distribution.* Gurney and Jackson. London,

DEKEYSER, P.L. (1955). Les Mammifères de l'Afrique Noire Française. I.F.A.N., Dakar, *Initiations Africaines,* nº 1.

DOLAN, JAMES (1966). Notes on *Addax nasomaculatus* (de Blainville, 1816). *Z. Säugetierk.* 31(1): 23-31.

DUPUY, ANDRÉ (1966). La grande faune du Sahara algérien. *St. Hubert* nº 3: 90-93.

— (1967). Répartition actuelle des espèces menacées de l'Algérie. *Bull. Soc. Sci. nat. phys. Maroc.* 47(3 and 4): 355-386.

GILLET, HUBERT (1964). Pâturages et Faune Sauvage dans le Nord Tchad (rapport de mission). *J. Agric. trop. Bot. appl.* 11(5-6-7): 155-176.

GILLET, HUBERT (1965). L'Oryx Algazelle et l'Addax au Tchad. *La Terre et la Vie.* 112(3): 257-272.

GILLET, HUBERT (1966). The Scimitar Oryx and the Addax in the Tchad Republic. *Afr. Wild Life* 20(2): 103-115, 20(3): 191-196.

HONE, ELISABETH (1933). African Game Protection. *Spec. Publ. Am. Comm. Int. Wild Life Prot.,* vol. I., No. 3.

KHALIL, F. (1968). *The Present State of Wild Fauna in Libya.* Draft Report for the Technical Meeting on Conservation and Ecology of the Western Mediterranean, North Africa and the Sahara. Cyclostyled.

LYDEKKER, R. (1901). *The Great and Small Game of Europe, Western and Northern Asia and America.* Rowland Ward, London.

MACKENZIE, P.Z. (1954). Catalogue of Wild Mammals of the Sudan Occurring in the Natural Orders Artiodactyla and Perissodactyla. *Sudan Museum (Natural History), Publication No. 4.*

MACPHERSON, LORD (1968). *Report on the Addax in Darfur Province.* Cyclostyled.

MONOD, TH. (1958). Majâbat al-Koubrâ. Contribution à l'étude de l'« Empty Quarter » ouest-saharien. *Mém. Inst. fr. Afri. noire.* nº 52

SCHOMBER, HANS W. (1963). Wild Life in the Sudan. Part IV. Desert and semi-desert game animals. *African Wild Life.* 17(2): 117-124.

VALVERDE, J.A. (1968). Ecological Bases for Fauna Conservation in Western Sahara. *IBP/CT Technical Meeting, Hammamet.* Cyclostyled.

DUPUY, A. (1967) La faune menacée de l'Algérie et sa protection. *Bull. Soc. Sci. Nat. Phys. Maroc* 47(3-4): 329-354

BONTEBOK

BRAND, D.J. (1962). The Bontebok—Status and Distribution. *Department of Nature Conservation, Cape of Good Hope Province, Report* No. 19: 88-90.

SIDNEY, JASMINE (1965). The Past and Present Distribution of Some African Ungulates. *Trans. zool. Soc. London* 30: 1-397.

BIGALKE, R. (1955). The Bontebok (*Damaliscus pygargus* (Pall), with special reference to its history and preservation. *Fauna and Flora* No. 6: 94-115.

SELOUS, F.C. (1899). In BRYDEN, H.A. (1899) *Great and Small Game of Africa.* An account of the distribution, habits, and natural history of the sporting mammals, with personal hunting experiences. Rowland Ward, London.

ANON (1969). *The Bontebok. Provincial Administration of the Cape of Good Hope, Republic of South Africa. Report No. 25* 1968-69.

WALIA IBEX

BROWN, LESLIE (1966), *The Mobil Handbook of Conservation: Ethiopia.* Ethiopian Tourist Organization, Addis Ababa.

BROWN, LESLIE H. (1969). The Walia Ibex. *Walia,* No. 1., 9-14.

BROWN, L.H. (1966). Wildlife Conservation in Ethiopia. *Nature and Ressources* 2(1): 5-9.

BROWN, LESLIE (1965). *Ethiopian Episode.* Country Life, London.

GRIMWOOD, I.R. and BROWN, L.H. (1965). *Report on the Conservation of Nature and Natural Resources in Ethiopia.*

HUXLEY, J. et al (1963). *The Conservation of Nature and Natural Resources in Ethiopia,* UNESCO, Paris.

LONG-TAILED GROUND ROLLER

APPERT O. (1968). Zur Brutbiologie der Erdracke *Uratelornis chimaera* Rothschild. *Journal für Ornithologie* 109: 264-275.

OCEANIA

THYLACINE

GUILER, E. R. (1961). The Former Distribution and Decline of the Thylacine. *Australian Journal of Science* 23(7): 207-210.

SHARLAND, MICHAEL (1962). *Tasmanian Wild Life.* Melbourne University Press.

GUILER, ERIC R. (1966). In Pursuit of the Thylacine. *Oryx* 8(5): 307-310.

TROUGHTON, ELLIS (1962). *Furred Animals of Australia.* Angus & Robertson.

RENSHAW, GRAHAM (1938). The Thylacine. *J. Soc. Pres. Fauna Emp.* N. S. 35:47-49.

ANDREWARTHA, E. P. (1938). The Tasmanian Tiger. *J. Soc. F.P.E.* 34.

FLEMING, A. L. (1939). The Thylacine. *J. Soc. F.P.E.* 38.

FLEAY, DAVID (1946). Tasmanian Tiger Hunt. *Wild Life,* June 1946. pp. 186.

SHARLAND, M.S.R. (1939). Tracking the Thylacine. *Wild Life,* June 1939 1(8): 7-9.

WHITE-THROATED WALLABY

GOULD, J. (1863). *The Mammals of Australia.* London Taylor and Francis.

HARPER, FRANCIS (1945). Extinct and Vanishing Mammals of the Old World. *Spec. Publs. Amer. Comm. int. Wild Life Prot.* No. 12.

MARLOW, B. J. (1958). A Survey of the Marsupials of New South Wales *C.S.I.R.O. Wildl. Res.* 3, 71-114.

RIDE, W.D.L. (1957). *Protemnodon parma* (Waterhouse) and the Classification of Related Wallabies *(Protemnodon, Thylogale* and *Setonix). Proc. zool. Soc. London* 128(3): 237-346.

TATE, G.H.H. (1948). Studies on the Anatomy and Phylogeny of the Macropodidae (Marsupialia). Results of the Archbold Expeditions No. 59. *Bull. Amer. Mus. Nat. Hist.* 91(2): 233-352.

TROUGHTON, ELLIS (1962). *Furred Animals of Australia.* Angus and Robertson, Sydney. 7th edition.

WODZICKI, K. and FLUX, J.E.C. (1967). Rediscovery of the White-throated Wallaby, *Macropus parma* Waterhouse. 1846, on Kawau Island, New Zealand. *Aust. J. Sci.* 29(II): 429-430.

WODZICKI, K. (1969). *Report on a Visit to Kawau (25-27 January) and Motutapu (29 January, 1969)* Islands, Hauraki Gulf. Mimeographed.

KAKAPO

FALLA R. A., SIBSON R. B. & TURBOTT E. G. (1966). *A Field Guide to the Birds of New Zealand.* Collins, London.

STIVENS D. (1964). Last Call for New Zealand's Ground Parrot. *Animal Kingdom* 67: 101-106.

WILLIAM G. R., (1956). The Kakapo *Strigops habroptilus.* A review and reappraisal of a near extinct species. *Notornis* 7:29-56.

OCEANS

POLAR BEAR

COOLEY, RICHARD A. (1968). International Scientific Cooperation on the Polar Bear. *I.U.C.N. Bulletin.* N.S. 2(7): 54-56.

HARINGTON, C.R. (1964). Polar Bears and Their Present Status. *Canadian Audubon Magazine.*

— (1965). The Life and Status of the Polar Bear. *Oryx,* 8(3): 169-176.

FLYGER, VAGN (1967). The Polar Bear: a Matter for International Concern. *Arctic,* 20(3): 147-153.

LOUGHREY, ALAN G. (1956). The Polar Bear and Its Protection. *Oryx,* 3(5): 233-239.

LARSEN, THOR (1968). Ecological Investigations on the Polar Bear in Svalbard: a Progress Report. *Norsk Polarinstitut, Årbok,* pp. 92-98.

LARSEN, T. (1967). The Trapping and Study of Polar Bears, Spitsbergen, 1966. *The Polar Record* 13(86): 589-593.

SPÄRCK, R. (1956). Some Remarks on the Status of the Polar Bear *(Thalarctos maritimus)* in Greenland. *Proceedings and Papers of the 5th Technical Meeting of IUCN,* 1954. p. 85.

PEDERSEN, ALWIN (1957). *Der Eisbär.* Die Neue Brehm-Bücherei, Stuttgart.

USPENSKY, SAVVA (1965). The Future of the Polar Bear: Russia Shows the Way. *Animals Magazine,* 7(12): 318-319.

BARTLETT, E.L. and CHARLES, R.H. (1965). The Future of the Polar Bear: the Vital Need for More Information. *Animals Magazine,* 7(12): 310-317.

KOLENOSKY, G. and STANDFIELD, R.O. (1966). Polar Bears of Canada. *Animals,* 8(19): 528-531.

PERRY, RICHARD (1966). *The World of the Polar Bear.* Cassell, London.

HARINGTON, C.R. (1968). Denning Habits of the Polar Bear *(Ursus maritimus* Phipps). *Canadian Wildlife Service Report Series,* No. 5.

DUGONG

ALLEN, GLOVER M. (1938-40). *The Mammals of China and Mongolia.* New York.

TATE, G.H.H. (1947). *Mammals of Eastern Asia.* New York.

BERTRAM & BERTRAM (1966). Dugongs in Australian Waters, *Oryx* 8(4).

— (1968). The Sirenia: a Vanishing Order of Mammals. *Animal Kingdom.*

JONKLAAS, RODNEY (1961). Some Observations on Dugongs. *Loris* 9(1): 1-8.

NORRIS, C.E. (1960). The Dugong. *Loris* 8(5): 296-300.

CRUSZ, HILARY (1960). Dugongs—a Zoological Romance. *Loris* 8(5): 300-304.

TROUGHTON, ELLIS (1962). *Furred Animals of Australia.*

DECARY, RAYMOND (1950). *La Faune Malgache. Son rôle dans les croyances et les usages indigènes.* Payot, Paris. 236 pp. 22 figs.

JONES (1967). *International Zoological Year Book.*

MANI, S.B. (1960). *(See International Zoo Year Book p, 220).*

GOHAR, H.A.F. (1957). The Red Sea Dugong, *Dugong dugong* (Erxlb.), subsp. *tabernaculi* (Rüppell). *Publs. mar. biol. Stn. Ghardaqa* No. 9: 3-49. 5 pls.

TROUGHTON, ELLIS Le G. (1928). Sea-Cows. The Story of the Dugong. *Aust. Mus. Mag.,* vol. 3. pp. 220-228.

JONKLAAS, RODNEY (1960). The Vanishing Dugong. *Loris* 8(5): 302-304.

BLUE WHALE

JONSGARD, AGE (1955). The Stocks of Blue Whales *(Balaenoptera musculus)* in the Northern Atlantic Ocean and Adjacent Arctic Waters. *Norwegian Whaling Gazette* 44 (9): 505-519.

MACKINTOSH, N.S. (1965). *The Stocks of Whales.* Fishing News (Books) Ltd., London.

SLIJPER, E.J. (1965). A Hundred Years of Modern Whaling. *Netherlands Committee for International Protection, Information Bulletin* No. 19: 29-61.

SIMON, NOEL (1965). Of Whales and Whaling. *Science* 149 (3687): 943-946. International Whaling Commission (1964). *Final Report of the Committee of Three Scientists on the Special Scientific Investigation of the Antarctic Whale Stocks.*

HERSHKOVITZ (1966). *Catalog of Living Whales.* Smithsonian Institution, Bulletin 24 b.

ICHIHARA, TADAYOSHI (1961). Blue Whales in the Waters around Kerguelen Island. *Norwegian Whaling Gazette* 50(1): 1-22.

SCAMMON, CHARLES M. (1968). *The Marine Mammals of the North-Western Coast of North America.* Described and illustrated. Together with an account of the American whale-fishery. Dover Publications, New York 319 pp. 27 pls.

SLIJPER, E.J. (1962). *Whales.* Basic Books Inc. New York.

MEDITERRANEAN MONK SEAL

MURSALOGLU, B. (1964). Occurrence of the Monk Seal on the Turkish Coasts. *J. Mammal.* 45(2): 316-317.

MORALES-AGACINO, E. (1950). Notes sur les Phoques-Moines *(Monachus monachus Herm.)* du littoral saharien espagnol. *Mammalia* 14: 1-6.

KUMERLOEVE, HANS (1966). Zum Vorkommen der Mönchsrobbe, *Monachus m. monachus* (Hermann, 1779), im libanesischen Küstengebiet. *Säugetierkundliche Mitteilungen* 14(2): 114-118.

KING, JUDITH E. (1956). The Monk Seals (Genus *Monachus*). *Bull. Brit. Mus. (Nat. Hist.) Zool* 5(3): 201-256.

KING, JUDITH E. (1964). *Seals of the World.* British Museum (Natural History), London.

SCHEFFER, VICTOR B. (1958). *Seals, Sea Lions and Walruses : a Review of the Pinnipedia.* Stanford University Press, California.

WIJNGAARDEN, A. van (1969). The Monk Seal Colony at La Güera, Rio d'Oro. *I.U.C.N. Bulletin* N.S. 2(10): 77.

TROITZKY, A. (1953). Contribution à l'étude des Pinnipèdes à propos de deux phoques de la Méditerranée ramenés de croisière par S.A.S. le prince Rainier III de Monaco. *Bull. Inst. Océanogr. Monaco,* No. 1032. 46 pp.

MONOD, TH. (1932). Phoques Sahariens. *La Terre et la Vie* 12: 257-261.

VALVERDE, J.A. (1957). Aves del Sahara espanol. Madrid.

WIJNGAARDEN, A. van (1962) a). *On the State of the Mediterranean Monk Seal Monachus Monachus (Hermann).* 1962 b) *Additions to the Report...* 1964. *Additions...* (2nd list). Zeist, R.I.V.O.N., cyclostyled.

— 1962 c). The Mediterranean Monk Seal. *Oryx* 6 (5): 270-273.

JUAN FERNANDEZ FUR SEAL

KING, JUDITH E. (1954). The Otariid Seals of the Pacific Coast of America. *Bull. Brit. Mus. (Nat. Hist.), Zool.* 2: 309-337.

JORDAN, DAVID STARR *et al.* (1899). *The Fur Seals and Fur-Seal Islands of the North Pacific Ocean.* 4 vols.

ALLEN, GLOVER M. (1942). *Extinct and Vanishing Mammals of the Western Hemisphere with the Marine Species of all the Oceans.* American Committee for International Wild Life Protection. Special Publication No. 11.

ACKNOWLEDGMENTS

The subject of endangered wildlife has, of course, already been treated in several recent books, notably the *Red Data Book*, which comprises a series of volumes designed primarily for the specialist, and published by I.U.C.N., Morges, Switzerland. Of this series, the Mammalia volume by Noel Simon, and the Aves volume by Jack Vincent have provided much of the basic raw material used in writing this present book. A "popular" version of the *Red Data Book* has been published under the title *The Red Book : wildlife in danger* (Collins, 1969). We wish to acknowledge our indebtedness to I.U.C.N. and to the publishers for permission to adapt the chapters on the orang-utan and the mountain gorilla for use here.

Noel Simon has written the chapters on the mammals; Paul Géroudet those on the birds. The latter have been translated from the original French by Madame Marguerite Barbey. The writing of the mammal chapters has been sustained by a grant from the Foresta Institute for Ocean and Mountain Studies, without whose generous support the work could not have been accomplished.

The mammal paintings are the work of Helmut Diller, of Munich, Germany; those of the birds are by Paul Barruel, of Saint-Jean d'Arvey, Savoy, France. Their excellence is self-evident, and requires no embellishment.

Several specialists have been generous enough to read the chapters on species of which they have specialized knowledge. They include: Otto Appert (long-tailed ground roller); Douglass Branch (giant otter); Eskander Firouz (Persian fallow deer); Barbara Harrisson (orang-utan); Fred Kurt (Ceylon elephant); Vratislav Mazak (tiger); Bernhard Nievergelt (walia ibex); Jean-Jacques Petter (indris, aye-aye, and sifaka); Paul Schauenberg (mountain tapir); and Rudolf Schenkel (Javan rhinoceros). Their authoritative criticisms and constructive comments have been invaluable, and are gratefully acknowledged.

A significant contribution has been made by Arnold J. Koenen, I.U.C.N. Librarian, in obtaining the large number of books, papers, and other publications which have been consulted during the preparation of this work. His consistent help, extending over many months, has been of the greatest value.

Printed by Presses Centrales Lausanne S.A.
Colour illustrations by Lichtdruck S.A., Dielsdorf
Binding by Maurice Busenhart, Lausanne

PRINTED IN SWITZERLAND